D1590425

LECTURES ON TOPOLOGICAL DYNAMICS

MATHEMATICS LECTURE NOTE SERIES

J. Frank Adams	LECTURES ON LIE GROUPS
E. Artin and J. Tate	CLASS FIELD THEORY
Michael Atiyah	K-THEORY
Jacob Barshay	TOPICS IN RING THEORY
Hyman Bass	ALGEBRAIC K-THEORY
Melvyn S. Berger Marion S. Berger	PERSPECTIVES IN NONLINEARITY
Armand Borel	LINEAR ALGEBRA GROUPS
Raoul Bott	LECTURES ON K (X)
Andrew Browder	INTRODUCTION TO FUNCTION ALGEBRAS
Gustave Choquet	LECTURES ON ANALYSIS I. INTEGRATION AND TOPOLOGICAL VECTOR SPACES II. REPRESENTATION THEORY III. INFINITE DIMENSIONAL MEASURES AND PROBLEM SOLUTIONS
Paul J. Cohen	SET THEORY AND THE CONTINUUM HYPOTHESIS
Eldon Dyer	COHOMOLOGY THEORIES
Robert Ellis	LECTURES ON TOPOLOGICAL DYNAMICS
Walter Feit	CHARACTERS OF FINITE GROUPS
John Fogarty	INVARIANT THEORY
William Fulton	ALGEBRAIC CURVES
Marvin J. Greenberg	LECTURES ON ALGEBRAIC TOPOLOGY
Marvin J. Greenberg	LECTURES ON FORMS IN MANY VARIABLES
Robin Hartshorne	FOUNDATIONS OF PROJECTIVE GEOMETRY
J. F. P. Hudson	PIECEWISE LINEAR TOPOLOGY

Irving Kaplansky	RINGS OF OPERATORS
K. Kapp and H. Schneider	COMPLETELY O-SIMPLE SEMIGROUPS
Joseph B. Keller Stuart Antman	BIFURCATION THEORY AND NONLINEAR EIGENVALUE PROBLEMS
Serge Lang	ALGEBRAIC FUNCTIONS
Serge Lang	RAPPORT SUR LA COHOMOLOGIE DES GROUPES
Ottmar Loos	SYMMETRIC SPACES I. GENERAL THEORY II. COMPACT SPACES AND CLASSIFICATIONS
I. G. Macdonald	ALGEBRAIC GEOMETRY: INTRODUCTION TO SCHEMES
George W. Mackey	INDUCED REPRESENTATIONS OF GROUPS AND QUANTUM MECHANICS
Andrew Ogg	MODULAR FORMS AND DIRICHLET SERIES
Richard Palais	FOUNDATIONS OF GLOBAL NON-LINEAR ANALYSIS
William Parry	ENTROPY AND GENERATORS IN ERGODIC THEORY
D. S. Passman	PERMUTATION GROUPS
Walter Rudin	FUNCTION THEORY IN POLYDISCS
Jean-Pierre Serre	ABELIAN l-ADIC REPRESENTATIONS AND ELLIPTIC CURVES
Jean-Pierre Serre	ALGEBRES DE LIE SEMI-SIMPLE COMPLEXES
Jean-Pierre Serre	LIE ALGEBRAS AND LIE GROUPS
Shlomo Sternberg	CELESTIAL MECHANICS PART I
Shlomo Sternberg	CELESTIAL MECHANICS PART II
Moss E. Sweedler	HOPF ALGEBRAS

A Note from the Publisher

This volume was printed directly from a typescript prepared by the author, who takes full responsibility for its content and appearance. The Publisher has not performed his usual functions of reviewing, editing, typesetting, and proofreading the material prior to publication.

The Publisher fully endorses this informal and quick method of publishing lecture notes at a moderate price, and he wishes to thank the author for preparing the material for publication.

LECTURES ON TOPOLOGICAL DYNAMICS

ROBERT ELLIS
University of Minnesota

W. A. BENJAMIN, INC.
New York 1969

LECTURES ON TOPOLOGICAL DYNAMICS

Standard Book Numbers 8053-2420-8 (Clothbound)
8053-2421-6 (Paperback)

Library of Congress Catalog Card Number 76-99277
Manufactured in the United States of America
12345 MR 32109

*The manuscript was put into production on October 1, 1969;
this volume was published on December 1, 1969*

W. A. BENJAMIN, INC.
New York, New York 10016

TO

BETTY,

DAVID and VALERIE

PREFACE

These notes are an expanded version of a one quarter course and a series of seminars given at the University of Minnesota during the academic year 1967-68. My main aim is to give a unified presentation of the more recent results in topological dynamics. I have also tried to make available to the research student those techniques which have proved fruitful. Moreover, the notes are self-contained, complete proofs are given; and I hope that they can also serve as an introduction to the subject.

I would like to thank my colleague, Harvey Keynes for his help in the preparation of this book. His painstaking comments, interest, and encouragement turned a chore into a joy.

I am also grateful to Cheryl Keynes for her careful typing and to the National Science Foundation (NSF Grant GP-8691) for its support.

INTRODUCTION

In order to place these notes in the proper perspective let me discuss briefly three aspects of the theory of dynamical systems. For want of a better description I shall refer to them as the local, global, and abstract theories.

The local theory is concerned with the application of topological methods to the qualitative study of differential equations. The general setting is a differential equation in $\mathbb{R}^n$ and one is interested in such questions as, "What does the ω-limit set look like?"; "What happens in the neighborhood of a fixed point ?"; "Is it stable?"; etc.

By the global theory I am referring to the research of Smale and his co-workers. Here the object of study is the set of vector fields on a manifold. One is interested in characterizing the structurally stable vector fields and in studying the "orbit picture" of the flow associated with a given vector field.

The abstract theory is expounded by Gottschalk and Hedlund in their book, *Topological Dynamics*. Here the setting is a general transformation group but the notions studied are those arising in the qualitative study of differential equations. It is shown that many of the results first proved for differential equations are valid in a much wider setting.

The relevance of the abstract theory for the local one is that in the former the topological tools used are refined and the essence of the theorems displayed. However, it is not clear that the problems which are germane to abstract topological dynamics will have application to differential equations. The reason for this is that for all "practical purposes" the phase group involved may be assumed discrete. Thus not only is the differential structure ignored but the topological properties of the reals are not made essential use of.

At present there is little contact between the abstract and the global theories. One reason is: let X be a vector field and f a strictly positive differentiable function, then from the "global" point of view the dynamical properties of X and fX are the same but from the "abstract" point of view they are generally quite different.

There is an approach to the study of vector fields on manifolds which does concern itself with the notions defined in Topological Dynamics. This is set forth in Flows on Homogeneous Spaces by L. Auslander, L. Green, F. Hahn, et.al.. Here the dynamical system involved consists of a compact homogeneous space M of a Lie group, G together with the action on M induced by a one-parameter subgroup of G. The methods used are "Lie-algebraic" in flavor.

This book is concerned with those notions of the abstract theory which have developed a life of their own. The central theme is the classification of minimal sets. Although there remains much to be done, I felt it would be useful to present a unified account of the results obtained thus far. Recent work on the abstract theory indicates first, that the proper approach is to view a given minimal set as a "point" in the collection of all minimal sets rather than as an isolated object, and second that the abstract theory is closer in spirit to functional analysis than it is to differential equations. These two points are emphasized in the text.

Let me now discuss these notes in a little more detail. The first six chapters introduce the concepts which have proved most fruitful, concepts centering around the notions of minimal and distal. Here there is considerable overlap with Topological Dynamics with regards to material covered but the proofs differ. One purpose of these notes is to describe those techniques which have proved useful. Thus the enveloping semigroup is exploited repeatedly in these first chapters.

In chapter 7 the universal minimal set associated with a group T is introduced. This sets the stage for the consideration of the collection of all minimal sets with phase group T since these are all homomorphic images of the universal one.

Although all universal minimal sets are isomorphic it is desirable to have a "concrete" one at hand. For this reason the β-compactification, βT of the discrete group T is studied in detail in chapter 8. The "resources" of βT have barely begun to be tapped.

As was mentioned above I feel that one should study a class of transformation groups all at once rather than a particular one in isolation. The class studied herein consists of those transformation groups with phase group, T which are homomorphic images of $(\beta T,T)$. By a classical result of M. H. Stone's, the study of the above class is equivalent to the study of a certain collection of subalgebras of $\mathcal{C}(\beta T)$. Of the two points of view (the topological and the algebraic) I have chosen to describe the algebraic for the following reasons: First, it is easier to study sub-objects than quotient objects. Second, this point of view is new and there are many concepts which because they are algebraic in nature are obvious in this approach but are hidden in the topological one. Third, the algebraic approach suggests new problems and also displays the close relationship between abstract topological dynamics and functional analysis.

The algebraic theory is developed in chapters 9 through 14 and used in chapters 15 through 18 to give a unified treatment of Furstenberg's structure theorem, Knapp's work on "generalized" almost periodic functions, and some recent work on disjointness.

There are several other topics which I feel could be profitably considered from the algebraic point of view. (I have not included them because the results I have are only fragmentary.) These include Veech's recent work on almost automorphic functions and almost automorphic extensions, and the work of Hahn and Parry on flows with quasi-discrete spectrum.

I also think an intensive examination of the 0-dimensional case with special emphasis on expansive flows would prove rewarding.

Finally, since every T-invariant Borel measure on the minimal set (X,T) can be "lifted" to (βT,T) when T is abelian, it might prove fruitful to investigate some ergodic theory notions from this "universal" point of view.

At the end of each chapter is a section entitled Notes. These include the titles of the articles referred to in the body of the chapter and comments on various points raised. They often also mention unsolved problems and indicate general areas of research.

The definitions, lemmas, propositions, etc. are numbered consecutively in each chapter. Thus for example 2.15 refers to the fifteenth item in the second chapter.

Numbers enclosed in brackets, [ ] refer to items in the notes at the end of the chapter in which they occur.

TABLE OF CONTENTS

CHAPTER 1

TRANSFORMATION GROUPS

1.1 DEFINITION. A right transformation group is a triple (X,T,π) where X is a topological space called the phase space, T is a topological group called the phase group, and

$$\pi: X \times T \to X, \ (x,t) \to xt$$

is a continuous mapping such that

(i) $xe = x \quad (x \in X)$, where e is the identity of T,

(ii) $(xt)s = x(ts) \quad (x \in X,\ t,s \in T)$.

Similarly a left transformation group is a triple (ρ,G,X) where now $\rho: G \times X \to X$, $(g,x) \to gx$ is such that $ex = x$ $(x \in X)$ and $g(hx) = (gh)x \quad (x \in X,\ g,h \in G)$.

If (X,T,π) is a right transformation group then setting $\rho(t,x) = \pi(x,t^{-1}) \quad (x \in X,\ t \in T)$ turns it into a left transformation group (ρ,T,X).

Thus it is merely a matter of taste whether one writes the group elements on the right or left. In general, we will be concerned with right transformation groups.

It will be convenient to suppress the mapping π (or ρ in the case of a left transformation group) and then denote the transformation group (X,T,π) simply as (X,T).

A <u>bitransformation group</u> is a pair of transformation groups (G,X) and (X,T) with the same phase space X such that $g(xt) = (gx)t$ $(g \in G,\ x \in X,\ t \in T)$. The notation (G,X,T) will be used to signify that the pair (G,X), (X,T) constitute a bitransformation group, and $g(xt) = (gx)t$ will be denoted by gxt.

Let T be an abstract group, X a topological space, $\pi: X \times T \to X$ such that (i) and (ii) hold and such that the map $x \to \pi(x,t)$ of X into X is continuous $(t \in T)$. Then (X,T,π) is a transformation group when T is provided with the discrete topology.

Definition 1.1 requires that T be a topological group. If a transformation group is defined but no topology on T is specified, then the discrete topology is intended. It will become clear that for many of the problems considered, the topology on T is irrelevant and that one may assume it to be discrete.

1.2 <u>DEFINITION</u>. Let (X,T) be a transformation group. The group T <u>acts effectively</u> (<u>on</u> X) if $t \in T$ and $t \neq e$, then $xt \neq x$ for some $x \in X$. It <u>acts freely</u> (<u>on</u> X) if $t \in T$ and $t \neq e$, then $xt \neq x$ $(x \in X)$.

1.3 <u>REMARKS</u>.

(i) Let (X,T,π) be a transformation group, let $\pi^t: X \to X$ be the map such that $\pi^t(x) = xt$ $(x \in X,\ t \in T)$. Then π^t is a homeomorphism of X onto X $(t \in T)$. The inverse of π^t is just $\pi^{t^{-1}}$.

(ii) Let H denote the group (under composition) of homeomorphisms of X onto X, $\varphi: T \to H$ such that $\varphi(t) = \pi^{t^{1}}$.

Then φ is a group homomorphism into and T is effective if and only if ker φ = e. Indeed it is easy to see that in general if X is Hausdorff, ker φ is a closed invariant subgroup of T and that the map $(x,t(\ker \varphi)) \to xt$ makes $(X,T/\ker\varphi)$ into a transformation group. From our point of view, there is no need to distinguish between (X,T) and $(X, T/\ker \varphi)$. Thus we may assume that T acts effectively on X and may view T as a subgroup of H.

1.4 <u>EXAMPLES</u>.

1. Let X be a topological space, H the group of homeomorphisms of X onto X, S a subgroup of H. Then the map $(f,x) \to f(x)$ $(f \in S, x \in X)$ of S x X into X defines a transformation group (S,X).

2. Let $\varphi \in H$. Then the map $(x,n) \to \varphi^n(x)$ defines an action of the integers $\mathbb{Z}$ on X (i.e. a transformation group $(X, \mathbb{Z})$). Indeed every transformation group $(X, \mathbb{Z},\pi)$ with phase group $\mathbb{Z}$ arises in this fashion (set $\varphi(x) = \pi(x,1)$ $(x \in X)$).

3. Let X be a topological group, and G,T subgroups of X. Then $(x,t) \to xt$ (group product) $(x \in X, t \in T)$ defines a right transformation group (X,T) and $(g,x) \to gx$ $(x \in X, g \in G)$ a left transformation group (G,X). Moreover, the pair (G,X), (X,T) determine a bitransformation group (G,X,T).

1.5 <u>THE CONSTRUCTION OF NEW TRANSFORMATION GROUPS FROM GIVEN ONES.</u>

1. Let (X,T,π) be a transformation group. A subset M of X is <u>invariant</u> if $Mt \subset M$ $(t \in T)$. If M is invariant, then $\pi(M \times T) \subset M$ and π restricted to M x T induces a transformation group (M,T,π).

2. Let (X_i,T) $(i \in I)$ be a family of transformation

groups, let $X = \Pi X_i$ and set $xt = (x_i t \mid i \in I)$, where $x = (x_i \mid i \in I) \in X$. Then (X,T) is again a transformation group.

A particular case of the above construction which occurs frequently is when I consists of two elements $\{1,2\}$ and $(X_1,T) = (X_2,T) = (Y,T)$. Then $(X,T) = (Y \times Y,T)$. The action of T on $Y \times Y$ is given by $(y,z)t = (yt,zt)$ $(y,z \in Y, t \in T)$.

3. Let (X,T) be a transformation group, R an equivalence relation on X. Then R is <u>invariant</u> if $(x,y) \in R$ implies $(xt,yt) \in R$ $(t \in T)$. Let R be an invariant equivalence relation on X, $k: X \to X/R$ the canonical map. Then the map $(k(x),t) \to k(xt)$ $(x \in X, t \in T)$ defines a discrete (i.e. T discrete) transformation group $(X/R,T)$. If R is open (i.e. k is an open map) or if X is compact Hausdorff and R is a closed subset of $X \times X$, then the map $(k(x),t) \to k(xt)$ is jointly continuous with the original topology on T.

4. A particular case of 3. arises in the presence of a bitransformation group (G,X,T). Set $R = \{(x,y) \mid y \in Gx\} \subset X \times X$. Then R is an open equivalence relation on X. The quotient space X/R is usually denoted X/G. Since the action of G commutes with that of T, R is invariant and there is a naturally defined transformation group $(X/G,T)$.

1.6 <u>DEFINITION</u>. Let (X,T) and (Y,T) be transformation groups, $\varphi: X \to Y$. Then φ is a <u>homomorphism</u> if φ is continuous and $\varphi(xt) = \varphi(x)t$ $(x \in X, t \in T)$. If φ is onto we write $\varphi: (X,T) \underset{\to}{\simeq} (Y,T)$ or $\varphi: X \underset{\to}{\simeq} Y$.

In 1 of 1.5 the inclusion map of M into X is a monomorphism (one-one homomorphism) of (M,T) into (X,T). In 2 of 1.5 the projections of X onto its various factors are epimorphisms (onto homomorphisms), and in 3 and 4 of 1.5 the canonical maps are epimorphisms.

1.7 DEFINITION. Let (X,T) be a transformation group and $x \in X$. Then the set $xT = \{xt \mid t \in T\}$ is called the orbit of x and the set $\overline{xT}$ the orbit closure of x.

As was remarked in 4 of 1.5 the relation $R = \{(x,y) \mid y \in xT\} \subset X \times X$ is an equivalence relation on X. Since the equivalence class to which x belongs is just the orbit of x, this relation is usually referred to as the orbit relation.

One approach to the study of the transformation group (X,T) is to deduce properties of the action of T from the topological properties of X/T. This method works well when T is compact since in this case X/T is a "nice" space if X is "nice". However in topological dynamics we deal essentially with discrete groups T so that even if X is nice, X/T need not be. Thus this method has not been used in topological dynamics.

One might try using $S = \{(x,y) \mid y \in \overline{xT}\}$ instead of R but this is not an equivalence relation in general (e.g. X the unit interval and $\varphi: X \to X$ such that $\varphi(x) = x^2$). For the most interesting cases in which S is an equivalence relation, it turns out to be $X \times X$ so that the quotient is a one point space thus telling us nothing about the action of T on X.

CHAPTER 2

MINIMAL SETS

We now begin the study of one of the most fruitful notions in the abstract theory of topological dynamics. For the purpose of motivation let us consider a transformation group $(X, \mathbb{R})$, where the phase group is the real numbers $\mathbb{R}$. Such transformation groups are often referred to as dynamical systems since they first arose in the qualitative study of differential equations associated with problems in dynamics.

Now let us try to classify the points of X. The "simplest type" is the fixed point (x is _fixed_ if $xt = x$ $(t \in \mathbb{R})$). Next comes the periodic point (x is a _periodic point_ if x is not a fixed point but $xt = x$ for some $t \in \mathbb{R}$ with $t \neq 0$). The smallest number t for which $xt = x$ is called the _period_ of x.

In both of the above cases the orbit of x coincides with its orbit closure. When x is fixed this is merely x itself and when x is periodic it is a circle.

One might note, by the way, that these concepts can obviously be extended to arbitrary transformation groups.

It is of interest to know when there are periodic points but in general there need not be any. Again the problem of classifying the orbit closures of periodic points is trivial. Thus we are led to relax the conditions and consider points which are not quite periodic but rather "almost" periodic.

Fortunately this can be done in such a way that if X is compact Hausdorff, then there is always at least one almost periodic point. Moreover, the problem of classifying the orbit closures of almost periodic points is far from trivial.

Let $x \in X$ and U a neighborhood of x. Set $A(U) = \{t \mid xt \in U\}$. If x is periodic with period r, then $\mathbb{R} = A(U) + K$ where K is the interval $[o,r]$. Thus $\mathbb{R}$ may be written as the sum of A(U) plus a compact set K. In the case of a periodic point, the compact set K may be chosen independently of the neighborhood U. A natural weakening of the condition on x would be to allow K to depend on U. Thus x is an <u>almost periodic point</u> if for every neighborhood U of x there exists a compact subset K(U) of $\mathbb{R}$ such that $\mathbb{R} = A(U) + K(U)$. This amounts to requiring that A(U) be a relatively dense subset of $\mathbb{R}$.

Before beginning the study of almost periodic points, let me describe a classical example: here X is the set of bounded real valued continuous functions on $\mathbb{R}$ provided with the metric $d(x,y) = \sup \{|x(t) - y(t)| \mid t \in \mathbb{R}\}$. The pair $(X, \mathbb{R})$ is made into a transformation group by means of the map $(x,t) \to xt$, where $xt(s) = x(t + s)$ $(x \in X,\ t,s \in \mathbb{R})$. Then $x \in X$ is a periodic point if and only if it is a periodic function, and it is an almost periodic point if and only if it is an almost periodic function in the sense of

Bohr.

2.1 DEFINITION. Let T be a topological group and A a subset of T. Then A is syndetic if there exists a compact subset K of T with T = AK.

Let (X,T) be a transformation group and $x \in X$. Then x is an almost periodic point (with respect to (X,T)) if $\{t \mid xt \in U\}$ is a syndetic subset of T for all neighborhoods U of x.

Notice that the notion of a syndetic set and hence that of being an almost periodic point depends upon the topology of T.

With regard to the existence of almost periodic points, there is the following:

2.2 PROPOSITION. Let (X,T) by a transformation group and let Y be a non-vacuous, compact T_2 invariant subset of X. Then there exists an almost periodic point $y \in Y$.

The proof of 2.2 follows from 2.4 and 2.5 below.

2.3 DEFINITION. Let (X,T) be a transformation group, and $M \subset X$. Then M is a minimal subset of X if

(i) M is closed, non-vacuous, and invariant.

(ii) M is minimal with respect to the above properties (i.e. if N is closed, non-vacuous and invariant with $N \subset M$, then N = M).

The transformation group (X,T) is called a minimal set if X is minimal.

Notice the M is a minimal subset of X if and only if $\overline{xT} = M$ $(x \in M)$.

2.4 PROPOSITION. Let (X,T) be a transformation group with X compact T_2. Then there exists a minimal subset of X.

PROOF. Let $\mathcal{C}$ be the collection of closed, non-vacuous, invariant subsets of X. Then $X \in \mathcal{C}$ shows that $\mathcal{C} \neq \emptyset$. Moreover, when partially ordered downward by inclusion, $\mathcal{C}$ is inductive. Then Zorn's lemma guarantees the existence of a minimal element of $\mathcal{C}$. This minimal element of $\mathcal{C}$ is a minimal subset of X.

2.5 PROPOSITION. Let (X,T) be a transformation group, X locally compact T_2, and $x \in X$. Then x is an almost periodic point iff (if and only if) $\overline{xT}$ is a compact minimal subset of X.

PROOF. Let x be an almost periodic point, and U a compact neighborhood of x. There exists a compact subset K of T such that $T = AK$ where $A = \{t \mid xt \in U\}$. Then $xT \subset xAK = UK$, and hence $\overline{xT}$ is compact, since UK is.

Let $y \in xT$ and U an arbitrary compact neighborhood of x. Then as above $y \in \overline{xT} \subset UK$. Thus $yT \cap U \neq \emptyset$ and since X is locally compact this implies that $x \in \overline{yT}$. Hence $\overline{xT} = \overline{yT}$.

Now suppose that $\overline{xT}$ is a compact minimal subset of X and let U be an open neighborhood of x. Since $\overline{xT} - UT$ is a closed, invariant proper subset of $\overline{xT}$, it must be vacuous. Then $\overline{xT} \subset UT$ and therefore $\overline{xT} \subset UF$ for some finite subset F of T.

Let $A = \{t \mid xt \in U\}$ and $t \in T$. Then $xt = uf$ for some $u \in U$, $f \in T$. Thus $xtf^{-1} \in U$ whence $tf^{-1} \in A$ and $t \in AF$. Consequently $T = AF$ and F is finite.

The proof of 2.5 shows that $\overline{xT}$ is compact minimal iff x is an almost periodic point relative to the discrete topology of T. Hence, whether or not x is an almost periodic point does not depend on the topology on T. It turns out that this is true of most of the notions studied in topological dynamics. This means that for most purposes we may assume that T is discrete.

2.6 PROPOSITION. Let (X,T) be a transformation group with X locally compact T_2. Then every point of X is an almost periodic point iff $\{\overline{xT} \mid x \in X\}$ is a partition of X consisting of compact sets.

PROOF. Assume every point of X is an almost periodic point. Since minimal sets are disjoint or equal by 2.3, it follows by 2.5 that $\{\overline{xT} \mid x \in X\}$ forms the desired partition.

On the other hand if $\{\overline{xT} \mid x \in X\}$ is a partition every set $\overline{xT}$ must be minimal. Since $\overline{xT}$ is also compact, x is an almost periodic point by 2.5.

2.7 PROPOSITION. Let $\varphi\colon (X,T) \to (Y,T)$ be a homomorphism, and let x be an almost periodic point of (X,T). Then $\varphi(x)$ is an almost periodic point of (Y,T).

PROOF. Let V be a neighborhood of $\varphi(x)$, and U a neighborhood of x with $\varphi(U) \subset V$. If A is syndetic and $xA \subset U$, then $\varphi(x)A = \varphi(xA) \subset \varphi(U) \subset V$.

2.8 PROPOSITION. (Inheritance theorem). Let (X,T) be a transformation group, X locally compact T_2, S a syndetic invariant subgroup of T, and $x \in X$. Then x is an almost periodic point of (X,S) iff x is an almost periodic point of (X,T).

PROOF. Let x be an almost periodic point of (X,S), U a neighborhood of x, and $A = \{t \mid xt \in U\}$. Then there exists a compact subset L of S such that $S = (A \cap S)L$. Let K be a compact subset of T with $T = SK$. Then LK is compact and $T = ALK$. Hence x is an almost periodic point of (X,T).

Now assume that x is an almost periodic point of (X,T). I shall show that $\overline{xS}$ is a compact minimal subset of

X.

By 2.5 $\overline{xT}$ is compact, hence so is $\overline{xS}$.

Set $R = \{t \mid xt \in \overline{xS}\}$. Then R is closed and syndetic (it contains S). Let $r,t \in R$. Then $xrt \in \overline{xS}t = \overline{xSt} = \overline{xtS} \subset \overline{\overline{xS}S} \subset \overline{xS}$; i.e. $rt \in R$. Thus R is a closed, syndetic, semigroup containing S. This implies by 2.12 below that R is a subgroup of T.

Let $y \in \overline{xS}$. I must show that $x \in \overline{yS}$.

Let $T = SK$ with K compact. Since $\overline{xT}$ is minimal and $y \in \overline{xT}$, $x \in \overline{yT} = \overline{yS}K$. Hence $xk^{-1} \in \overline{yS} \subset \overline{xS}$ for some $k \in K$. Thus $k^{-1} \in R$, whence $k \in R$. This implies $xk \in \overline{xS}$, whence $x \in \overline{xS}k^{-1} = \overline{xSk^{-1}} = \overline{xk^{-1}S} \subset \overline{\overline{yS}S} \subset \overline{yS}$.

The next few lemmas, although not directly concerned with minimal sets, are very useful in their study.

2.9 <u>LEMMA</u>. Let E be a compact T_1 topological space provided with a semigroup structure such that the maps L_x: $y \to xy$ are closed and continuous ($x \in E$). Then there exists an <u>idempotent</u> u in E. (i.e. an element u such that $u^2 = u$).

<u>PROOF</u>. Let $\mathfrak{S}$ be the collection of all non-vacuous closed subsets S of E with $S^2 \subset S$. Then $\mathfrak{S} \neq \emptyset$ since $E \in \mathfrak{S}$.

If $\mathfrak{S}$ is ordered downward by inclusion, it is inductive and hence contains a minimal set S.

Let $x \in S$. Then $xS = L_x(S)$ is a closed, non-vacuous subset of S with $(xS)(xS) \subset xSSS \subset xS$. Hence by the minimality of S, $xS = S$. Therefore there exists $u \in S$ with $xu = x$.

Since $u \in W = L_x^{-1}(x) \cap S$, W is a non-vacuous closed subset of S. In addition $W^2 \subset W$. Hence $W = S$. Then $x \in W$ whence $x^2 = x$.

2.10 <u>COROLLARY</u>. Let E be a compact T_2 topological

space provided with a semigroup structure such that the maps L_x: $y \to xy$ are continuous ($x \in E$). Then there exists an idempotent in E.

PROOF. Since E is compact T_2 every continuous map is closed.

2.11 COROLLARY. Let E be a compact T_1 topological space provided with a group structure such that the maps L_x: $y \to xy$ are continuous ($x \in E$), and let M be a non-vacuous closed subset of E with $M^2 \subset M$. Then M is a subgroup of E.

PROOF. Since E is a group, the maps L_x ($x \in E$) are homeomorphisms. Hence they are closed.

Now let $x \in M$. Then xM satisfies the hypotheses of 2.9. Hence xM contains an idempotent. But there is only one idempotent element in a group, the identity e. Thus $e \in xM$ and so $x^{-1} \in M$.

2.12 COROLLARY. Let T be a topological group, S a syndetic invariant subgroup of T, and R a closed subset of T with $S \subset R$ and $R^2 \subset R$. Then R is a subgroup of T.

PROOF. Let Π be the canonical map of T onto $T/\overline{S}$. Since S is syndetic, $T/\overline{S}$ is a compact topological group.

Since R is closed, $\overline{S} \subset R$ whence $\Pi^{-1}\Pi(R) = R$. Thus $\Pi(R)$ is a closed subset of $T/\overline{S}$ such that $\Pi(R)\Pi(R) \subset \Pi(R)$. By 2.10 $\Pi(R)$ is a subgroup of $T/\overline{S}$. Therefore $R = \Pi^{-1}\Pi(R)$ is a subgroup of T.

NOTES

The problem of classifying minimal sets is central to topological dynamics. Along this line let me mention some important results which I shall not discuss.

Let x be an almost periodic point of $(X, \mathbb{R})$ where X is the plane. Then the Poincare-Bendixon theorem states that $\overline{x\mathbb{R}}$ is either a point or a circle.

The case when X is a two torus was discussed by Denjoy. He showed that in general $\overline{x\mathbb{R}}$ can be quite complicated. However if the action of $\mathbb{R}$ is induced by a differential equation with some mild differentiability assumptions on the coefficients, then $\overline{x\mathbb{R}}$ is either a point, a circle, or the entire torus.

For a discussion of these results see the book: "Qualitative Theory of Differential Equations" (Princeton Univ. Press, 1960) by Nemytskii and Stepanov.

Arthur J. Schwartz in his paper "A generalization of the Poincare-Bendixon theorem to closed two-dimensional manifolds" (Amer. Jour. of Math. vol. 85 (1963)) extended Denjoy's result to arbitrary compact 2 manifolds: If X is not the torus and if the action of $\mathbb{R}$ is induced by a vector field of class C^2, then $\overline{x\mathbb{R}}$ is a point or a circle.

CHAPTER 3

THE ENVELOPING SEMIGROUP

Our goal is the classification of minimal sets with compact T_2 phase spaces. However, before embarking on this study I wish to introduce a technical device, the enveloping semigroup, which has proved useful in topological dynamics.

Henceforth I shall assume that the phase spaces of the transformation groups considered are compact T_2 unless specified otherwise.

3.1 DEFINITION. Let (X,T,π) be a transformation group. Then for $t \in T$, π^t is a map of X into X, hence an element of the compact T_2 space X^X. The enveloping semigroup $E(X)$ (or simply E) of (X,T,π) is the closure of $\{\pi^t \mid t \in T\}$ in X^X.

The space X^X is naturally provided with a semigroup structure: if $p,q \in X^X$ then $pq: X \to X$ is such that $x(pq) = (xp)q$ $(x \in X)$. (i.e. the composition first p then q).

Since (X,T) is a right transformation it will be convenient to write the elements of X^X on the right as was done above.

There are many ways to describe the topology on X^X. One way which will be useful is: a net (p_α) in X^X converges to p (i.e. $p_\alpha \to p$) if the net (xp_α) in X converges to xp $(x \in X)$. This topology is merely the topology of pointwise convergence.

Let $p_\alpha \to p$ and let $q \in X^X$. Then $xq \in X$ implies that $(xq)p_\alpha \to (xq)p$ $(x \in X)$. In other words $x(qp_\alpha) \to x(qp)(x \in X)$. Thus the maps $L_q : p \to qp$ of X^X into X^X are continuous $(q \in X^X)$. In general the maps $R_q : p \to pq$ are not continuous. However, if q is a continuous function on X, then it is immediate that R_q is also continuous. Thus the maps $p \to p\pi^t$ are continuous $(t \in T)$.

It will be convenient to regard T as a subset of E via the map $t \to \pi^t$ even though it is in general not one-one. This means that there are now two topologies on T, the original one and the one it inherits from E. Henceforth when I write $t_\alpha \to t$ it will mean that the net (t_α) converges to t in the latter topology. When I wish to refer to the original topology on T, I shall write $t_\alpha \to t$ in T.

3.2 <u>PROPOSITION</u>. Let (X,T,π) be a transformation group and E its enveloping semigroup. Then:

1. E is a sub-semigroup of X^X.
2. The map $(p,t) \to pt$ of E x T into E defines an action of T on E.
3. The maps $L_q : p \to qp$ of E into E are continuous $(q \in E)$.

4. The maps R_t: $p \to pt$ of E into E are continuous ($t \in T$).

PROOF. 1. Let $p,q \in E$ and nets (t_α), (s_β) in T with $t_\alpha \to p$ and $s_\beta \to q$. Fix β. Then $t_\alpha s_\beta \to ps_\beta$ by the continuity of s_β, whence $ps_\beta \in E$. Now (ps_β) is a net in E which converges to pq by the continuity of L_p. Hence $pq \in E$.

2. Let $p_\alpha \to p$ and $t_\beta \to t$ in T. Then $xp_\alpha \to xp$ and $\pi(xp_\alpha, t_\beta) \to \pi(xp,t)$ $(x \in X)$. Hence $p_\alpha t_\beta \to pt$.

3. and 4. follow from the remarks preceding 3.2.

3.3 PROPOSITION. Let (X,T) be a transformation group and E its enveloping semigroup. Then:

1. The orbit of the identity e of E is dense; i.e. $\overline{eT} = E$.

2. For each $x \in X$, the map θ_x: $p \to xp$ of E into X is a homomorphism, and its image is just the orbit closure $\overline{xT}$ of x, i.e. θ_x: $(E,T) \rightrightarrows (\overline{xT},T)$.

PROOF. 1. follows immediately from the way T acts on E.

2. That θ_x is a continuous mapping with $\theta_x(pt) = \theta_x(p)t$ follows immediately from the definitions involved.

From 1 and the fact that θ_x is closed, it follows that $\theta_x(E) = \theta_x(\overline{eT}) = \overline{\theta_x(eT)} = \overline{xT}$.

3.4 PROPOSITION. Let (X,T) be a transformation group and E its enveloping semigroup. Then the minimal subsets of the transformation group (E,T) coincide with the minimal right ideals of the semigroup E. (Recall that a right ideal is a non-vacuous subset I of E with $IE \subset I$).

PROOF. Let M be a minimal subset of (E,T), and $p \in M$. Then $L_p(T) = pT \subset M$ and M closed imply $pE = L_p(\overline{T}) \subset M$. Thus M is a right ideal.

Now let I be a non-vacuous right ideal with $I \subset M$ and let $p \in I$. Then $\overline{pT} = pE \subset IE = I$. Since M is a minimal subset of E, $\overline{pT} = M$. Hence M = I and M is a minimal right ideal.

Now suppose I is a minimal right ideal. Then $IT \subset IE \subset I$ shows that I is an invariant subset of (E,T).

Let $p \in I$. Then $\overline{pT} = pE$ is a right ideal contained in I. Thus $\overline{pT} = I$ and I is a minimal subset of E.

3.5 PROPOSITION. Let (X,T) be a transformation group, E its enveloping semigroup, and I a minimal right ideal. Then:

1. The set J of idempotents of I is non-vacuous.
2. If $v \in J$ and $p \in I$, $vp = p$.
3. Iv is a subgroup of I with identity v ($v \in J$).
4. $(Iv \mid v \in J)$ is a partition of I.

PROOF. 1. I is a compact T_2 space provided with a semigroup structure such that the maps $L_q : q \to pq$ of I into I are continuous ($p \in I$). Hence 1. follows from (2.10).

2. Let $v \in J$, $p \in I$. Then vI is a right ideal contained in I. Hence vI = I. Thus there exists $q \in I$ with $vq = p$. Then $vp = vvq = v^2q = vq = p$.

3. Let $q \in Iv$. Then $q = pv$ whence $qv = pv^2 = pv = q$. Thus v is a right identity for Iv. By 2. it is also a left identity.

Moreover, qI = I implies that qr = v for some $r \in I$. Then $qrv = v^2 = v$, and $rv \in Iv$. Thus given $q \in Iv$ there exists $s \in Iv$ with qs = v. Again sx = v for some $x \in Iv$.

Then $q = qv = qsx = vx = x$ shows that s is an inverse for q in Iv.

4. Let $p \in I$. Then $pI = I$ and so the set $K = \{q \mid q \in I \text{ and } pq = p\}$ is a non-empty closed subsemigroup of I. Hence $K \cap J \neq \emptyset$ by (2.10). Thus $I = \bigcup\{Iv \mid v \in J\}$.

Now let $p \in Iv \cap Iu$, where $u, v \in J$. Then by 3. above $p = pu = pv$ and there exists $q \in Iv$ with $qp = v$. Finally, by 2., $u = vu$, whence $u = vu = qpu = qp = v$.

3.6 PROPOSITION. Let (X,T) be a transformation group, E its enveloping semigroup, and I, K and L minimal right ideals in E. Then:

1. Given any idempotent $u \in I$ there exists a unique idempotent $v \in K$ with $uv = u$ and $vu = v$.

2. If u, v, w are idempotents in I, K, and L respectively with $uv = u$, $vu = v$ and $uw = u$, $wu = w$, then $vw = v$, $wv = w$.

The transformation groups (I,T) and (K,T) are isomorphic. (Recall that I and K are invariant subsets of E, and so the original action of T on E induces actions on I and K.)

PROOF. 1. Let $u^2 = u \in I$. Then uK is a right ideal in I. Hence $uK = I$ and $L = \{p \mid p \in K,\ up = u\}$ is a closed, non-empty subsemigroup of K. Thus there exists $v^2 = v \in L$ by (2.10); i.e. $uv = u$.

Similarly there exists $w^2 = w \in I$ with $vw = v$. Then $w = uw$ by 3.5 whence $w = uw = uvw = uv = u$. Thus $vu = v$.

Now suppose $v_1^2 = v_1 \in K$ with $uv_1 = u$ and $v_1u = v_1$. Then $v_1 = vv_1 = vuv_1 = vu = v$.

2. $vw = vuw = vu = v$ and $wv = wuv = wu = w$.

3. Let u, v be as above. Then $L_uL_v(p) = uvp = up = p$

$(p \in I)$ and $L_v L_u (x) = vux = vx = x$ $(x \in K)$ show that L_v restricted to I is an isomorphism of (I,T) onto (K,T), its inverse being the restriction of L_u to K.

3.7 PROPOSITION. Let (X,T) be a transformation group, E its enveloping semigroup, I a minimal ideal in E, and $x \in X$. Then the following statements are equivalent:

1. x is an almost periodic point of (X,T).
2. $\overline{xT} = xI = \{xp \mid p \in I\}$.
3. There exists an idempotent $u \in I$ with $xu = x$.

PROOF. 1. implies 2. Let x be an almost periodic point. Then $\overline{xT}$ is a minimal subset of X (2.5). Moreover, $\overline{xT} = xE \supset xI$ by (3.3 number 2). Since xI is closed and invariant, $\overline{xT} = xI$.

2. implies 3. Let $\overline{xT} = xI$. Then $x \in xI$ whence $L = \{p \mid p \in I, xp = x\}$ is a non-empty closed subsemigroup of I. Hence there exists an idempotent $u \in I \cap L$. Then $xu = x$.

3. implies 1. We have $\theta_x(u) = x$ where $\theta_x\colon p \to xp$ is the homomorphism of E into X discussed in (3.3). Since I is a minimal subset of E, u is an almost periodic point of (E,T) (2.5). Hence x is an almost periodic point of (X,T) (2.7).

3.8 PROPOSITION. Let $\theta\colon (X,T,\pi) \overset{\rightarrow}{\rightarrow} (Y,T,\rho)$ be an epimorphism. Then there exists a unique epimorphism $\psi\colon (E(X),T) \overset{\rightarrow}{\rightarrow} (E(Y),T)$ such that the diagram

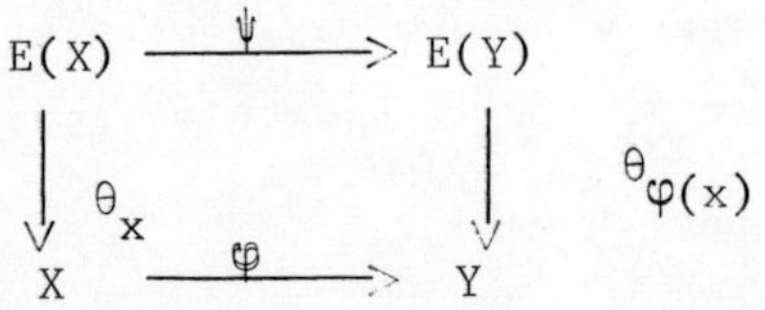

$$\begin{array}{ccc} E(X) & \xrightarrow{\psi} & E(Y) \\ \downarrow \theta_x & & \downarrow \theta_{\varphi(x)} \\ X & \xrightarrow{\varphi} & Y \end{array}$$

commutes $(x \in X)$.

Moreover ψ is also a semigroup homomorphism.

PROOF. Let $p \in E(X)$ and (t_α), (s_α) nets in T with $t_\alpha \to p$ and $s_\alpha \to p$. Let $y \in Y$. Then $y = \varphi(x)$ for some $x \in X$, and $yt_\alpha \to \varphi(xp)$ and $ys_\alpha \to \varphi(xp)$. This shows that both (t_α) and (s_α) converge to the same element in $E(Y)$ and thus allows us to define $\psi(p) = \lim t_\alpha$ in $E(Y)$. Also, $y\psi(p) = \lim yt_\alpha = \varphi(xp)$ shows that the above diagram is commutative.

Now let (p_α) be a net in $E(X)$ with $p_\alpha \to p$. Then $y\psi(p_\alpha) = \varphi(xp_\alpha) \to \varphi(xp) = y\psi(p)$. Thus $\psi(p_\alpha) \to \psi(p)$ whence ψ is continuous.

Let $t \in T$. Then the one element net $(t) \to t$ in both $E(X)$ and $E(Y)$. Thus $\psi(t) = t$. Hence ψ is onto.

Now let $p \in E(X)$, $t \in T$ and (t_α) a net in T with $t_\alpha \to p$. Then $t_\alpha t \to pt$ and $\psi(pt) = \lim t_\alpha t = \lim \psi(t_\alpha)t = \psi(p)t$. Thus ψ is a transformation group homomorphism.

Let $p,q \in E(X)$ and (t_α) a net in T with $t_\alpha \to q$. Then $pt_\alpha \to pq$ and $\psi(pq) = \lim \psi(pt_\alpha) = \lim \psi(p)t_\alpha = \psi(p)\lim \psi(t_\alpha) = \psi(p)\psi(q)$.

The uniqueness of ψ follows immediately from the fact that φ is onto.

3.9 PROPOSITION. Let (X_i,T) $(i \in I)$ be transformation groups and $(X,T) = \Pi(X_i,T)$. Then $E(X) \cong \overline{uT} \subset \Pi E(X_i)$ where $u = (e_i \mid i \in I)$ and e_i = identity of $E(X_i)$ $(i \in I)$.

PROOF. Let $\varphi_i\colon (X,T) \overset{\sim}{\to} (X_i,T)$ be the projection. Then by 3.8 there exist epimorphisms $\psi_i\colon E(X) \overset{\sim}{\to} E(X_i)$ such that $\varphi_i(xp) = \varphi_i(x)\psi_i(p)$ $(x \in X,\ p \in E(X),\ i \in I)$.

Then ψ: $p \to (\psi_i(p) \mid i \in I)$ is a homomorphism of $E(X)$ into $\Pi E(X_i)$.

If $\psi(p) = \psi(q)$ then $\psi_i(p) = \psi_i(q)$ $(i \in I)$ whence $\varphi_i(xp) = \varphi_i(xq)$ $(x \in X,\ i \in I)$. Hence $xp = xq$ $(x \in X)$ and so $p = q$. Thus ψ is one-one and consequently $E(X)$ is isomorphic with the image of ψ.

Since $\psi_i(e) = e_i$ $(i \in I)$, $\psi(e) = u$. Hence $\psi(E(X)) = \psi(\overline{eT}) = \overline{\psi(e)T} = \overline{uT}$.

3.10 COROLLARY. Let (X,T) be a transformation group and I a non-empty set. Then $(E(X),T) \cong (E(X^I),T)$.

PROOF. Let $(X_i,T) = (X,T)$ $(i \in I)$, ρ_i: $E(X) \xrightarrow{\sim} E(X_i)$ the identity map, and ρ the induced map of $E(X) \to \Pi E(X_i)$. Then ρ is an isomorphism of $E(X)$ onto $\overline{uT}$ where $u = (e_i \mid i \in I)$ and e_i is the identity of $E(X_i)$.

By 3.9 $E(X^I) \cong \overline{uT} \subset \Pi E(X_i)$.

Note that if ψ: $E(X) \xrightarrow{\sim} E(X^I)$ is the isomorphism produced above, $(x_i \mid i \in I)\psi(p) = (x_i p \mid i \in I)$ $(p \in E(X),\ x_i \in X)$.

CHAPTER 4

UNIFORM ALMOST PERIODICITY OR EQUICONTINUITY

One way of attempting to classify minimal sets is to add properties to minimality with the hope of simplifying the problem. Thus one studies minimal sets which also have some additional property P. This forms a subclass of the class of all minimal sets, and if P is wisely chosen this subclass will be rich enough to be worth investigating but not so rich that the investigation is hopeless.

In this chapter, the additional property studied is uniform almost periodicity. For our purposes it is too strong. Indeed if (X,T) is uniformly almost periodic and minimal, then there exists a compact topological group G such that T is dense in G and $(X,T) \cong (G/H,T)$ where H is a closed subgroup of G. (If moreover T is abelian, then H reduces to the identity.) This means that the action of T on X is "more or less equivalent" to the action of the compact group G on the homogeneous space G/H. In topological dynamics we are interested in the action of discrete rather than compact groups.

Despite the above remarks we investigate the class of

almost periodic transformation groups rather thoroughly because these serve as a touchstone for the theory. They serve as the "nice" transformation groups, and one wishes to know how far a given transformation group "differs from" a nice one.

4.1 DEFINITION. The transformation group (X,T) is (uniformly) almost periodic if given any index α on X, there exists a syndetic subset A of T such that $xA \subset x\alpha (x \in X)$. (Recall that X is assumed to be compact T_2 and so is endowed with a unique uniform structure.)

Notice that by a standard argument in uniform spaces this is equivalent to: given any index α on X there exist an index β on X and a syndetic subset A of T such that $(xt,yt) \in \alpha \quad ((x,y) \in \beta,\ t \in A)$. (In terms of the product transformation group $(X \times X,T)$, $\beta A \subset \alpha$).

Of course if (X,T) is uniformily almost periodic, then x is an almost periodic point of (X,T) $(x \in X)$.

The study of uniform almost periodicity is facilitated by the introduction of the so called regionally proximal relation, $Q(X,T) = \bigcap\{\overline{\alpha T} \mid \alpha \text{ an index of } X\}$. (The reason for the above terminology will become apparent in Chapter 5.)

4.2 LEMMA. Let (X,T) be almost periodic and I a nonempty set. Then (X^I,T) is almost periodic.

PROOF. A basic index of X^I is of the form $\alpha_J = \Pi\alpha_i$ where J is a finite subset of I, α_i an index of X $(i \in J)$ and $\alpha_i = X \times X$ $(i \notin J)$. Let $\alpha = \bigcap_J \alpha_i$, β an index, and A a syndetic subset of T with $\beta A \subset \alpha$. Then $\beta_J A \subset \alpha_J$ where $\beta_J = \Pi\beta_i$, $\beta_i = \beta$ $(i \in J)$, and $\beta_i = X \times X$ $(i \notin J)$.

4.3 LEMMA. Let (X,T) be a transformation group and Q the regionally proximal relation on X. Then

1. Q is a closed invariant subset of $(X \times X,T)$
2. (X,T) is almost periodic iff $Q = \Delta$, the diagonal iff given α, $\beta T \subset \alpha$ for some β (i.e. T is equicontinuous).

PROOF. 1. is immediate.

2. Let (X,T) be almost periodic and α a closed index. Let $AK = T$ with K compact and let β be an index with $\beta A \subset \alpha$. Then $\overline{\beta T} = \overline{\beta AK} \subset \overline{\alpha K} = \alpha K \subset \alpha T$, whence $Q \subset \cap\{\alpha T \mid \alpha \text{ index}\}$. But if $(x,y) \in \cap\{\alpha T \mid \alpha \text{ index}\}$, $\Delta \cap \overline{(x,y)T} \neq \emptyset$ whence $(x,t) \in \Delta$ by 4.2.

Now suppose $Q = \Delta$ and let α be an open index of X. If the family of closed sets $(\overline{\beta T} \cap \alpha' \mid \beta \text{ index})$ has the finite intersection property, then $Q \cap \alpha' \neq \emptyset$. Hence there exists β with $\overline{\beta T} \subset \alpha$. The last equivalence is clear.

4.4 PROPOSITION. The following statements are pairwise equivalent:

1. (X,T) is uniformly almost periodic.
2. T is equicontinuous.
3. $E(X,T)$ is a group of continuous maps of X into X.

PROOF. 1. and 2. are equivalent by 4.3.

2 implies 3. Let α be a closed index of X and β an index with $\beta T \subset \alpha$. Then $\beta p \subset \overline{\alpha} = \alpha$ $(p \in E)$, whence every element of E is continuous.

Now let $u^2 = u \in E$, $x \in X$, and $y = xu$. Then $(y,y) = (x,y)u \in \overline{(x,y)T}$ and since (x,y) is an almost periodic point of $(X \times X,T)$ (4.2), $x = y$. Thus $u = e$ and E is a group.

3 implies 1. Let α be an index on X. Then by [1] the map $f\colon (x,p) \to xp$ of $X \times E \to X$ is continuous. Hence

there exists a neighborhood N of the identity e of E with $xN \subset x\alpha$ $(x \in X)$.

Since $\overline{T} = E$ and E is compact there exists a finite subset F of T with $E = NF$. Then if $A = T \cap N$, $T = AF$ and $xA \subset x\alpha$ $(x \in X)$.

In view of the equivalence of statements 1 and 2 above we shall often say that (X,T) is equicontinuous rather than that (X,T) is uniformly almost periodic.

4.5 <u>COROLLARY</u>. Let (X,T) be almost periodic. Then:

1. E(X,T) is a group of homeomorphisms of X onto X.

2. The map ψ: $(x,p) \to xp$ of $X \times E$ into X defines a transformation group structure on (X,E).

3. The transformation group (X,T_d) is almost periodic, where T_d is T provided with the discrete topology.

(Since it is evident that if (X,T_d) is almost periodic so is (X,T), the notion of uniform almost periodicity does not depend on the topology of T.)

<u>PROOF</u>. 1. This follows from 3 of 4.4.

2. The continuity of ψ follows from 3 of 4.4 and [1].

3. This follows from 4.4 and the fact that whether or not T is equicontinuous does not depend on the topology of T.

4.6 <u>REMARKS AND EXAMPLES</u>.

1. Let (X,T) be uniformly almost periodic and minimal, $x \in X$, and θ_x: $(E,T) \xrightarrow{\simeq} (X,T)$ where $\theta_x(p) = xp$ $(p \in E)$. Let $H = \{p \mid \theta_x(p) = x\}$. Then H is a closed subgroup of the compact topological group E, (H,E,T) is a bitransformation group and θ_x induces an isomorphism of (E/H,T) onto (X,T).

2. If in addition to the above assumptions T is abelian, $H = \{e\}$. (If T is abelian, $tp = pt$ $(t \in T, p \in E)$. Then by continuity E is abelian. Hence $p \in H$ implies $xp = x$,

whence $xtp = xpt = xt$ $(x \in X)$. Since p is continuous and $\overline{xT} = X$, $yp = y$ $(y \in X)$, i.e. $p = e$). Thus in this case $(E,T) \cong (X,T)$, i.e. X is essentially a compact abelian topological group, and T is a dense subgroup of X which acts by right multiplication.

3. The classic example of a uniformly almost periodic transformation group is a rotation of a circle. Here X is the group of complex numbers of modulus 1 and φ: $x \to xa$ $(x \in X)$ where $a \in X$.

Then the orbit closure of the point $1 \in X$ is the subgroup $H = \mathrm{cl}\{a^n \mid n = 0, \pm 1, \ldots\}$.

Now the only closed proper subgroups of X are finite. Hence $H = X$ or H is finite. Thus (X, φ) is minimal or H is finite. In the latter case there exists an integer n with $a^n = 1$. If we write $a = e^{i\theta}$ then $a^n = e^{in\theta}$ whence $n\theta = 2k\pi$ for some integer k. Thus in this case θ is a rational multiple of π.

Summing up: The transformation group (X, φ) is almost periodic; it is minimal iff φ is a rotation through an angle which is an irrational multiple of π.

4.7 <u>PROPOSITION</u>. Let θ: $(X,T) \overset{\sim}{\to} (Y,T)$ be an epimorphism, and let (X,T) be almost periodic. Then (Y,T) is almost periodic.

<u>PROOF</u>. Let η be an index of Y. Then there exists an index α of X with $\theta(x\alpha) \subset \theta(x)\eta$ $(x \in X)$. If $xA \subset x\alpha$ with A syndetic $(x \in X)$, then $\theta(x)A = \theta(xA) \subset \theta(x)\eta$. Since θ is onto, $yA \subset y\eta$ $(y \in Y)$.

4.8 <u>PROPOSITION</u>. 1. Let (X,T) be almost periodic and let M be a closed invariant subset of X. Then (M,T) is also almost periodic.

2. Let (X_i,T) $(i \in I)$ be a family of transformation groups, and $(X,T) = \Pi(X_i,T)$. Then (X,T) is almost periodic iff (X_i,T) is almost periodic $(i \in I)$.

PROOF. 1. is immediate.

2. Let (X,T) be almost periodic. Then (X_i,T) is almost periodic by 4.7.

Let (X_i,T) be almost periodic $(i \in I)$ and $\alpha_J = \Pi\alpha_i$ a basic index of ΠX_i. Thus α_i is an index of X_i $(i \in J)$ and $\alpha_i = X_i \times X_i$ $(i \notin J)$ where J is a finite subset of I. Then there exist indices β_i of X_i $(i \in J)$ with $\beta_i T \subset \alpha_i$ (2 of 4.4) Hence $\delta T \subset \alpha_J$ where $\delta = \Pi\delta_i$, $\delta_i = \beta_i$ $(i \in J)$ and $\delta_i = X_i \times X_i$ $(i \notin J)$.

I now wish to discuss almost periodicity in terms of the orbit closure relation (1.7) on (X,T). To this end I use the following well-known lemma.

4.9 LEMMA. Let X be a compact T_2 space, and R an equivalence relation on X. Then X/R is T_2 iff R is a closed subset of $X \times X$.

4.10 PROPOSITION. Let (X,T) be almost periodic, and $R = \{(x,y) \mid y \in \overline{xT}\}$ the orbit closure relation on X. Then R is a closed invariant equivalence relation on X. (Thus in this case X/R is T_2).

PROOF. By 3 of 4.4 and [1] $E(X)$ is a compact topological group. Proposition 4.10 now follows from 1 of 4.5 and the fact that R is just the orbit relation of (X,E).

Proposition 4.10 shows that when (X,T) is almost periodic it is necessary that the orbit closure relation R be a closed invariant equivalence relation. However, this condition is not sufficient since if (X,T) is minimal $R = X \times X$ but (X,T) need not be almost periodic

To obtain a sufficient condition we must consider $(X \times X,T)$ rather than (X,T).

4.11 PROPOSITION. Let (X,T) be a transformation group, and let S be the orbit closure relation on $(X \times X,T)$. Then (X,T) is almost periodic iff S is a closed invariant equivalence relation on $X \times X$.

PROOF. Let (X,T) be almost periodic. Then $(X \times X,T)$ is almost periodic by 4.2. Hence S is a closed invariant equivalence relation (4.10).

Now suppose S is a closed invariant equivalence relation on X.

Let α be an open index on X. Then the diagonal, Δ of $X \times X$ is a closed saturated subset of α. ($\Delta T = \Delta$ implies $\Delta S = \Delta$).

Now let Π: $X \times X \to X \times X/S$ be the canonical map. Then $\Pi(\alpha')$ is compact hence closed since $X \times X/S$ is T_2. Thus $\Pi^{-1}\Pi(\alpha') = \alpha' S$ is a closed invariant subset of $X \times X$. Then $\Delta \subset (\alpha' S)' \subset \alpha$ and $(\alpha' S)'$ is an open invariant neighborhood of Δ. Set $\beta = (\alpha' S)'$. Then β is an index with $\beta T \subset \alpha$.

I would now like to characterize the almost periodicity of (X,T) in terms of $C(X)$, the algebra of real-valued continuous functions on X. This will be done by means of the notion of an almost periodic function on (X,T). To motivate this concept let us recall some classical definitions.

4.12 DEFINITION. (von-Neumann) Let T be a topological group, $C_o(T)$ the Banach algebra of bounded real-valued functions on T with the supremum norm, and let $f \in C_o(T)$.

Then f is a (right) almost periodic function if the closure of $\{R_t f \mid t \in T\}$ is a compact subset of $C_o(T)$, where $R_t f(s) = f(st)$ $(s,t \in T)$.

4.13 REMARKS. 1. We could, of course, have defined the notion of a left almost periodic function. However in [2] von-Neumann showed that f is right almost periodic iff f is left almost periodic.

2. When $T = \mathbb{R}$, we already have the notion of an almost periodic function due to Bohr (see beginning of Chapter 2). Bochner showed that in this case the two notions coincide when we restrict ourselves to continuous functions.

Since we have the notion of relatively dense (i.e. syndetic) for arbitrary groups we might mimic Bohr's definition viz.: f is Bohr-right almost periodic if given $\varepsilon > 0$ there exists a syndetic subset A of T such that $| f(ta) - f(t) | < \varepsilon$ $(t \in T, a \in A)$.

When T is abelian one can show that the two notions (von-Neumann and Bohr almost periodicity) yield the same class of continuous functions. However, all that can be said in the general case is that a continuous von-Neumann almost periodic function is also Bohr almost periodic. In [3] Wu shows that a Bohr left almost periodic function need not be Bohr-right almost periodic.

It will be convenient for us to mimic the von-Neumann rather than the Bohr definition of almost periodicity in defining an almost periodic function on (X,T).

4.14 DEFINITION. Let (X,T) be a transformation group, C(X) the Banach algebra of real-valued continuous functions on X with the supremum norm, and let $f \in C(X)$. Then f is almost periodic if the closure of $\{tf \mid t \in T\}$ is a compact subset of C(X), where $tf(x) = f(xt)$ $(t \in T, x \in X)$.

4.15 <u>PROPOSITION</u>. Let (X,T) be a transformation group. Then (X,T) is almost periodic iff f is almost periodic $(f \in C(X))$.

<u>PROOF</u>. Let (X,T) be almost periodic and $f \in C(X)$. Then by 2 of 4.4 the family $(tf \mid t \in T)$ is equicontinuous. Hence f is almost periodic by Ascoli's theorem.

Now assume f is almost periodic $(f \in C(X))$ and let α be an index on X. Then there exist $\varepsilon > 0$ and F a finite subset of $C(X)$ such that $|f(x) - f(y)| < \varepsilon$ $(f \in F)$ implies $(x,y) \in \alpha$. By Ascoli's theorem the families $(tf \mid t \in T)$ $(f \in F)$ are equicontinuous. Thus since F is finite, there exists an index β of X with $|tf(x) - tf(y)| = |f(xt) - f(yt)| < \varepsilon$ $(t \in T,\ f \in F,\ (x,y) \in \beta)$. Hence $\beta T \subset \alpha$ and T is equicontinuous.

4.16 <u>LEMMA</u>. Let (X,T) be a transformation and S a syndetic subgroup of T. Then $Q(X,T) = Q(X,S)$.

<u>PROOF</u>. Clearly $Q(X,S) \subset Q(X,T)$.

Let $T = SK = K^{-1}S$ with K compact and let α,β be indices of X with $\beta K^{-1} \subset \alpha$. Then $\beta T = \beta K^{-1}S \subset \alpha S$ shows that $Q(X,T) \subset Q(X,S)$.

4.17 <u>PROPOSITION</u>. (Inheritance theorem). Let (X,T) be a transformation group, and S a syndetic subgroup of T. Then (X,T) is almost periodic iff (X,S) is almost periodic.

<u>PROOF</u>. Use 4.16 and 2 of 4.3

In general we shall not be interested in almost periodic transformation groups per se. Rather we shall try to relate the study of an arbitrary transformation group to that of an almost periodic one. This is the reason for the introduction below of the structure group.

4.18 PROPOSITION. Let (X,T) be a transformation group, $\mathfrak{R}$ the collection of closed invariant equivalence relations R on X with $(X/R,T)$ almost periodic, and let $S = \cap \{R \mid R \in \mathfrak{R}\}$. Then $S \in \mathfrak{R}$.

PROOF. That S is a closed invariant equivalence relation on X is immediate.

Let Π_R: $(X/S,T) \overset{\sim}{\to} (X/R,T)$ be the canonical map $(R \in \mathfrak{R})$. Then the induced product map $\Pi_0:(X/S,T) \to (\Pi X/R,T)$ is an isomorphism of $(X/S,T)$ onto a closed invariant subset of $(\Pi X/R,T)$. Since the latter is almost periodic by 2 of 4.8, $(X/S,T)$ is almost periodic by 1 of 4.8.

4.19 REMARKS. 1. Notice that S is the smallest closed invariant equivalence relation R such that $(X/R,T)$ is almost periodic.

2. S is called the equicontinuous structure relation on (X,T).

3. $E(X/S,T)$ is a compact topological group called the structure group of (X,T).

4.20 PROPOSITION. Let (X,T) be a transformation group and S its equicontinuous structure relation. Then S is the smallest closed invariant equivalence relation on X which contains $Q(X,T)$.

PROOF. Let $Y = X/S$ and Π: $(X,T) \overset{\sim}{\to} (Y,T)$ the projection. Since (Y,T) is equicontinuous, $Q(Y,T) = \Delta_Y$, the diagonal of Y. Then the uniform continuity of Π implies that $\Pi \times \Pi\ (Q(X,T)) \subset \Delta_Y$, whence $Q(X,T) \subset S$.

Now let R be a closed invariant equivalence relation on X with $Q \subset R$ and $Z = X/R$. I shall show that (Z,T) is equicontinuous by showing that $E(Z)$ is a group of continuous maps of Z onto Z (4 of 4.4).

Let $\Pi: (X,T) \overset{\sim}{\to} (Z,T)$ be the projection and $\psi: E(X) \overset{\sim}{\to} E(Z)$ the epimorphism induced by Π.

Let $p \in E(Z)$, (z_α) a net in Z with $z_\alpha \to z \in Z$, $q \in E(X)$ with $\psi(q) = p$, and (x_α) a net in X with $\Pi(x_\alpha) = z_\alpha$ for all α. We may assume $x_\alpha \to x \in X$, and $x_\alpha q \to y \in X$.

Let β be an index of X. Then $(x_\alpha, x) \in \beta$ $(\alpha \geq \alpha_o)$. Hence $\overline{(x_\alpha, x)\ T} \subset \overline{\beta T}$ and so $(x_\alpha q, xq) \in \overline{\beta T}$ $(\alpha \geq \alpha_o)$. Thus $(y, xq) \in \overline{\beta T}$. Since β was arbitrary this implies that $(y, xq) \in Q(X,T)$ whence $\Pi(y) = \Pi(xq) = \Pi(x)\psi(q) = \Pi(x)p$.

Now $z = \lim z_\alpha = \lim \Pi(x_\alpha) = \Pi(x)$ and $z_\alpha p = \Pi(x_\alpha)\psi(q) = \Pi(x_\alpha q)$. Hence $\lim z_\alpha p = \lim \Pi(x_\alpha q) = \Pi(y) = \Pi(x)p = zp$.

Finally let $u^2 = u \in E(Z)$, $v^2 = v \in E(X)$ with $\psi(v) = u$, and α an index of X. Then $(xv, xv) \in \overline{(x, xv)T}$ implies $(x, xv) \in \overline{\alpha T}$ $(x \in X)$. Hence $(x, xv) \in Q(X,T)$ whence $\Pi(x) = \Pi(xv) = \Pi(x)u$ $(x \in X)$. Thus $u = e$ and $E(Y)$ is a group.

NOTES

1. Robert Ellis, *Locally compact transformation groups*, Duke Math. Journal, vol.24 (1957), 119-125.

2. John von-Neumann, *Almost periodic functions in a group I*, Trans. A.M.S., vol.36 (1934), 445-492.

3. T.S. Wu, *Left almost periodicity does not imply right almost periodicity*, Bull. A.M.S., vol.72 (1966), 314-316.

CHAPTER 5

DISTAL AND PROXIMAL

In this chapter we begin the study of distal transformation groups. The concept of "distallity" has proved to be a very fruitful one for topological dynamics, giving rise to a rather extensive theory. This will be discussed in subsequent chapters; here we just introduce the basic definitions and properties.

Before proceeding, let me remind the reader that the phase spaces of all the transformation groups involved are assumed to be compact T_2.

5.1 <u>DEFINITION</u>. The transformation group (X,T) is <u>distal</u> if given $x,y \in X$ with $x \neq y$, there exists an index α of X with $(xt,yt) \notin \alpha$ $(t \in T)$.

5.2 <u>REMARKS</u>. 1. In general the index α depends on the pair (x,y).

2. If X is a metric space with metric d, then (X,T) is distal iff $\inf\{d(xt,yt) \mid t \in T\} = 0$ implies $x = y$.

3. In general (X,T) is distal iff $xt_\alpha \to z$ and $yt_\alpha \to z$ implies $x = y$ $(x,y,z \in X$ and (t_α) a net in $T)$. In

terms of $(X \times X,T)$ this means that if $x \neq y$, then $\overline{(x,y)T} \cap \Delta = \emptyset$ where Δ is the diagonal of $X \times X$.

5.3 <u>PROPOSITION</u>. The following are pairwise equivalent:

1. (X,T) is distal.
2. $E(X)$ is a minimal right ideal.
3. $E(X)$ is a group.

(Caution: (X,T) distal does not imply that $E(X)$ is a topological group. It implies only that the elements of $E(X)$ are invertible. They need not be continuous.)

<u>PROOF</u>. 1 implies 2. Let I be a minimal right ideal in $E(X)$, $u^2 = u \in I$, $x \in X$ and $y = xu$. Then $(xu,yu) = (x,y)u \in \overline{(x,y)T}$ shows that $\overline{(x,y)T} \cap \Delta \neq \emptyset$. Hence $x = y$ (3 of 5.2) and $u = e$. Thus $I = E(X)$.

2 implies 3. Since $e^2 = e$, $E(X) = E(X)e$ is a group by 3 of 3.5.

3 implies 1. Let $(z,z) \in \overline{(x,y)T} \cap \Delta$. Then there exists $p \in E(X)$ with $z = xp = yp$. Hence $x = xpp^{-1} = zp^{-1} = ypp^{-1} = y$.

5.4 <u>COROLLARY</u>. If (X,T) is almost periodic then it is distal.

<u>PROOF</u>. (4.4) and (5.3).

The following examples illustrate the fact that distal is an "orbital property" (i.e. (X,T) is distal if $(\overline{xT},T)$ is distal $(x \in X)$) whereas almost periodicity is not.

1. Let X be the set of complex numbers z with $|z| \leq 1$ and $\varphi: z \to ze^i$. Then (X,φ) is both almost periodic and distal

2. Let X be as above but now set $\psi(z) = ze^{i|z|}$ $(z \in X)$. Then on the orbit closure of each point everything is fine so that (X,ψ) is distal. However, it is not too hard

to see that it is not almost periodic.

Even if (X,T) is minimal and distal it need not be almost periodic. However, I defer giving an example until later (2 of 6.19).

5.5 COROLLARY. Let (X,T) be distal. Then x is an almost periodic point $(x \in X)$. (In this case (X,T) is said to be pointwise almost periodic in contrast to uniformly almost periodic.)

PROOF. When (X,T) is distal, $E(X)$ is a minimal right ideal (5.3) and $e \in E(X)$. The corollary now follows from 3 of 3.7.

5.6 EXAMPLE. (The roving circle) Let X be the circle and T the group of all homeomorphisms of X onto X. Then $xT = X$ $(x \in X)$ whence (X,T) is a minimal set. However, given any two points $x,y \in X$, there exists a net (t_α) in T with $xt_\alpha \to x$ and $yt_\alpha \to x$. Thus (X,T) is "highly" non-distal.

5.7 COROLLARY. Let (X,T) be distal and let $\varphi: (X,T) \overset{\sim}{\to} (Y,T)$ be an epimorphism. Then (Y,T) is distal.

PROOF. By 3.8 there exists a semigroup homomorphism Ψ of $E(X)$ onto $E(Y)$. Hence $E(Y)$ is a group and (Y,T) is distal.

5.8 PROPOSITION. Let (X_i,T) $(i \in I)$ be distal. Then $(\Pi X_i,T)$ is distal.

PROOF. $E(X_i)$ is a group $(i \in I)$. Hence $E(\Pi X_i)$ is a group since it is isomorphic to a closed subsemigroup of the group $\Pi E(X_i)$ (3.9 and 2.11).

5.9 PROPOSITION. Let (X,T) be a transformation group. Then the following statements are pairwise equivalent:

1. (X,T) is distal.

2. (X^I,T) is pointwise almost periodic where I is a set with at least two elements.

3. $(X \times X,T)$ is pointwise almost periodic.

<u>PROOF</u>. 1. implies 2. Use 5.8 and 5.5.

2. implies 3. Clear.

3. implies 1. Let $x,y \in X$ with $\overline{(x,y)T} \cap \Delta \neq \emptyset$. Then $\overline{(x,y)T} \subset \Delta$ since Δ is closed and invariant. Hence $x = y$.

5.10 <u>DEFINITION</u>. Let (X,T) be a transformation group and $x,y \in X$. Then x and y are <u>proximal</u> if given an index α of X, there exists $t \in T$ with $(xt,yt) \in \alpha$. The set of proximal pairs will be denoted $P(X,T)$ or simply P.

5.11 <u>REMARKS</u>. 1. It follows immediately from 5.10 that $P(X,T) = \cap \{\alpha T \mid \alpha \text{ an index of } X\}$.

2. Another characterization of $P(X,T)$ is that $(x,y) \in P(X,T)$ iff $\overline{(x,y)T} \cap \Delta \neq \emptyset$ and since $\overline{(x,y)T} = (x,y)E$, $(x,y) \in P(X,T)$ iff $(x,y)E \cap \Delta \neq \emptyset$.

3. Recall that the regionally proximal relation $Q(X,T)$ was defined to be $\cap \{\overline{\alpha T} \mid \alpha \text{ index}\}$. It is a simple exercise to show that $(x,y) \in Q(X,T)$ iff given an index α and neighborhoods U and V of x and y respectively there exist $x_1 \in U$, $y_1 \in V$, and $t \in T$ with $(x_1t,y_1t) \in \alpha$.

4. Let $(x,y) \in P$ and let (x,y) be an almost periodic point of $(X \times X,T)$. Then $x = y$ for if $(z,z) \in \overline{(x,y)T}$ then $(x,y) \in \overline{(z,z)T} \subset \Delta$ since Δ is a closed invariant subset of $X \times X$.

The proofs of the next three results are straightforward and will be omitted.

5.12 <u>LEMMA</u>. The transformation group (X,T) is distal iff $P(X,T) = \Delta$, the diagonal of $X \times X$.

5.13 LEMMA. Let S be a syndetic subgroup of T. Then $P(X,S) = P(X,T)$.

5.14 PROPOSITION. (Inheritance theorem) Let (X,T) be a transformation group, and let S be a syndetic subgroup of T. Then (X,T) is distal iff (X,S) is distal.

5.5 LEMMA. Let (X,T) be a transformation group, and $x,y \in X$. Then the following statements are pairwise equivalent:

1. $(x,y) \in P(X,T)$.
2. There exists $p \in E(X)$ with $xp = yp$.
3. There exists a minimal right ideal I in $E(X)$ such that $xq = yq$ $(q \in I)$.

PROOF. The equivalence of 1 and 2 is just 2 of 5.11.

2 implies 3. Let I be a minimal right ideal in $E(X)$. Then so is pI and $xq = yq$ $(q \in pI)$.

Clearly 3 implies 2.

5.16 PROPOSITION. Let (X,T) be a transformation group. Then:

1. $P(X,T)$ is invariant, reflexive and symmetric.
2. $P(X,T)$ is transitive iff there is only one minimal right ideal in $E(X)$.

PROOF. 1. is immediate.

2. Let $P(X,T)$ be transitive, I,K minimal right ideals in $E(X)$, and $u^2 = u \in I$, $v^2 = v \in K$ with $uv = u$ and $vu = v$. Let $x \in X$. Then $(x,xu) \in P(X,T)$ and $(x,xv) \in P(X,T)$ implies $(xu,xv) \in P(X,T)$. But $(xu,xv)v = (xu,xv)$ implies that (xu,xv) is an almost periodic point of $(X \times X,T)$. Hence $xu = xv$ (4 of 5.11) and $I = K$.

Now let I be the only minimal right ideal in $E(X)$ and $(x,y) \in P$ and $(y,z) \in P$. Then $xp = yp = zp$ $(p \in I)$ by 3 of

5.15 and so $(x,z) \in P$ (5.15).

5.16 <u>REMARKS</u>. 1. In general $P(X,T)$ need not be an equivalence relation as the following example shows. Let X be the closed unit interval and $\varphi: X \to X$ such that $\varphi(x) = x^2$. Then $P(X,\varphi) = X \times X - \{(0,1),(1,0)\}$.

2. Statement 3 of 5.16 gives a necessary and sufficient condition for $P(X,T)$ to be an invariant equivalence relation. However, it need not be closed. Let X be the set of complex numbers z such that $1 \leq |z| \leq 2$ and $\varphi(r \exp(2\pi it)) = r \exp(2\pi it^r)$ $(1 \leq r \leq 2,\ 0 \leq t \leq 1)$. Then $P = \Delta \cup \{(u,v) \mid |u| = |v| \neq 1\}$.

It is an open question whether (X,T) minimal and $P(X,T)$ an equivalence relation implies that $P(X,T)$ is closed.

On the other hand we have the following:

5.17 <u>LEMMA</u>. Let $P(X,T)$ be closed. Then it is an equivalence relation on X.

<u>PROOF</u>. Let I,K be minimal right ideals in E(X), $u^2 = u \in I$ and $v^2 = v \in K$ with $uv = u$ and $vu = v$. Let $x \in X$. Then $(x,xu) \in P$ implies that $(xv,xu) = (x,xu)v \in P$. But (xv,xu) is also an almost periodic point of $(X \times X,T)$. Hence $xv = xu$ (4 of 5.11) and $I = K$. Lemma 5.17 now follows from 5.15.

5.18 <u>COROLLARY</u>. Let $P(X,T) = Q(X,T)$. Then $P(X,T)$ is a closed invariant equivalence relation on X and $(X/P,T)$ is equicontinuous.

<u>PROOF</u>. Since $Q(X,T)$ is closed, $P(X,T)$ is a closed invariant equivalence relation by 5.17. By 4.20 $(X/P,T)$ is equicontinuous.

The proof of the following lemma is immediate.

5.20 LEMMA. Let (X,T) be distal and let M be a closed invariant subset of X. Then (M,T) is distal.

5.21 PROPOSITION. Let (X,T) be a transformation group, let $\mathfrak{R}$ be the collection of closed invariant equivalence relations R on X such that (X/R,T) is distal, and let $S = \bigcap \mathfrak{R}$. Then $S \in \mathfrak{R}$.

Thus S is the smallest closed invariant equivalence relation R on X such that X/R is distal. The relation S is called the distal structure relation of (X,T).

PROOF. It is clear that S is a closed invariant equivalence relation on X.

Let Π_R: (X/S,T) $\tilde{\to}$ (X/R,T) be the canonical epimorphism ($R \in \mathfrak{R}$). Then the induced product map Π_o: (X/S,T) $\to$ (ΠX/R,T) is an isomorphism onto a closed invariant, subset of (ΠX/R,T). 5.21 now follows from 5.8 and 5.20.

5.22 PROPOSITION. Let φ: (X,T) $\tilde{\to}$ (Y,T) be an epimorphism, and $\check{\varphi}$: X x X $\to$Y x Y the map induced by φ. Then:

1. If P(X,T) is an equivalence relation, so is P(Y,T).

2. $\check{\varphi}$ P(X,T) $\subset$ P(Y,T).

3. If (Y,T) is pointwise almost periodic, $\check{\varphi}$ P(X,T) = P(Y,T). (Thus in this case P(X,T) closed implies that P(Y,T) is also closed.)

PROOF. 1. Let ψ: E(X) $\tilde{\to}$ E(Y) be the epimorphism induced by φ and let K be a minimal right ideal in E(Y). Then ψ^{-1}(K) is a right ideal in E(X) whence it contains the unique minimal right ideal I of E(X). Then ψ(I) $\subset$ K, and by the minimality of K, ψ(I) = K. Thus E(Y) has only one minimal right ideal and 1 follows from 5.16.

2. Let $(x_1,x_2) \in$ P(X,T). Then by 5.15 there exists

$p \in E(X)$ with $x_1p = x_2p$. Therefore $\varphi(x_1)\psi(p) = \varphi(x_1p) = \varphi(x_2p) = \varphi(x_2)\psi(p)$ and $\check{\varphi}(x_1,x_2) = (\varphi x_1, \varphi x_2) \in P(Y,T)$.

3. Let $(y_1,y_2) \in P(Y,T)$. Then there exists a minimal right ideal K in $E(Y)$ such that $y_1p = y_2p$ $(p \in K)$ (3 of 5.15).

Since y_2 is an almost periodic point of (Y,T) there exists an idempotent v in K with $y_2v = y_2$ (3.7). Now $\psi^{-1}(v)$ is a closed non-vacuous subsemigroup of $E(X)$ whence it contains an idempotent u.

Finally pick $x_1 \in X$ with $\varphi(x_1) = y_1$. Then $(x_1,x_1u) \in P(X,T)$ and $\check{\varphi}\,(x_1,x_1u) = (\varphi(x_1), \varphi(x_1u)) = (y_1,y_1v) = (y_1,y_2v) = (y_1,y_2)$.

5.23 PROPOSITION. The distal structure relation S of (X,T) is the smallest closed invariant equivalence relation on X which contains $P(X,T)$.

PROOF. Let $\Pi\colon (X,T) \xrightarrow{\sim} (X/S,T)$ be the canonical map. By 2 of 5.22 $\Pi \times \Pi\,(P(X,T)) \subset P(X/S,T) =$ diagonal of $X/S \times X/S$ (5.21 and 5.12). Thus $P(X,T) \subset S$.

Now let R be a closed invariant equivalence relation on X with $P(X,T) \subset R$, let $\varphi\colon (X,T) \xrightarrow{\sim} (X/R,T)$ be the canonical map and $\psi\colon E(X) \xrightarrow{\sim} E(X/R)$ the map induced by φ.

If $u^2 = u \in E(X/R)$ then $\psi^{-1}(u)$ is a closed subsemigroup of $E(X)$. Hence there exists $v^2 = v \in E(X)$ with $\psi(v) = u$. Since $(x,xv) \in P(X,T)$, $\varphi(x) = \varphi(xv) = \varphi(x)u$ $(x \in X)$. Thus $u = e$, $E(X/R)$ is a group and $(X/R,T)$ is distal (5.3).

I would now like to impose a condition on (X,T) which will guarantee that $P(X,T)$ be a closed equivalence relation.

5.24 DEFINITION. The transformation group (X,T) is

<u>locally almost periodic</u> if given $x \in X$ and U a neighborhood of x there exist a neighborhood V of x and a syndetic subset A of T with $VA \subset U$.

5.25 <u>REMARK</u>. Again the notion of local almost periodicity does not depend on the topology of T. Thus if (X,T) is discretely locally almost periodic it is evidently locally almost periodic.

Conversely, let (X,T) be locally almost periodic. I shall show that it remains locally almost periodic when the original topology on T is replaced by the discrete topology.

Let $x \in X$ and U a neighborhood of X. Then there exist neighborhoods W of x and N of e in T with $WN \subset U$.

Since (X,T) is locally almost periodic there exist a neighborhood V of x and a syndetic subset A of T with $VA \subset W$. Let K be a compact subset of T with $AK = T$. Then there exists a finite subset F of T with $K \subset NF$.

Finally set $B = AN$. Then $BF = ANF \supset AK = T$ so that B is discretely syndetic and $VB = VAN \subset WN \subset U$.

5.26 <u>LEMMA</u>. Let (X,T) be locally almost periodic and α an index on X. Then there exists an index β on X such that $\overline{\beta T} \subset \alpha T$.

<u>PROOF</u>. Let γ be a closed index on X and δ a symmetric index with $\delta^2 \subset \gamma \subset \alpha$.

Let $x \in X$. Then there exist a syndetic subset A of T and a neighborhood W_x of x such that $W_x A \subset x\delta$. This implies that $(W_x \times W_x) A \subset x\delta \times x\delta \subset \delta^2 \subset \gamma$. Let K be compact with $AK = T$. Then $\overline{(W_x \times W_x)T} \subset \overline{\delta^2 K} \subset \overline{\gamma K} = \gamma K \subset \alpha T$.

Let F be a finite subset of X such that $\cup \{W_x \mid x \in F\} = X$. Then $\beta = \cup \{W_x \times W_x \mid x \in F\}$ is an index on X and $\overline{\beta T} = \cup \{\overline{(W_x \times W_x)T} \mid x \in F\} \subset \alpha T$.

5.27 PROPOSITION. Let (X,T) be locally almost periodic. Then P is a closed invariant equivalence relation on X and (X/P,T) is uniformly almost periodic.

PROOF. By 5.26 P(X,T) = Q(X,T). Now use 5.18.

5.28 COROLLARY. The transformation group (X,T) is uniformly almost periodic iff it is locally almost periodic and distal.

PROOF. If (X,T) is locally almost periodic and distal (X/P,T) is uniformly almost periodic (5.27) and X/P = X by 5.12.

The converse is clear.

5.29 EXAMPLE. Let Y be the circle. For $a,b \in Y$ let (a,b) be the open arc from a to b traversed in a counterclockwise direction, and $[a,b) = \{a\} \cup (a,b)$.

Let $X = (Y \times 1) \cup (Y \times 2)$ i.e. two copies of Y, $\tau: X \to X$ such that $\tau(a,1) = (a,2)$ and $\tau(a,2) = (a,1)$ $(a \in Y)$.

Make X into a topological space by defining a typical neighborhood of the point (a,1) to be the set $[a,b) \times 1 \cup (a,b) \times 2$ with $b \neq a$ and a typical neighborhood of (a,2) to be the set $(b,a) \times 1 \cup [b,a) \times 2$ with $b \neq a$. Then X is compact T_2 and 0-dimensional.

Now let φ be a rotation through one radian on Y and $\psi: X \to X$ such that $\psi(a,i) = (\varphi(a),i), i = 1,2$. Then (X,ψ) is minimal and locally almost periodic, $P = \{(x,x) \mid x \in X\} \cup \{(x,\tau x) \mid x \in X\}$, and $(X/P,\psi) \cong (Y,\varphi)$.

CHAPTER 6

BITRANSFORMATION GROUPS

In this chapter I would like to consider the previous notions in the context of bitransformation groups. The problem is this: let $\varphi: (X,T) \stackrel{\sim}{\to} (Y,T)$ be an epimorphism, then which 'dynamical' properties of (Y,T) lift to (X,T)? In general very little can be said. (Set Y equal to a one point space. Then any transformation group (X,T) can be mapped homomorphically onto (Y,T)). However, if we start with a bitransformation group (H,X,T) and $Y = X/H$ then it is possible to lift 'information' from (Y,T) to (X,T).

A bitransformation group (H,X,T) involves two transformation groups (H,X) and (X,T), so that from the notation $E(X)$ it is not clear which enveloping semigroup is being referred to. However, I shall always use it to designate the enveloping semigroup of (X,T).

Notice also that H commutes with $E(X)$ as well as T since H is a group of automorphisms of (X,T).

6.1 <u>PROPOSITION</u>. Let $\pi: (X,T) \stackrel{\sim}{\to} (Y,T)$ be an epimorphism and let y be an almost periodic point of (Y,T). Then there exists an almost periodic point x of (X,T) with

$\pi(x) = y$.

PROOF. $\pi^{-1}(\overline{yT})$ is a closed invariant subset of X. Hence it contains a minimal set M. Since $\pi(M)$ is a closed invariant subset of $\overline{yT}$, it must coincide with the latter. Consequently there exists $x \in M$ with $\pi(x) = y$.

6.2 PROPOSITION. Let (H,X,T) be a bitransformation group such that X/H is T_2 and (X/H,T) is pointwise almost periodic. Then (X,T) is also pointwise almost periodic.

PROOF. Let $\pi: X \rightrightarrows X/H$ be the canonical map and let $x \in X$. Since $\pi(x)$ is an almost periodic point of (X/H,T) there exists an almost periodic point z of (X,T) with $\pi(z) = \pi(x)$ (6.1). Since $x = hz$ for some $h \in H$ and h is a homomorphism of (X,T) into (X,T), x is also an almost periodic point of (X,T).

6.3 REMARKS. 1. Notice that in general X/H is compact but it need not be T_2. Thus it is necessary to assume this when nothing further is known about H. However if H is compact T_2 then X/H is T_2 by (4.9).

2. If (X/H,T) is minimal the structure of (X,T) becomes particularly transparent as the following shows.

6.4 PROPOSITION. Let (H,X,T) be such that X/H is T_2 (X/H,T) is minimal and $x \in X$. Then:

1. $\{\overline{hxT} \mid h \in H\}$ is a partition of X.

2. $H_x = \{h \mid h \in H, hx \in \overline{xT}\}$ is a closed subgroup of H with $H_{hx} = hH_xh^{-1}$ $(h \in H)$.

3. Let R be the orbit closure relation on X. Then the map $\varphi: H \to X/R$ such that $\varphi(h) = \overline{hxT}$ induces a continuous bijective map $\overline{\varphi}$ of $H/H_x = \{gH_x \mid g \in H\}$ onto X/R. If in

addition H is compact then R is closed and $\bar{\varphi}$ is a homeomorphism.

PROOF. 1. Let $\pi: X \to X/H$ be the canonical map, and $y \in X$. Then $\pi(y) \in \pi(\overline{xT})$ since X/H is minimal. Hence $y \in \overline{HxT}$ and $X = \cup \{\overline{hxT} \mid h \in H\}$. Now use 6.2.

2. Let $h \in H_x$. Then $h\overline{xT} = \overline{hxT} = \overline{xT}$ by 1. Thus $H_x = \{h \mid h \in H, h\overline{xT} = \overline{xT}\}$ from which it follows immediately that H_x is a closed subgroup of H.

Now $g \in H_{hx}$ iff $g\overline{hxT} = \overline{hxT}$ iff $h^{-1}g\overline{hxT} = \overline{xT}$ iff $h^{-1}gh \in H_x$ iff $g \in hH_xh^{-1}$.

3. The map φ is continuous because it is the composition of the continuous maps $h \to hx$ of H into X and the projection of X onto X/R. It is onto by 1 above.

Let $g,h \in H$. Then $\varphi(g) = \varphi(h)$ iff $\overline{gxT} = \overline{hxT}$ iff $h^{-1}g \in H_x$ iff $g \in hH_x$. Hence $\bar{\varphi}$ is bijective.

Finally let H be compact and (u_α, v_α) a net in $R \subset X \times X$ with $u_\alpha \to u$ and $v_\alpha \to v$. Then by 1 there exists a net (h_α) in H such that $h_\alpha u_\alpha, h_\alpha v_\alpha \in \overline{xT}$ for all α. We may suppose $h_\alpha \to h \in H$. Then $h_\alpha u_\alpha \to hu$ and $h_\alpha v_\alpha \to hv$, whence $hu, hv \in \overline{xT}$ and $(u,v) \in R$. Thus in this case X/R is T_2 and H/H_x is compact and so $\bar{\varphi}$ is a homeomorphism.

6.5 REMARK. Notice that if in addition to the assumptions of 6.4, X is a principal bundle over X/H with structure group H then $(H_x, \overline{xT})$ is a reduction of the group of the bundle to H_x.

6.6 PROPOSITION. Let (H,X,T) be such that X/H is T_2 and (X/H,T) is distal. Then (X,T) is also distal.

PROOF. Let $\pi: X \to X/H$, $\psi: E(X) \to E(X/H)$ be the canonical maps and let u be an idempotent in E(X). Then $\psi(u) = e$ since E(X/H) is a group.

Now let $x \in X$. Then $\pi(xu) = \pi(x)\psi(u) = \pi(x)$. Hence there exists $h \in H$ with $hx = xu$. Then $hxu = xu^2 = xu = hx$ implies that $xu = x$. Thus $u = e$ and E(X) is a group, whence (X,T) is distal.

Thus pointwise almost periodicity and "distallity" lift from (X/H,T) to (X,T). However, we shall see that in general uniform almost periodicity does not. For further comments see [1].

For the remainder of this chapter I would like to consider the following situation: G will denote a topological group, H a closed syndetic subgroup of G, G/H = $\{Hg \mid g \in G\}$, and T an arbitrary subgroup of G. Then G/H is compact T_2 and the multiplication in G induces a transformation group structure on (G/H,T).

I shall investigate (G/H,G) and deduce results about (G/H,T) from the fact that $T \subset G$.

For the rest of this chapter $\mathfrak{n}$ will denote the neighborhood filter at the identity of G, P = P(G/H,G) the proximal relation on (G/H,G) and Q = Q(G/H,G) the regionally proximal relation on (G/H,G). (Recall that since H is a syndetic subgroup of G, P = P(G/H,H) and Q = Q(G/H,H)).

6.7 PROPOSITION. Let $x,y \in G$. Then the following statements are pairwise equivalent:

1. $(Hx,Hy) \in Q$.
2. $(Hxy^{-1},H) \in Q$.
3. $xy^{-1} \in \cap \{\overline{HUH} \mid U \in \mathfrak{n}\}$.

PROOF. That 1 and 2 are equivalent is clear since Q is invariant.

2 implies 3. Let $U,V,W \in \mathfrak{n}$ with $VV^{-1} \subset U$. Since the orbit under G of every point is all of G/H, there exist $w_1, w_2 \in W$ and $g \in G$ such that $Hxy^{-1}w_1g$, $Hw_2g \in HV$. Thus $xy^{-1} \in HVg^{-1}w_1^{-1}$ and $g \in w_2^{-1}HV$ whence $xy^{-1} \in HVV^{-1}Hw_2w_1^{-1} \subset HUHWW^{-1}$. Since W is arbitrary, $xy^{-1} \in \overline{HUH}$.

3 implies 2. Let $V,W \in \mathfrak{n}$. Then $xy^{-1}W \cap HVH \neq \emptyset$. Hence there exist $w \in W$ and $h \in H$ with $xy^{-1}wh \in HV$. Thus $(Hxy^{-1}w)h$, $(H)h \in HV$ whence $(Hxy^{-1},H) \in Q$.

6.8 <u>COROLLARY</u>. The transformation group (G/H,G) is equicontinuous iff given $U \in \mathfrak{n}$ there exists $V \in \mathfrak{n}$ with $VH \subset HU$.

<u>PROOF</u>. (G/H,G) is equicontinuous iff Q is the diagonal. The equivalence of 2 and 3 of 6.7 shows that this will occur iff $\cap \{\overline{HUH} \mid U \in \mathfrak{n}\} = H$.

Now $\cap \{\overline{HUH} \mid U \in \mathfrak{n}\} = \cap \{HUHW \mid U,W \in \mathfrak{n}\}$ so that if the condition of 6.8 is satisfied this is equal to $\cap \{HV \mid V \in \mathfrak{n}\} = \overline{H} = H$.

On the other hand if $\cap \{\overline{HUH} \mid U \in \mathfrak{n}\} = H$, then since G/H is compact, given $U \in \mathfrak{n}$ there exists $V \in \mathfrak{n}$ with $HVH \subset HU$.

6.9 <u>REMARKS</u>. 1. It follows immediately from 6.8 that (G/H,G) is equicontinuous when H is normal.

2. The equivalence of 2 and 3 of 6.7 shows that Q is an equivalence relation iff $\cap \{\overline{HUH} \mid U \in \mathfrak{n}\}$ is a group.

6.10 <u>PROPOSITION</u>. Consider the following:

1. Given $U \in \mathfrak{n}$ there exists $V \in \mathfrak{n}$ such that $gVg^{-1} \subset U (g \in G)$.

2. (G/H,G) is equicontinuous.

Then 1 implies 2. When G is locally connected and H discrete then 2 implies 1.

PROOF. That 1 implies 2 follows from 6.8.

Now suppose $(G/H,G)$ is equicontinuous, G locally connected and H discrete. Let $U \in \mathfrak{n}$ and K compact with $G = HK$. Then there exists $W \in \mathfrak{n}$ with $kWk^{-1} \subset U (k \in K)$. Since H is discrete we may assume that W is such that if $x,y \in H$ with $xW \cap yW \neq \emptyset$, then $x = y$.

By 6.8 there exists a connected set $V \in \mathfrak{n}$ with $VH \subset HW$.

Let $h \in H$. Then Vh is connected and $(lW \mid l \in H)$ is an open partition of $HW \supset Vh$. Since $hW \cap Vh \neq \emptyset$ this implies that $Vh \subset hW$. Thus $h^{-1}Vh \subset W$.

Let $g \in G$. Then $g = kh^{-1}$ for some $k \in K$, $h \in H$ and $gVg^{-1} = kh^{-1}Vhk^{-1} \subset kWk^{-1} \subset U$.

6.11 REMARKS. 1. Condition 1 is equivalent to the coincidence of the left and right uniformities of G.

2. The fact that condition 1 does not involve H implies that if G is locally connected and if $(G/H,G)$ is equicontinuous for some closed, syndetic discrete group H, then $(G/L,G)$ is equicontinuous for any closed syndetic subgroup L.

6.12 PROPOSITION. Let $x,y \in G$. Then the following statements are pairwise equivalent:

1. $(Hx,Hy) \in P(G/H)$.
2. $(Hxy^{-1},H) \in P(G/H)$.
3. $xy^{-1} \in \cap \{HUH \mid U \in \mathfrak{n}\} = K(H)$.
4. $e \in \overline{Hxy^{-1}H}$.

PROOF. It is immediate that 1 and 2 are equivalent since $P(G/H)$ is invariant.

2 implies 3. Let $U,V \in \mathfrak{n}$ with $VV^{-1} \subset U$. Then there

exists $g \in G$ such that $Hxy^{-1}g$, $Hg \in HV$. Thus $xy^{-1}g$, $g \in HV$, whence $xy^{-1} \in HVV^{-1}H \subset HUH$.

Reading the above "backwards" proves that 3 implies 2.

The proof that 3 and 4 are equivalent is left to the reader.

6.13 <u>COROLLARY</u>. $P(G/H)$ is an equivalence relation iff $K(H)$ is a group.

<u>PROOF</u>. Immediate from the equivalence of 1 and 3 of 6.12.

6.14 <u>COROLLARY</u>. The following are pairwise equivalent:

1. P is closed.
2. P is a closed equivalence relation.
3. K(H) is closed.
4. K(H) is a closed subgroup of G.

<u>PROOF</u>. 1 and 2 are equivalent by 5.17.

1 implies 3. Let $x_\alpha \to x$ with $x_\alpha \in K(H)$ for all α. Then $(Hx_\alpha, H) \in P$ by 6.12. Since $(Hx_\alpha, H) \to (Hx, H)$, $(Hx, H) \in P$ and $x \in H$.

3 implies 1. Let $(Hx_\alpha, Hy_\alpha) \in P$ for all α where $Hx_\alpha \to Hx$ and $Hy_\alpha \to Hy$. Then (using subnets if necessary) there exists nets (u_α) and $v_\alpha)$ such that $u_\alpha \in Hx_\alpha$, $v_\alpha \in Hy_\alpha$ for all α, $u_\alpha \to x$ and $v_\alpha \to y$. Then $u_\alpha v_\alpha^{-1} \in K(H)$ whence $xy^{-1} \in K(H)$ and so $(Hx, Hy) \in P$.

Clearly 4 implies 3. Now it follows from the above that 3 implies 2, whence 3 implies 4 by 6.13.

6.15 <u>PROPOSITION</u>. The following statements are

pairwise equivalent:

1. $(G/H,G)$ is distal.

2. $K(H) = H$.

3. If $e \in \overline{HgH}$ then $g \in H$.

PROOF. This follows from 6.12 and the fact that $(G/H,G)$ is distal iff P is the diagonal of $G/H \times G/H$.

6.16 DEFINITION. H is subnormal in G if there exist subgroups $H_o = H \subset H_1 \subset \ldots \subset H_n = G$ such that H_i is a normal subgroup of H_{i+1}.

6.17 PROPOSITION. Let H be subnormal in G. Then $(G/H,G)$ is distal.

PROOF. Let $H_o = H \subset H_1 \subset \ldots \subset H_n = G$ be subgroups of G with H_i a normal subgroup of H_{i+1} $(0 \leq i \leq n-1)$. We may assume H_i closed for all i. (Otherwise use $\overline{H}_i$ instead of H_i).

Now let $g \in G$ with $e \in \overline{HgH}$. Assume $g \in H_i$ with $i > 0$. Then $e \in H_{i-1}gH_{i-1}$ and $(H_i/H_{i-1},H_i)$ equicontinuous (1 of 6.9) implies $g \in H_{i-1}$ by 6.15. (Note that since H_{i-1} is syndetic in G, it is also syndetic in H_i.) Hence $g \in H$ and $(G/H,G)$ is distal (6.15).

6.18 REMARK. 1. If G is nilpotent then every subgroup is subnormal [3] whence in this case $(G/H,G)$ is distal and therefore so is $(G/H,T)$ for every subgroup T of G.

6.19 EXAMPLES. 1. Let $G = \mathbb{R}^n$ and $H = \mathbb{Z}^n$. Then G/H is the n-torus and $(G/H,G)$ is equicontinuous (6.9).

Now I would like to find $x \in G$ such that $(G/H,T)$ is minimal where T is the one parameter subgroup $\{xt \mid t \in \mathbb{R}\}$

of G, where xt is scalar multiplication of the vector x by the scalar t.

This is a classical problem, the solution to which is that (G/H,T) will be minimal if the components $x_1,\ldots,x_n$ are rationally independent.

However instead of proving this let me sketch a general method for finding such an x. This will illustrate the technique used in [4 and V1 of 5] for constructing minimal sets in more general situations.

Let U be an open subset of G. Set $A(U) = \{x \mid xt \in H + U \text{ for some } t \in \mathbb{R}\}$. Then clearly A(U) is an open subset of G. Notice also that if V is open in G then the set Vt "swells" as $t \to \infty$ whence for some $t \in T$, $H + Vt = G$. If $u = h + vt$ with $u \in U$, $h \in H$ and $v \in V$, $v \in A(U)$. Hence A(U) is also dense. Finally let $\mathfrak{U}$ be a countable base for the topology on G and set $A = \cap \{A(U) \mid U \in \mathfrak{U}\}$. Then A is a residual subset of G and if $x \in A$, $x\mathbb{R} \cap (H + W) \neq \emptyset$ for any open set W of G.

Let $x \in A$ and set $T = \{xt \mid t \in \mathbb{R}\}$. Then the orbit of H in (G/H,T) is just $\{H + xt \mid t \in \mathbb{R}\}$ whence it is dense by the above remark. Since (G/H,T) is equicontinuous this implies that (G/H,T) is minimal.

2. [4] Let $G = \left\{\begin{bmatrix} 1 & x & y \\ 0 & 1 & z \\ 0 & 0 & 1 \end{bmatrix} \mid x,y,z \in \mathbb{R}\right\}$, a group under matrix multiplication. For convenience I denote $\begin{bmatrix} 1 & x & y \\ 0 & 1 & z \\ 0 & 0 & 1 \end{bmatrix}$ by $[x,y,z]$.

Let $H = \{[x,y,z] \mid x,y,z \in \mathbb{Z}\}$ and $K = \{[x,y,z] \mid x,z \in \mathbb{Z},\ y \in \mathbb{R}\}$.

Statements 1 through 5 below are standard or easily

verified.

2.1 G is a simply connected nilpotent Lie group.

2.2 H is a closed, syndetic discrete subgroup of G. I denote G/H by X.

2.3 K is a closed normal subgroup of G such that Y = G/K is the two torus.

2.4 H is a normal subgroup of K such that L = K/H is the circle group.

2.5 L acts on X via the map $(Hk, Hg) \to Hkg$ and $X/L \cong G/K = Y$.

2.6 Now suppose S is a group which acts on X such that (L,X,S) is a bitransformation group with (Y,S) minimal. Then (X,S) is minimal.

<u>PROOF</u>. Let $x \in X$, $Z = \overline{xS}$ and $M = \{l \mid l \in L, lx \in Z\}$. Then M is a closed subgroup of L (6.4) whence M is finite or M = L. If M = L then X = Z (6.4). I shall complete the proof by showing that M cannot be finite.

Since M is an invariant subgroup of L and (M,Z) is a reduction of the bundle (L,X) by 6.5, X/M is homeomorphic to L/M x Y. (This is standard fiber bundle theory see e.g. page 57 of [7]. One can prove this directly by defining $\varphi: X \to L/M \times Y$ to be such that $\varphi(u) = (Ml, \sigma(u))$, where $\sigma: X \to Y$ is the canonical map and $l \in L$ with $lu \in Z$, and verifying that φ induces a homeomorphism of X/M onto L/M x Y).

Now if M is finite L/M is homeomorphic to a circle so that the fundamental group $\Pi_1(L/M \times Y) = \mathbb{Z}^3$ and the part $\Pi_1(M) \to \Pi_1(X) \to \Pi_1(X/M)$ of the homotopy sequence of the fiber bundle $X \to X/M$ shows that $\Pi_1(X)$ is a subgroup of $\Pi_1(X/M)$ ($\Pi_1(M) = 0$). This is impossible since $\Pi_1(X) = H$ which is not abelian.

2.7 Let $[a,b,c] \in G$, T the one parameter subgroup $\{[at, bt + \frac{act^2}{2}, ct] \mid t \in \mathbb{R}\}$ of G, and $\Pi: G \to \mathbb{R}^2$ such that $\Pi([x,y,z]) = (x,z)$. Then Π is a homomorphism onto which maps T onto the one parameter subgroup $\{(at,ct) \mid t \in \mathbb{R}\}$ of $\mathbb{R}^2$ which I shall also denote by T. Moreover Π induces a transformation group isomorphism of $(G/K,T)$ onto $(\mathbb{R}^2/\mathbb{Z}^2,T)$. Thus if a and c are properly chosen (example 1), (G,K,T) is minimal. Hence by 2.6 of 6.19 $(G/H,T)$ is also minimal. In addition $(G/H,T)$ is distal by 6.17. However $(G/H,T)$ is not equicontinuous for if it were, G/H would be an abelian topological group (4.6) whence G/H would be a torus because it is a manifold. This is impossible because the fundamental group of a torus is abelian but $\Pi_1(G/H) = H$ is not.

2.8 $(G/H,G)$ is distal (6.17) but not equicontinuous since if it were so would $(G/H,T)$ be, where T is as in 2.7 of this example.

NOTES

1. Example 2 of 6.19 shows that there are bitransformation groups (H,X,T) such that (X/H,T) is equicontinuous and (X,T) is minimal but not equicontinuous. It would be of interest to know whether this phenomenon could still occur when H is finite. In this case one can show that (X,T) will be equicontinuous if in addition one of the following conditions is satisfied:

(i) X is locally connected

(ii) T is connected

(iii) X is 0-dimensional and T is finitely generated.

2. The situation discussed from 6.7 onwards is that of a transformation group (X,G) where G acts transitively on X i.e. the orbit of any point is all of X. If one fixes $x \in X$, then $(X,G) \cong (G/H,G)$ where $H = \{g \mid xg = x\}$.

Now let S be the equicontinuous structure relation on X. Then (X/S,G) is of the form (G/L,G) where L is a closed subgroup of G with $H \subset L$. Then from 6.7 it can be deduced that L is the least closed subgroup of G containing H with $M = \cap \{\overline{MUM} \mid U \in \mathcal{N}\}$.

Similarly if D denotes the distal structure relation on $(G/H,G) \cong (X,G)$ then $(X/D,G) \cong (G/K,G)$ where K is the least closed subgroup M of G with $H \subset M$ and $M = \cap \{MUM \mid U \in \mathcal{N}\}$.

For a discussion of the above results and the related propositions see: (1) W. Gottschalk, A study of minimal sets, Annales de L'Institut Fourier, Tome XIV, 1964, 55-60. (2) Harvey B. Keynes, Invariant relations on coset transformation groups, (to appear), and (3) _____, A study of the proximal relation in coset transformation groups,

Trans. Amer. Math Soc., 128(1967), 389-402.

3. W. R. Scott, Group Theory, Prentice-Hall, 1965.

4. Example 2 of 6.19 is due to L. Auslander, F. Hahn, and L. Markus. For an extensive discussion of transformation groups of the form (G/H,T) where G is a Lie group and T a one parameter subgroup of G see:

Auslander, L; Green, L.; Hahn, F.; Flows on Homogeneous Spaces, Annals of Mathematics Studies, No.53, Princeton University Press, Princeton, 1963.

5. The problem touched on briefly in example 1 of 6.19 is the following:

Let X be a compact T_2 space and T a group. Define an action of T on X making (X,T) minimal. Usually one is interested in the case where $T = \mathbb{R}$ or $T = \mathbb{Z}$.

One outstanding conjecture in this direction is that it is impossible to define an action of $\mathbb{R}$ on the three sphere S^3 with $(S^3, \mathbb{R})$ minimal. (This is 'weaker' than the Seifert conjecture that the action of $\mathbb{R}$ on S^3 produced by a vector field must have at least one compact orbit.) It can be shown that if $(S^3, \mathbb{R})$ is minimal, then its structure group is trivial. Also it is known (Furstenberg) that $(S^3, \mathbb{R})$ cannot be minimal distal.

For these and related results see:

(i) H. Chu and M. A. Geraghty, The fundamental group and the first cohomology group of a minimal set, Bull. A. M. S. 69(1963), 377-381.

(ii) H. Furstenberg, The structure of distal flows, Amer. J. Math. 85(1963), 477-515.

(iii) P. J. Kahn and A. W. Knapp, Equivariant maps onto minimal sets, (to appear).

(iv) H. Keynes and J. Robertson, _Eigenvalue theorems in topological transformation groups_, Trans. A.M.S., (to appear - May, 1969).

For a discussion of the general problem see:

(v) H. Chu, _Algebraic topology criteria for minimal sets_, Proc. A.M.S., Vol.13 (1962), 503-508.

(vi) R. Ellis, _The construction of minimal discrete flows_, Amer. J. Math., Vol.87 (1965), 564-574.

6. Closely related to the problem discussed in 5 is: given (H,X) with H compact, Y = X/H, and T a minimal action on Y when can it be lifted to a minimal action on X. Indeed the minimal discrete flows of (vi) in 5 were constructed by solving special cases of the above problem.

Suppose further that X and Y are manifolds, H a compact Lie group, and T the reals whose action is the solution curves of a vector field A on Y. Then [7] the action of T may be lifted to X yielding a bitransformation group (H,X,T) with $(X/H,T) \cong (Y,T)$. However, (X,T) need not in general be minimal. When H is a torus it can be shown using a method analogous to that of 1 of 6.19 that a minimal lift can be found. What happens in the case of an arbitrary compact Lie group H is still an open question. It seems that 6.4 and 6.5 might be applied to advantage here.

7. Kobayashi, S. and Nomizu, K., _Foundations of Differential Geometry_, Interscience Publishers, New York.

CHAPTER 7

UNIVERSAL TRANSFORMATION GROUPS

In this chapter we begin the exposition of an approach to the study of minimal sets which is proving to be fruitful. Instead of studying a given minimal set in isolation, it is considered in relation to the totality of minimal sets. This is done by means of the notion of a universal minimal set.

The main technical device employed is the Stone-Čech or β-compactification βT of the discrete group T. This will be studied in detail in the next chapter; here we assume the following facts about βT:

(a) βT is a compact T_2 space.

(b) T is a dense subset of βT.

(c) t is open in βT $(t \in T)$.

(d) If φ: $T \to X$ and X is compact T_2 then there exists a unique continuous map $\psi : \beta T \to X$ with $\psi(t) = \varphi(t)$ $(t \in T)$. Indeed these characterize βT.

7.1 PROPOSITION. There exists a semigroup structure on βT such that:

(i) L_x: $y \to xy$ is continuous $(x \in \beta T)$.

(ii) R_x: $y \to yx$ is continuous $(x \in T)$.

(iii) The semigroup structure on βT induces the group structure on T.

PROOF. Let $t \in T$. Then by (d) of the above the map $s \to st$ of T into βT has a continuous extension R_t to βT. Indeed R_t is a homeomorphism onto since $R_t R_{t^{-1}}$ is the identity on the dense subset T of βT.

Now let $x \in \beta T$. Then again by (d) there exists a continuous map $L_x : \beta T \to \beta T$ such that $L_x(t) = R_t(x)$ $(T \in T)$.

Finally set $xy = L_x(y)$ $(x,y \in \beta T)$. Then (i), (ii), and (iii) can be verified directly.

7.2 REMARKS AND DEFINITION. 1. By (iii) the multiplication on βT induces an action of T on βT. (The map $(x,t) \to xt$ of $\beta T \times T \to \beta T$ is continuous because T is discrete and R_t is continuous). The transformation group $(\beta T, T)$ is point transitive, i.e. there exists $x \in \beta T$ with $\overline{xT} = \beta T$. (In this case x may be chosen to be the identity of T by (b)).

2. In general R_x is not continuous if $x \notin T$.

7.3 PROPOSITION. Let (X,T) be a point transitive transformation group. Then there exists an epimorphism $\varphi: (\beta T, T) \rightrightarrows (X,T)$.

PROOF. Let $x \in X$ with $\overline{xT} = X$. Then by (d) there exists a continuous map $\varphi: \beta T \to X$ such that $\varphi(t) = xt$ $(t \in T)$. Then $\varphi(ts) = \varphi(t)s$ $(t,s \in T)$ whence $\varphi(ps) = \varphi(p)s$ by the continuity of $\varphi(p \in \beta T)$.

Also $\varphi(\beta T) = \varphi(\overline{T}) = \overline{\varphi(T)} = \overline{xT} = X$.

Proposition 7.3 motivates the following.

7.4 DEFINITION. The transformation group (Z,T) is a universal point transitive transformation group if (i) (Z,T) is point transitive and (ii) if (X,T) is point transitive then there exists $\varphi: (Z,T) \overset{\sim}{\to} (X,T)$.

It is a <u>universal minimal set</u> if (i) (Z,T) is minimal and (ii) if (X,T) is minimal, then there exists $\varphi:(Z,T) \overset{\sim}{\to} (X,T)$.

Thus 7.3 says that $(\beta T,T)$ is a universal point transitive transformation group. We shall see in a moment that it is unique up to isomorphism.

7.9 <u>PROPOSITION</u>. Let $\varphi: (\beta T,T) \to (\beta T,T)$ be a homomorphism. Then:

1. There exists $p \in \beta T$ with $\varphi = L_p$.
2. If φ is onto, then $\varphi = L_t$ for some $t \in T$ and φ is an isomorphism.

<u>PROOF</u>. 1. Let $p = \varphi(e)$. Then $\varphi(t) = \varphi(et) = \varphi(e)t = pt = L_p(t)$ $(t \in T)$, and thus $\varphi = L_p$.

2. Let $\varphi = L_p$ and $\varphi(x) = e$. Since e is an open set, there exists a neighborhood N of x with $\varphi(y) = e$ $(y \in N)$. Let $s \in N \cap T$. Then $ps = L_p(s) = \varphi(s) = e$ whence $p = s^{-1} \in T$.

That φ is an isomorphism follows from $\varphi^{-1} = L_p^{-1} = L_s$.

7.10 <u>COROLLARY</u>. Let (Z,T) be point transitive and $\varphi: (Z,T) \overset{\sim}{\to} (\beta T,T)$. Then φ is an isomorphism.

<u>PROOF</u>. By 7.3 there exists $\psi: (\beta T,T) \overset{\sim}{\to} (Z,T)$. Then $\varphi\psi: (\beta T,T) \overset{\sim}{\to} (\beta T,T)$ and so is one-one by 7.9. Hence ψ is one-one and so is $\varphi = (\varphi\psi)\psi^{-1}$.

The following corollaries are immediate.

7.11 <u>COROLLARY</u>. Any two universal point transitive transformation groups are isomorphic.

7.12 <u>COROLLARY</u>. The map $\theta_e: p \to ep$ of $(E(\beta T),T) \to (\beta T,T)$ is an isomorphism onto.

Henceforth I shall identify $E(\beta T)$ with βT and apply the notions and results of chapter 2 to βT.

7.13 PROPOSITION. Let M be a minimal right ideal in βT. Then (M,T) is a universal minimal set.

PROOF. Let (X,T) be a minimal set. Then it is point transitive, and thus by 7.3 there exists $\varphi: (\beta T,T) \overset{\sim}{\to} (X,T)$. Since $\varphi(M)$ is closed and invariant $\varphi(M) = X$. Thus $\varphi/M: (M,T) \overset{\sim}{\to} (X,T)$.

7.14 PROPOSITION. Let (X,T) be a transformation group, M a minimal right ideal in E(X), and φ a homomorphism from (M,T) into (M,T). Then $\varphi = L_p$ for some $p \in M$ and φ is an isomorphism onto.

PROOF. Let u be an idempotent in M and set $p = \varphi(u)$. Then $\varphi(ut) = \varphi(u)t = pt = L_p(t)$ $(t \in T)$.

Now let $q \in M$ and (t_α) a net in T with $t_\alpha \to q$. Then (ut_α) is a net in M with $ut_\alpha \to uq = q$. Hence $\varphi(q) = \lim \varphi(ut_\alpha) = \varphi(u) \lim t_\alpha = pq = L_p(q)$. Thus $\varphi = L_p$.

There exist $r,v \in M$ such that $v^2 = v$, and $rp = pr = v$. Then $L_rL_p = L_{rp} = L_{pr} = L_pL_r = L_v$ = identity on M. Hence $\varphi^{-1} = L_r$.

The proofs of the following results are similar to those of 7.10 and 7.11.

7.15 COROLLARY. Let M be a minimal right ideal in βT, (X,T) a minimal set, and $\varphi: (X,T) \to (M,T)$ a homomorphism. Then φ is an isomorphism onto.

7.16 COROLLARY. Any two universal minimal sets are isomorphic.

NOTES

1. The results of this chapter may be used to produce all sorts of universal transformation groups as follows:

Let $\mathcal{P}$ denote the class of point transitive transformation groups. Call a property P of such transformation groups <u>intersective</u> if

(i) (X,T), $(Y,T) \in \mathcal{P}$ with $(X,T) \cong (Y,T)$ implies (X,T) has P iff (Y,T) has P.

(ii) If $\mathcal{R}$ is a collection of closed invariant equivalence relations on βT such that $(\beta T/R,T)$ has P $(R \in \mathcal{R})$, then $(\beta T/S,T)$ also has P where $S = \cap \mathcal{R}$.

Let P be intersective and $S(P) = \cap \mathcal{R}$ where $\mathcal{R}$ is the set of closed invariant equivalence relations R on βT such that $(\beta T/R,T)$ has P. It is easy to see that if $(X,T) \in \mathcal{P}$ and (X,T) has P then it is a homomorphic image of $(\beta T/S(P),T)$. Thus $(\beta T/S(P),T)$ is a universal P-transformation group.

Some examples of intersective properties are:

1.1 Let (X,T) have P if it is point transitive and distal.

1.2 Let $\mathfrak{J}$ be a topology on T such that $(T,\mathfrak{J})$ is a topological group. Let $(X,T,\pi) \in \mathcal{P}$ have P if π: $X \times (T,\mathfrak{J}) \to X$ is continuous. Then P is intersective and $(\beta T/S(P),T)$ is a universal point transitive transformation group when T is required to have the topology $\mathfrak{J}$ rather than the discrete topology. The reader is cautioned that in general $\beta T/S(P)$ is not the β-compactification of $(T,\mathfrak{J})$.

1.3 With $\mathfrak{J}$ as in 1.2, let (X,T,π) have P_o if (X,T,π) is minimal and π: $X \times (T,\mathfrak{J}) \to X$ is continuous. Then P_o is intersective and $(\beta T/S(P_o),T)$ is a universal minimal set when T is required to have the topology $\mathfrak{J}$ rather than the discrete topology.

It is not known whether T acts freely on $\beta T/S(P_o)$.

CHAPTER 8

THE β-COMPACTIFICATION OF T

There are several ways of describing βT. In this chapter it is viewed as the collection of all ultrafilters on T. Properties (a), (b), (c), and (d) of βT assumed in chapter 7 are proved below but the chief reason for investigating this representation of βT in detail is to develop techniques for the study of minimal sets.

We recall the following facts. Let $\mathcal{F}$ be a collection of subsets of T. Then:

1. $\mathcal{F}$ is a filter if $\emptyset \notin \mathcal{F}$, A,B, $\in \mathcal{F}$ implies $A \cap B \in \mathcal{F}$, and $A \subset B$ with $A \in \mathcal{F}$ implies $B \in \mathcal{F}$.

2. $\mathcal{F}$ is a filter base if $\emptyset \notin \mathcal{F}$ and given $A,B \in \mathcal{F}$ there exists $C \in \mathcal{F}$ with $C \subset A \cap B$.

3. $\mathcal{F}$ is a filter subbase if $\mathcal{F}$ has the finite intersection property, i.e. if I is a finite set and $F_i \in \mathcal{F}$ $(i \in I)$ then $\cap \{F_i \mid i \in I\} \neq \emptyset$.

If $\mathcal{F}$ is a filter subbase then the collection of all subsets of T which are the intersection of finitely many elements of $\mathcal{F}$ is a filter base.

If $\mathcal{F}$ is a filter base then $\{A \mid F \subset A \text{ for some } F \in \mathcal{F}\}$

is a filter.

Thus when $\mathcal{F}$ is a filter base or a filter subbase it makes sense to speak of the filter generated by $\mathcal{F}$.

4. Finally a collection u of subsets of T is an ultrafilter if it is a maximal filter; i.e. u is a filter and if $\mathcal{F}$ is a filter with $u \subset \mathcal{F}$ then $u = \mathcal{F}$.

I shall denote the collection of all ultrafilters on T by βT. (This is of course an 'abuse of notation' for it has not yet been shown how the set of ultrafilters can be provided with a topology such that it satisfies the conditions of chapter 7.)

8.1 <u>DEFINITION</u>. Let $\Gamma \subset \beta T$. The <u>kernel</u> of Γ, $k(\Gamma) = \cap \{u \mid u \in \Gamma\}$. Then $k(\Gamma)$ is a filter on T with $k(\Gamma) \subset u$, $(u \in \Gamma)$.

Let $\mathcal{F}$ be a filter on T. Then the hull of $\mathcal{F}$, $h(\mathcal{F}) = \{u \mid u \in \beta T, \mathcal{F} \subset u\}$.

Finally, for each subset Γ of βT let $\overline{\Gamma} = hk(\Gamma)$.

8.2 <u>LEMMA</u>. Let Γ, Δ be subsets of βT. Then:

1. $\Gamma \subset \overline{\Gamma}$.

2. $\Gamma \subset \Delta$ implies $\overline{\Gamma} \subset \overline{\Delta}$.

3. $k(\Gamma) = k(\overline{\Gamma})$.

4. $\overline{\overline{\Gamma}} = \overline{\Gamma}$.

5. $\overline{\Gamma \cup \Delta} = \overline{\Gamma} \cup \overline{\Delta}$.

<u>PROOF</u>. 1 and 2 are evident from the definitions.

3. Since $\Gamma \subset \overline{\Gamma}$, $k(\overline{\Gamma}) \subset k(\Gamma)$. On the other hand $k(\Gamma) \subset u$ $(u \in \overline{\Gamma})$ by the definition of $\overline{\Gamma}$. Hence $k(\Gamma) \subset k(\overline{\Gamma})$.

4. $\overline{\overline{\Gamma}} = hk(\overline{\Gamma}) = hk(\Gamma) = \overline{\Gamma}$.

5. Since both Γ and Δ are contained in $\Gamma \cup \Delta$, $\overline{\Gamma} \cup \overline{\Delta} \subset \overline{\Gamma \cup \Delta}$ by 2.

Now suppose $u \notin \overline{\Gamma} \cup \overline{\Delta}$. Then there exist $A \in k(\Gamma)$ and $B \in k(\Delta)$ such that $A \notin u$ and $B \notin u$. By a fundamental property of ultrafilters this implies that $A' \in u$ and $B' \in u$, whence $(A \cup B)' = A' \cap B' \in u$.

Since $k(\Gamma \cup \Delta) = k(\Gamma) \cap k(\Delta)$ and $A \cup B \in k(\Gamma) \cap k(\Delta)$, $u \notin \overline{\Gamma \cup \Delta}$.

Lemma 8.2 shows that the map $\Gamma \to \overline{\Gamma}$ defines a closure operator on βT. The resulting topology is called the <u>hull-kernel</u> topology. I now wish to investigate some of its properties.

Let $\emptyset \neq A \subset T$. Then $\{A\}$ is a filter base on T. The hull of the resulting filter will be denoted $h(A)$.

Notice that the filter generated by A is an ultrafilter if and only if A consists of a single element t of T. In this case the resulting ultrafilter will be denoted t. In this way T becomes a subset of βT.

8.3 <u>LEMMA</u>. 1. Let $\emptyset \neq A \subsetneq T$. Then $(h(A))' = h(A')$.

2. Let $\emptyset \neq A \subset T$. Then $h(A)$ is an open and closed subset of βT.

3. The set $\{h(A) \mid \emptyset \neq A \subset T\}$ is a base for the topology on βT.

<u>PROOF</u>. 1 follows from the fact that if $A \subset T$ and $u \in \beta T$, then $A \in u$ or $A' \in u$. (Of course both A and A' cannot be in u.)

2. Let $\emptyset \neq A \subset T$. Then it is a straightforward exercise to show that $kh(A)$ is the filter generated by A. Hence $hkh(A) = h(A)$ whence $h(A) = \overline{h(A)}$. Thus $h(A)$ is closed.

If $A = T$, then $h(A) = \beta T$ and it is open. Otherwise $h(A)' = h(A') = \overline{h(A')}$.

3. Let Γ be an open subset of βT and $u \in \Gamma$. Then u is not in the closed set Γ', whence there exists $B \in k(\Gamma')$ with $B \notin u$. Set $A = B'$. Then $A \in u$, whence $u \in h(A)$. Moreover, if $v \in h(A)$ then $B \notin v$ and so $v \notin hk(\Gamma') = \Gamma'$. Thus $u \in h(A) \subset \Gamma$.

8.4 <u>REMARKS</u>. 1. Since h(t) is the ultrafilter generated by t, 2 of 8.3 shows that t is an open-closed subset of βT $(T \in T)$.

2. Let Γ be a non-empty open subset of βT. Then by 3 of 8.3 there exists $\emptyset \neq A \subset T$ with $h(A) \subset \Gamma$. If $t \in A$ then the ultrafilter $t \in h(A) \subset \Gamma$. Thus $\overline{T} = \beta T$.

Thus conditions (b) and (c) of chapter 7 are satisfied.

8.5 <u>LEMMA</u>. Let Γ be a non-empty open subset of βT and $C = \cap \{B \mid B \in k(\Gamma)\}$. Then $k(\Gamma)$ is the filter generated by C.

<u>PROOF</u>. Let $u \in \Gamma$. Then by 3 of 8.3 there exists $A \subset T$ with $u \in h(A) \subset \Gamma$. Hence $k(\Gamma) \subset kh(A)$ and $A \in u$. Since kh(A) is the filter generated by A, $A \subset B$ $(B \in k(\Gamma))$. Thus $A \subset C$, whence $C \in u$. Consequently $C \in k(\Gamma)$ and the proof is completed.

8.6 <u>COROLLARY</u>. Let Γ be an open subset of βT. Then $\overline{\Gamma}$ is open and closed.

<u>PROOF</u>. If $\Gamma = \emptyset$ then so is $\overline{\Gamma}$.

Now suppose $\Gamma \neq \emptyset$. Set $C = \cap \{B \mid B \in k(\Gamma)\}$. Then $\overline{\Gamma} = hk(\Gamma) = h(C)$ by 8.5, whence $\overline{\Gamma}$ is open and closed by 2 of 8.3.

The proof of the following corollary is left to the reader.

8.7 COROLLARY. The non-empty subset Γ of βT is open and closed iff $\Gamma = h(A)$ for some subset A of T.

8.8 PROPOSITION. The hull-kernel topology is compact T_2.

PROOF. Let $(\Gamma_i \mid i \in I)$ be a family of closed subsets of βT with the finite intersection property. Then $\bigcup k\Gamma_i$ is a filter subbase on T and if $u \in \beta T$ with $\bigcup k\Gamma_i \subset u$, $u \in \bigcap \overline{\Gamma}_i = \bigcap \Gamma_i$.

Now let $u,v \in \beta T$ with $u \neq v$. Then there exists a subset A of T with $A \in u$ and $A' \in v$. Then $h(A)$ and $h(A')$ are disjoint open sets with $u \in h(A)$ and $v \in h(A')$.

8.9 PROPOSITION. Let X by a compact T_2 space and φ a map of T into X. Then there exists a unique continuous extension ψ of φ to all of βT.

PROOF. Let $u \in \beta T$. Then $\varphi(u) = \{\varphi(A) \mid A \in u\}$ is a filter base on X such that the filter it generates is an ultrafilter. Hence there exists a unique $x \in X$ such that $\varphi(u)$ converges to x. Set $\psi(u) = x$. Then it is left to the reader to show that ψ is continuous and extends φ.

The uniqueness of ψ follows from continuity and the fact that $\overline{T} = \beta T$.

By 8.4, 8.8, and 8.9 βT provided with the hull-kernel topology satisfies (a), (b), (c), and (d) of chapter 7. I would now like to exhibit explicitly the semigroup structure on βT. To this end let $Au = \{t \mid At^{-1} \in u\}$ for $A \subset T$ and $u \in \beta T$.

The proof of the following lemma is straightforward and will be omitted.

8.10 LEMMA. Let $u \in \beta T$, and A,B subsets of T. Then

1. $(A \cup B)\, u = Au \cup Bu$.

2. $\emptyset u = \emptyset$ and $Tu = T$.

3. $(At)u = (Au)t \ (t \in T)$.

4. $(Au)' = A'u$.

5. $A \subset B$ implies $Au \subset Bu$.

6. $(A \cap B)u = Au \cap Bu$.

8.11 <u>REMARKS</u>. 1. Lemma 8.10 shows that the map $A \to Au$ of the power set $\mathcal{P}T$ of T into itself is a Boolean algebra homomorphism.

2. Statement 3 of 8.10 is ambiguous, since one might interpret At as $\{at \mid a \in A\}$ or $At = \{s \mid As^{-1} \in t\}$. In the former, t is viewed as an element of T and in the latter as the principal ultrafilter that it generates. In statement 3 of 8.10 the former interpretation is intended. Indeed no confusion will result if every element of T is viewed as such rather than as an ultrafilter. When there is a possibility for confusion and the ultrafilter is intended, then $h(t)$ rather than t will be used.

8.12 <u>DEFINITION</u>. Let $u,v \in \beta T$. Then the product w of u and v ($w = uv$) is the ultrafilter $w = \{A \mid Au \in v\}$.

Statements 2, 5, and 6 of 8.10 show that w is a filter on T. To see that w is an ultrafilter one uses 4 of 8.10 and the characterization: a filter $\mathcal{F}$ is an ultrafilter iff $A \in \mathcal{F}$ or $A' \in \mathcal{F}$ for every subset A of T.

8.13. <u>LEMMA</u>. Let $u,v,w \in \beta T$ and $t,s \in T$. Then

1. $(uv)w = u(vw)$.

2. $h(ts) = h(t)h(s)$.

3. $uh(t) = \{At \mid A \in u\}$. (Thus writing ut instead of $uh(t)$ leads to no confusion.)

4. The map $L_u : p \to up$ of βT into βT is continuous.

5. The map R_t: $p \to pt$ of βT into βT is continuous.

PROOF. Statements 1, 2, and 3 follow directly from the definitions. (Note that $(Au)v = A(uv)$, $A \subset T$, $uv \in \beta T$).

4. Let Γ be a neighborhood of up. There exists a subset A of T with $up \in h(A) \subset \Gamma$. Then $A \in up$ whence $Au \in p$. Thus $h(Au)$ is a neighborhood of p, and if $q \in h(Au)$, $Au \in q$ whence $A \in uq$ and $uq \in h(A) \subset \Gamma$.

5. Let Γ be a neighborhood of pt, and $A \in pt$ with $h(A) \subset \Gamma$. By 3, $At^{-1} \in p$. Thus $h(At^{-1})$ is a neighborhood of p, and if $q \in h(At^{-1})$, $At^{-1} \in q$, whence $A \in qt$ and $qt \in h(A) \subset \Gamma$.

8.14 PROPOSITION. The group T acts freely on βT.

PROOF. Let $u \in \beta T$ and $t \in T$ with $t \neq e$. I shall show that $ut \neq u$.

Let $\mathcal{S} = \{F \mid F \subset T, Ft \cap F = \emptyset\}$. Then $\mathcal{S} \neq \emptyset$ since $\{e\} \in \mathcal{S}$. When $\mathcal{S}$ is ordered upwardly by inclusion, it is inductive. Hence there exists a maximal element F of $\mathcal{S}$.

Let $r \in T$ with $r \notin F \cup Ft$. Then $F \subsetneqq G = \{r\} \cup F$ whence $G \notin \mathcal{S}$. Hence $GT \cap G \neq \emptyset$ from which it follows that $r \in Ft^{-1}$. Thus $T = F \cup Ft \cup Ft^{-1}$.

Now suppose $ut = u$. Since u is an ultrafilter one of F, Ft, Ft^{-1} is in u. Hence all three are in u because $u = ut$ implies $u = ut^{-1}$. This contradicts the fact that $F \in \mathcal{S}$.

8.15 LEMMA. Let $A \subset T$. Then A is syndetic iff $Ap \neq \emptyset$ $(p \in \beta T)$.

PROOF. Let A be syndetic, $p \in \beta T$. There exists a finite subset F of T with $AF = T$. Since p is an ultrafilter there exists $t \in F$ with $At \in p$. Then $t^{-1} \in Ap$.

Conversely suppose $Ap \neq \emptyset$ $(p \in \beta T)$. Then it follows in this case that $\beta T = h(A)T$. Since βT is compact and $h(A)$ open there exists a finite subset F of T with $\beta T \subset h(A)F$. Then $T = AF$.

8.16 <u>DEFINITION</u>. Let $\mathcal{F}$ be a filter on T. Then $\mathcal{F}$ is <u>invariant</u> if $Ft \in \mathcal{F}$ $(F \in \mathcal{F}, t \in T)$.

Let $R \subset T$. Then R is <u>replete</u> if $R \cap A \neq \emptyset$ for all syndetic subsets A of T.

8.17 <u>LEMMA</u>. Let $\mathcal{F}$ be an invariant filter on T and $F \in \mathcal{F}$. Then F is replete.

<u>PROOF</u>. Let $u \in \beta T$ with $\mathcal{F} \subset u$. Then $Ft \in u$ $(t \in T)$ whence $Fu = T$.

Now let A be a syndetic subset of T. If $A \cap F = \emptyset$, then $Au = Au \cap T = Au \cap Fu = (A \cap F)u = \emptyset u = \emptyset$, which contradicts 8.15.

8.18 <u>LEMMA</u>. Let $\emptyset \neq \Gamma \subset \beta T$. Then $\overline{\Gamma}$ is invariant iff $k(\Gamma)$ is invariant.

<u>PROOF</u>. Since $k(\Gamma) = k(\overline{\Gamma})$ (8.2), $\overline{\Gamma}$ invariant implies that $k(\Gamma)$ is invariant.

The converse follows from the fact that $\overline{\Gamma} = hk(\Gamma)$.

8.19 <u>PROPOSITION</u>. Let M be a non-empty closed invariant subset of βT. Then M is minimal iff $k(M)$ is a maximal invariant filter on T.

<u>PROOF</u>. Let M be minimal and $\mathcal{F}$ an invariant filter with $k(M) \subset \mathcal{F}$. Let $\Gamma = h(\mathcal{F})$. Since every filter is the intersection of the ultrafilters containing it, $k(\Gamma) = \mathcal{F}$ and Γ is closed. Moreover $k(M) \subset \mathcal{F}$ implies $\Gamma \subset M$. Since Γ is invariant, $\Gamma = M$ whence $\mathcal{F} = k(\Gamma) = k(M)$.

Conversely suppose $k(M)$ is a maximal invariant filter and let $p \in M$. Then $k(pT) = k(\overline{pT})$ is an invariant filter with $k(M) \subset k(\overline{pT})$. Hence $k(\overline{pT}) = k(M)$ whence $\overline{pT} = hk(\overline{pT}) = hk(M) = M$.

NOTES

1. Let $\mathrm{Hom}_T(\mathcal{P}T,\mathcal{P}T)$ denote the set of maps $f\colon \mathcal{P}T \to \mathcal{P}T$ such that $f(\emptyset) = \emptyset$, $f(A \cup B) = f(A) \cup f(B)$, $f(A') = (f(A))'$, and $f(At) = f(A)t$ $(A,B \in \mathcal{P}T,\ t \in T)$.

For $u \in \beta T$ let $F(u)\colon \mathcal{P}T \to \mathcal{P}T$ be such that $F(u)(A) = Au$ $(A \in \mathcal{P}T)$. Then 8.10 shows that $F(u) \in \mathrm{Hom}_T(\mathcal{P}T,\mathcal{P}T)$. Thus $F\colon u \to F(u)$ is a map of βT into $\mathrm{Hom}_T(\mathcal{P}T,\mathcal{P}T)$.

Let $u,v \in \beta T$ with $F(u) = F(v)$. Then $A \in u$ iff $e \in F(u)(A)$ iff $e \in F(v)(A)$ iff $A \in v$. Thus F is one-one.

Now let $f \in \mathrm{Hom}_T(\mathcal{P}T,\mathcal{P}T)$. Then it is easy to verify that $u = \{A \mid e \in f(A)\}$ is an ultrafilter on T. (Use the fact that a filter $\mathcal{B}$ on T is an ultrafilter iff $A \in \mathcal{B}$ or $A' \in \mathcal{B}$ $(A \in \mathcal{P}T)$).

Then $t \in F(u)(A)$ iff $t \in Au$ iff $At^{-1} \in u$ iff $e \in f(At^{-1})$ iff $e \in f(A)t^{-1}$ iff $t \in f(A)$. Thus $F(u) = f$ whence F is onto.

Let $u,v \in \beta T$, $A \in \mathcal{P}T$. Then $F(uv)(A) = A(uv) = (Au)v = F(v)(F(u)(A))$. Hence $F(uv) = F(v)F(u)$.

To sum up:

1.1 PROPOSITION. Let $F\colon \beta T \to \mathrm{Hom}_T(\mathcal{P}T,\mathcal{P}T)$ be such that $F(u)(A) = Au$ $(A \in \mathcal{P}T,\ u \in \beta T)$. Then F is an anti-isomorphism.

CHAPTER 9

THE REPRESENTATION OF POINT TRANSITIVE TRANSFORMATION GROUP

In chapter seven we saw that every point transitive transformation group (X,T) is a homomorphic image of $(\beta T,T)$. This implies that $(X,T) \cong (\beta T/R,T)$ where R is an invariant closed equivalence relation on βT. Thus we can study the class of all point transitive transformation groups $\mathcal{P}$ by studying the set of closed invariant equivalence relations on βT.

The remainder of this work will be devoted to exploiting this "global" point of view. However, rather than considering closed invariant equivalence relations on βT, I shall study certain subalgebras of $\mathcal{C}(\beta T)$. That these approaches are equivalent will be made clear in this chapter.

Henceforth all transformation groups will be assumed point transitive.

Let (X,T) be such a transformation group. Then in general there are many homomorphisms of $(\beta T,T)$ onto (X,T). Let φ,ψ be two such homomprphisms. If $\varphi(e) = \psi(e)$, then $\varphi(t) = \varphi(et) = \varphi(e)t = \psi(e)t = \psi(t)$ $(t \in T)$ whence $\varphi = \psi$. Thus $\pi\colon (\beta T,T) \rightrightarrows (X,T)$ is completely determined by $\pi(e)$.

This is the motivation for the following.

9.1 DEFINITION. A pointed transformation group (X,x_o) is a transformation group (X,T) together with a point $x_o \in X$ such that $\overline{x_oT} = X$. The point x_o is the base point of (X,x_o).

Let (X,x_o) and (Y,y_o) be pointed transformation groups. Then a homomorphism $\varphi\colon (X,x_o) \overset{\simeq}{\to} (Y,y_o)$ is a homomorphism φ of (X,T) onto (Y,T) such that $\varphi(x_o) = y_o$. Notice that if φ exists, it is unique.

9.2 REMARKS. 1. Let (X,T) be a transformation group. Then its enveloping semigroup $(E(X),T)$ will always be considered a pointed transformation group with base point e. Thus βT will be identified with $(\beta T,e)$.

2. Let (X,T) be a transformation group and $\varphi\colon \beta T \overset{\simeq}{\to} X$. Then φ induces $\psi\colon (\beta T,e) \overset{\simeq}{\to} (E(X),e)$ (3.8) which is independent of φ. This permits one to consider an element p of βT as a map of X into X viz. $xp = x\psi(p)$ $(x \in X)$ i.e. identifying p with $\psi(p)$. With this convention $\varphi(qp) = \varphi(q)p$ $(p,q \in \beta T)$.

If p is viewed as an ultrafilter on T, then xp is the point to which the ultrafilter base $\theta_x(p)$ converges, where $\theta_x\colon T \to X$ is such that $\theta_x(t) = xt$ $(t \in T)$.

Again let $\varphi\colon \beta T \overset{\simeq}{\to} X$. Then φ induces an injective algebra homomorphism, $\varphi^*\colon \mathcal{C}(X) \to \mathcal{C}(\beta T)$, where for any topological space Y, $\mathcal{C}(Y)$ denotes the Banach algebra of bounded complex-valued continuous functions on Y. Since all the "information" about X is contained in $\mathcal{C}(X)$, (X,T) may be investigated by studying the subalgebra $\operatorname{im}\varphi^*$ of $\mathcal{C}(\beta T)$. Thus instead of quotients of βT we can study certain kinds of subalgebras of $\mathcal{C}(\beta T)$. The rest of this chapter will be devoted to making these notions precise

9.2 DEFINITIONS AND NOTATION. Let (X,T) be a transformation group. Then $\mathcal{C}(X)$ will denote the Banach algebra of complex-valued continuous functions on X provided with the supremum norm.

Let $f \in \mathcal{C}(X)$, $x \in X$. Then it will be convenient to denote the image of x under f by $\langle f,x\rangle$ rather than $f(x)$.

Now let $t \in T$ and $f \in \mathcal{C}(X)$. Then tf will denote that element of $\mathcal{C}(X)$ such that $\langle tf,x\rangle = \langle f,xt\rangle$ $(x \in X)$.

In the case of βT, $\mathcal{C}(\beta T)$ will be denoted simply by $\mathcal{C}$. Moreover if $p \in \beta T$, $f \in \mathcal{C}$, then fp is defined by $\langle fp,x\rangle = \langle f,px\rangle$ and pf by $\langle pf,x\rangle = \langle f,xp\rangle$. Notice that $fp \in \mathcal{C}$ $(p \in \beta T)$ but that in general $pf \in \mathcal{C}$ only if $p \in T$.

Now let $\mathfrak{A} \subset \mathcal{C}$. Then $\mathfrak{A}$ is a T-subalgebra if $\mathfrak{A}$ is a subalgebra of $\mathcal{C}$ such that $\mathfrak{A}$ is closed, the constant functions $\mathbb{C} \subset \mathfrak{A}$, $tf \in \mathfrak{A}$ and $\bar{f} \in \mathfrak{A}$ $(f \in \mathfrak{A},\ t \in T)$, where $\bar{f}(x) = \overline{f(x)}$ (complex conjugate) $(x \in \beta T)$.

Let $\mathfrak{A}$ and $\mathfrak{B}$ be T-subalgebras and $\varphi\colon \mathfrak{A} \to \mathfrak{B}$. Then φ is a T-homomorphism if φ is an algebra homomorphism (i.e. φ is a homomorphism with $\varphi(1) = 1$ and $\varphi(\bar{f}) = \overline{\varphi(f)}$) such that $\varphi(tf) = t\varphi(f)$ $(t \in T,\ f \in \mathfrak{A})$. The set of T-homomorphisms of $\mathfrak{A}$ into $\mathbb{C}$ will be denoted $|\mathfrak{A}|$.

The next few results are directed towards providing $|\mathfrak{A}|$ with a transformation group structure.

Let $t \in T$ and $L_t^*\colon \mathcal{C} \to \mathcal{C}$ be such that $L_t^*(f) = fL_t = ft$. Then $L_t^* \in |\mathcal{C}|$. Moreover $L_tL_s = L_{ts}$ implies that $L_{ts}^* = L_s^*L_t^*$

Thus if $\varphi \in |\mathfrak{A}|$ so is $\varphi t = L_t^*\varphi$ and it is immediate from the above that $\varphi e = \varphi$ and $(\varphi t)s = \varphi(ts)$ $(t,s \in T)$. The reader is cautioned that $(\varphi t)f \neq \varphi(tf)$.

Now we have to provide $|\mathcal{A}|$ with a compact T_2 topology such that $(|\mathcal{A}|,T)$ is point transitive. To this end let me remind the reader of some classical results of M. H. Stone: Let X and Y be compact T_2 spaces and $\varphi: X \to Y$ continuous. Then φ induces an algebra homomorphism φ^* of $\mathcal{C}(Y)$ into $\mathcal{C}(X)$. (Indeed, $\varphi^*(f) = f\circ\varphi$ $(f \in \mathcal{C}(Y))$). Conversely if $\psi: \mathcal{C}(Y) \to \mathcal{C}(X)$ is an algebra homomorphism, then it induces a continuous map $\overline{\psi}: X \to Y$ such that $\langle g,\overline{\psi}(x)\rangle = \langle\psi(g),x\rangle$. Moreover $\overline{\varphi^*} = \varphi$ and $\overline{\psi}^* = \psi$, and φ is one-one iff φ^* is onto and conversely.

9.3 <u>LEMMA</u>. Let $\mathcal{A}$ be a T-subalgebra of $\mathcal{C}$ and $R = \{(x,y) \mid \langle f,x\rangle = \langle f,y\rangle \ (f \in \mathcal{A})\}$. Then:

1. R is a closed invariant equivalence relation on βT.

2. If $\pi: \beta T \to \beta T/R$ is the canonical map and $\pi^*: \mathcal{C}(\beta T/R) \to \mathcal{C}(\beta T)$ the induced homomorphism, then $\mathrm{im}\pi^* = \mathcal{A}$. Thus π^* induces an algebra isomorphism of $\mathcal{C}(\beta T/R)$ onto $\mathcal{A}$.

<u>PROOF</u>. 1. This is immediate.

2. For $f \in \mathcal{A}$ set $\langle f^*,\pi x\rangle = \langle f,x\rangle$ $(x \in \beta T)$. Then f^* is a well-defined, continuous complex-valued function on $\beta T/R$ with $f = \pi^*(f^*)$. Hence $\mathcal{A} \subset \mathrm{im}\pi^*$.

Now $\mathcal{B} = (\pi^*)^{-1}(\mathcal{A})$ is a closed subalgebra of $\mathcal{C}(\beta T/R)$ such that $\mathbb{C} \subset \mathcal{B}$, $\overline{g} \in \mathcal{B})$, and $\mathcal{B}$ separates points of $\beta T/R$. Hence $\mathcal{B} = \mathcal{C}(\beta T/R)$ by the Stone-Weierstrass theorem; and $\mathcal{A} = \mathrm{im}\pi^*$.

Statement 2 of 9.3 provides the clue for identifying $(|\mathcal{A}|,T)$ with $(\beta T/R,T)$. Thus let $\varphi \in |\mathcal{A}|$. Then $\varphi\pi^*$ is a homomorphism of $\mathcal{C}(\beta T/R)$ into $\mathbb{C}$ and so induces a continuous map $\overline{(\varphi\pi^*)}$ of βT into $\beta T/R$.

Notice that if $f \in \mathcal{C}(\beta T/R)$ then tf makes sense and is again in $\mathcal{C}(\beta T/R)$. Moreover $\pi^*(tf) = t\pi^*(f)$.

9.4 LEMMA. With the same notation as above let $F\colon |\mathcal{A}| \to \beta T/R$ be such that $F(\varphi) = \overline{(\varphi\pi^*)}(e)$ $(\varphi \in |\mathcal{A}|)$. Then F is a bijective map such that $F(\varphi t) = F(\varphi)t$ $(\varphi \in |\mathcal{A}|, t \in T)$.

PROOF. Let $\varphi, \psi \in |\mathcal{A}|$ with $F(\varphi) = F(\psi)$. Let $f \in \mathcal{A}$ and $g \in \mathcal{C}(\beta T/R)$ with $\pi^*(g) = f$. Then $\langle\varphi(f),e\rangle = \langle\varphi\pi^*(g),e\rangle = \langle g,(\varphi\pi^*)^-(e)\rangle = \langle g,F(\varphi)\rangle = \langle g,F(\psi)\rangle = \langle g,(\psi\pi^*)^-(e)\rangle = \langle\psi\pi^*(g),E\rangle = \langle\psi(f),e\rangle$.

Now replace f by tf. Then $\langle\varphi(f),t\rangle = \langle t\varphi(f),e\rangle = \langle\varphi(tf),e\rangle = \langle\psi(tf),e\rangle = \langle\psi(f),t\rangle$. Hence $\varphi(f) = \psi(f)$ and thus F is one-one.

Now let $y \in \beta T/R$ and $x \in \beta T$ with $\pi(x) = y$. Then it is easy to verify that $L_x^* \in |\mathcal{C}|$, whence $\varphi = L_x^* \,|\, \mathcal{A} \in |\mathcal{A}|$.

Let $g \in \mathcal{C}(\beta T/R)$. Then $\langle g,F(\varphi)\rangle = \langle g,(\varphi\pi^*)^-(e)\rangle = \langle(\varphi\pi^*)(g),e\rangle = \langle L_x^*(\pi^*g),e\rangle = \langle\pi^*g,x\rangle = \langle g,y\rangle$. Hence $F(\varphi) = y$ and F is onto.

Finally let $\varphi \in |\mathcal{A}|$, $t \in T$, and $g \in \mathcal{C}(\beta T/R)$. Then $\langle g,F(\varphi t)\rangle = \langle g,(\varphi t\pi^*)^-(e)\rangle = \langle\varphi\pi^*(tg),e\rangle = \langle tg,F(\varphi)\rangle = \langle g,F(\varphi)t\rangle$, whence $F(\varphi t) = F(\varphi)t$.

9.5 REMARKS. 1. Henceforth $(|\mathcal{A}|,T)$ will be identified with the transformation group $(\beta T/R,T)$ by means of the map F. (The latter is point transitive since it is a homomorphic image of βT.) Then $F^*\colon \mathcal{C}(\beta T/R) \cong \mathcal{C}(|\mathcal{A}|)$ and $\pi^*\colon \mathcal{C}(\beta T/R) \cong \mathcal{A}$ allows us to identify $\mathcal{A}$ with $\mathcal{C}(|\mathcal{A}|)$ by means of the map $f \to \tilde{f}$ where $\tilde{f}(\varphi) = \langle\varphi(f),e\rangle$ $(\varphi \in |\mathcal{A}|)$.

Now the orbit of $\pi(e)$ is dense in $\beta T/R$ and $F(i_{\mathcal{A}}) = \pi(e)$ where $i_{\mathcal{A}} = L_e|\mathcal{A}$ is the inclusion map of $\mathcal{A}$ into $\mathcal{C}$ (see proof of 9.4). Hence the orbit of $i_{\mathcal{A}}$ is dense in $|\mathcal{A}|$ and so it may be used as a base point for $(|\mathcal{A}|,T)$.

2. When $\mathcal{A} = \mathcal{C}$, R reduces to the identity relation and π and π^* are just the identity maps on βT and $\mathcal{C}$ respectively. In this case F is a bijective map of $|\mathcal{C}|$ onto βT.

Let $\varphi \in |\mathcal{C}|$ and $p = F(\varphi) = \overline{\varphi}(e)$. Since φ is a T-homomorphism, $\overline{\varphi}$: $(\beta T,T) \to (\beta T,T)$ is also a homomorphism. Hence $\overline{\varphi}(q) = \overline{\varphi}(eq) = \overline{\varphi}(e)q = pq = L_p(q)$ $(q \in \beta T)$. Thus $\overline{\varphi} = L_p$ and $\varphi = L_p^*$.

The above considerations motivate the identification of $p \in \beta T$ with the homomorphism L_p^*, i.e. the map $f \to fp$ of $\mathcal{C}$ onto $\mathcal{C}$.

3. There are other ways of recovering a transformation group from a T-subalgebra. The reason for the above method is the following:

9.6 <u>PROPOSITION</u>. Let $\mathcal{A}$ be a T-subalgebra of $\mathcal{C}$ and $\varphi \in |\mathcal{A}|$. Then there exists $p \in \beta T$ such that $\varphi = p|\mathcal{A}$. (Recall that p has been identified with L_p^*. Thus $\varphi(f) = fp$ $(f \in \mathcal{A})$).

<u>PROOF</u>. With the notation as in 9.4 let $\pi(p) = F(\varphi)$. Then as in the proof of 9.4 $F(L_p^*|\mathcal{A}) = F(\varphi)$ whence $\varphi = L_p^*|\mathcal{A}$.

9.7 <u>REMARKS</u>. 1. In general there will be more than one element p of βT with $p|\mathcal{A} = \varphi$. If $p,q \in \beta T$ with $p|\mathcal{A} = q|\mathcal{A}$, I shall often express this fact by writing $p = q$ on $\mathcal{A}$.

2. In view of 9.6, I shall often write $p \in |\mathcal{A}|$ when $p \in \beta T$. This is of course an "abbreviation" for $p|\mathcal{A} \in |\mathcal{A}|$.

3. The power of this approach to the study of dynamical systems is that it allows us to study the relationship between two transformation groups $|\mathcal{A}|$ and $|\mathcal{B}|$ by comparing

the way the elements of βT act on $\mathcal{A}$ with the way they act on $\mathcal{B}$.

9.8 PROPOSITION. Let $F: (\beta T, e) \to (X, x_o)$ and $\mathcal{A} = \mathrm{im} F^*$. Then $(|\mathcal{A}|, i_{\mathcal{A}}) \cong (X, x_o)$. (Notice that by 9.1 the above isomorphism is unique.)

PROOF. Let $R = \{(p,q) \mid F(p) = F(q)\}$. Then R is a closed invariant equivalence relation on βT, and $(\beta T/R, \pi(e)) \cong (X, x_o)$ where $\pi: \beta T \to \beta T/R$ is the canonical map.

Now $F(p) = F(q)$ iff $\langle g, F(p)\rangle = \langle g, F(q)\rangle$ iff $\langle F^* g, p\rangle = \langle F^* g, q\rangle$ $(g \in C(X))$. Hence $R = \{(p,q) \mid \langle f,p\rangle = \langle f,q\rangle$ $(f \in \mathcal{A})\}$ and so $(|\mathcal{A}|, i_{\mathcal{A}}) \cong (X, x_o)$ by 1 of 9.5.

9.9 PROPOSITION. Let $F: (\beta T, e) \to (X, x_o)$, $H: (\beta T, e) \to (E(X), e)$, $\mathcal{A} = \mathrm{im} F^*$ and $\mathcal{B} = \mathrm{im} H^*$. Then $\mathcal{B}$ is the T-subalgebra $\mathcal{L}$ of $\mathcal{C}$ generated by $\{\mathcal{A}p \mid p \in \beta T\}$.

(Notice that H is the canonical map induced by F.)

PROOF. Let $f \in \mathcal{A}$, $p \in \beta T$, $g \in C(X)$ with $F^*(g) = f$ and $q = H(p) \in E(X)$. Since H is a semigroup homomorphism, $HL_p = L_q H$ whence $L_p^* H^* = H^* L_q^*$.

Now let $\pi: (E(X), e) \to (X, x_o)$ $(\pi(r) = x_o r$ $(r \in E(X)))$. Then by unicity $\pi H = F$ whence $F^* = H^* \pi^*$.

Thus $fp = L_p^*(f) = L_p^* F^*(g) = L_p^* H^* \pi^* g = H^* L_q^* \pi^* g \in \mathcal{B}$ since $L_q^* \pi^*(g) \in C(E(X))$. Hence $\mathcal{L} \subset \mathcal{B}$.

Now let $a,b \in \beta T$ with $a|\mathcal{L} = b|\mathcal{L}$. I shall show that $a|\mathcal{B} = b|\mathcal{B}$. This will imply that $\mathcal{L}$ separates points of $|\mathcal{B}|$ whence $\mathcal{L} = \mathcal{B}$. It suffices to show that $H(a) = H(b)$ or in other words that $xH(a) = xH(b)$ $(x \in X)$. Let $x \in X$, $p \in \beta T$ with $F(p) = x$, $g \in C(X)$ and $f = F^* g$. Then $\langle g, xH(a)\rangle = \langle g, F(p)H(a)\rangle = \langle g, F(pa)\rangle = \langle f, pa\rangle = \langle fp, a\rangle = \langle fp, b\rangle$ (since

$fp \in \mathcal{L}) = \langle f, pb \rangle = \ldots = \langle g, xH(b) \rangle$ whence $xH(a) = xH(b)$.

NOTES

1. Using the notions of category theory one might summarize chapter 9 as follows:

Let $\mathcal{K}$ and $\mathcal{L}$ be the categories such that

a) objects of $\mathcal{K}$ = T-subalgebras of $\mathcal{C}$.

b) if $\mathfrak{A},\mathfrak{B}$ are objects of $\mathcal{K}$ then $\mathrm{mor}(\mathfrak{A},\mathfrak{B}) = \emptyset$ if $\mathfrak{A} \not\subset \mathfrak{B}$ and $\mathrm{mor}(\mathfrak{A},\mathfrak{B})$ = inclusion map if $\mathfrak{A} \subset \mathfrak{B}$.

c) objects of $\mathcal{L}$ = pointed transformation groups.

d) if (X,x_o) and (Y,y_o) are in $\mathcal{L}$ then $\mathrm{mor}((X,x_o),(Y,y_o))$ is the unique homomorphism $\varphi\colon (X,x_o) \stackrel{\rightarrow}{\rightarrow} (Y,y_o)$ if this exists; otherwise it is null.

Then $S(\mathfrak{A}) = (|\mathfrak{A}|, i_{\mathfrak{A}})$ determines a contravariant functor of $\mathcal{K}$ into $\mathcal{L}$ and $G(X,x_o) = \mathrm{im}\varphi^*$ defines a contravariant functor from $\mathcal{L}$ into $\mathcal{K}$ where $\varphi\colon (\beta T,e) \stackrel{\rightarrow}{\rightarrow} (X,x_o)$.

Moreover GS is the identity functor on $\mathcal{K}$ and SG is naturally equivalent to the identity functor $id_{\mathcal{L}}$ on $\mathcal{L}$, i.e. there exists a natural transformation $\tau\colon SG \to id_{\mathcal{L}}$ such that $\tau(X,x_o)$ is an isomorphism for all objects (X,x_o) of $\mathcal{L}$. (For details see: Horelick, <u>An algebraic approach to the study of minimal sets in topological dynamics</u>, thesis, Wesleyan University, 1967.)

Thus all the information contained in $\mathcal{L}$ is reflected in $\mathcal{K}$ by the functor G.

2. Let $\mathcal{P}$ be the category of all transformation groups (recall they are all assumed point-transitive) with Hom(X,Y) the set of homomorphisms of X into Y. Now there is no "natural" way of assosiating a unique T-subalgebra of $\mathcal{C}$ with each object of $\mathcal{P}$. However, the T-subalgebras of $\mathcal{C}$ still faithfully reflect the properties of $\mathcal{P}$.

Thus let M be the category whose objects are the T-subalgebras of $\mathfrak{C}$ and where Hom($\mathfrak{A}$,$\mathfrak{B}$) is the set of T-homomorphisms of $\mathfrak{A}$ into $\mathfrak{B}$.

Set $F(\mathfrak{A}) = |\mathfrak{A}|$ for each object $\mathfrak{A}$ of M. Then F determines a contravariant functor from M into $\mathfrak{P}$ with the following properties:

(A) If $\mathfrak{A}, \mathfrak{B}$ are T-subalgebras of $\mathfrak{C}$ then the map $\mathrm{Hom}(\mathfrak{A},\mathfrak{B}) \to \mathrm{Hom}(|\mathfrak{B}|,|\mathfrak{A}|)$ induced by F is bijective. $(F(\varphi)(x) = x\,\varphi,\ (\varphi \in \mathrm{Hom}(\mathfrak{A},\mathfrak{B}),\ x \in |\mathfrak{B}|))$.

(B) If X,Y are objects of $\mathfrak{P}$ then there exist objects $\mathfrak{A}, \mathfrak{B}$ of M with $F(\mathfrak{A}) \cong X$ and $F(\mathfrak{B}) \cong Y$.

Thus if we wish to study Hom(X,Y) we can do so by studying Hom($\mathfrak{B}$,$\mathfrak{A}$) and this can be identified with $\{p|\mathfrak{B} \mid p \in \beta T,\ \mathfrak{B}p \subset \mathfrak{A}\}$ (9.6).

3. Let $\mathfrak{J}$ be a topology on T which makes it into a topological group and let $\mathfrak{R}$ be the set of bounded right uniformly continuous complex-valued functions on T. (Thus $f \in \mathfrak{R}$ if f is bounded and $\lim_{t\to e} \|tf - f\| = 0$)

Let $f \in \mathfrak{R}$. Then f is bounded and so there exists a unique $\bar{f} \in \mathfrak{C}$ with $\bar{f}|T = f$. It is convenient to identify f with $\bar{f}$ and view $\mathfrak{R}$ as a subset of $\mathfrak{C}$.

3.1 <u>LEMMA</u>. $\mathfrak{R}$ is a T-subalgebra of $\mathfrak{C}$.

<u>PROOF</u>. It is clear that $\mathfrak{R}$ is a closed subalgebra of $\mathfrak{C}$ which is closed under conjugation.

Let $f \in \mathfrak{R}$ and $t \in T$. I show that $tf \in \mathfrak{R}$.

Let $\varepsilon > 0$. Then there exists a $\mathfrak{J}$-neighborhood V of e such that $\|sf - f\| < \varepsilon$ $(s \in V)$. Let W be a $\mathfrak{J}$-neighborhood of e with $t^{-1}Wt \subset V$, and let $r \in W$. Then $t^{-1}rt \in V$ and $\|rtf - tf\| = \|t^{-1}rtf - f\| < \varepsilon$.

3.2 <u>LEMMA</u>. The map $\pi: |\mathfrak{R}| \times (T,\mathfrak{J}) \to |\mathfrak{R}|$ such that $\pi(x,t) = xt$. $(x \in |\mathfrak{R}|, t \in T)$ is continuous.

<u>PROOF</u>. Let $f \in \mathfrak{R}$. Then it suffices to show that the map $(x,t) \to \langle fx,t\rangle$ of $|\mathfrak{R}| \times T \to \mathbb{C}$ is continuous.

Let $x \in |\mathfrak{R}|$, $t \in T$, and $\varepsilon > 0$. Then there exist neighborhoods V of t and N of x such that

(i) $\|rf - tf\| < \varepsilon/2$ $(r \in V)$ and

(ii) $|\langle fx,t\rangle - \langle fy,t\rangle| < \varepsilon/2$ $(y \in N)$.

Hence by (i) $|\langle fi_{\mathfrak{R}}s,r\rangle - \langle fi_{\mathfrak{R}}s,t\rangle| =$

$|\langle f,sr\rangle - \langle f,st\rangle| = |\langle rf,s\rangle - \langle tf,s\rangle| < \varepsilon/2$ $(s \in T)$. Since $i_{\mathfrak{R}}T$ is dense in $|\mathfrak{R}|$, this implies

(iii) $|\langle fz,r\rangle - \langle fz,t\rangle| < \varepsilon/2$ $(z \in |\mathfrak{R}|)$.

Finally (ii) and (iii) imply that
$|\langle fy,r\rangle - \langle fx,t\rangle| < \varepsilon$ $(y \in N, r \in V)$.

3.3 <u>PROPOSITION</u>. Let (X,T,π) be a (point transitive) transformation group such that $\pi: X \times (T,\mathfrak{J}) \to X$ is continuous. Then (X,T) is a homomorphic image of $(|\mathfrak{R}|,T)$.

(Thus $(|\mathfrak{R}|,T)$ is a universal point transitive transformation group for the collection of point transitive transformation groups (X,T) where T is provided with the topology $\mathfrak{J}$.)

<u>PROOF</u>. Let $\mathfrak{A}$ be a T-subalgebra of $\mathfrak{C}$ such that the map $\varphi(x,t) = xt$ of $|\mathfrak{A}| \times (T,\mathfrak{J}) \to |\mathfrak{A}|$ is continuous. It suffices to show that $\mathfrak{A} \subset \mathfrak{R}$.

Let $f \in \mathfrak{A}$ and $\varepsilon > 0$. Then the map $(x,t) \to \langle fx,t\rangle$ of $|\mathfrak{A}| \times (T,\mathfrak{J}) \to C$ is continuous. Since $|\mathfrak{A}|$ is compact this implies that there exists a $\mathfrak{J}$-neighborhood V of e such that $|\langle fx,t\rangle - \langle fx,e\rangle| < \varepsilon$ $(x \in |\mathfrak{A}|, t \in V)$. Then
$|\langle tf,s\rangle - \langle f,s\rangle| = |\langle f,xt\rangle - \langle f,s\rangle| =$

$| \langle fi_{\alpha}s, t \rangle - \langle fi_{\alpha}s, e \rangle | < \varepsilon \; (s \in T, t \in V)$; i.e.

$\|tf - f\| < \varepsilon \; (t \in V)$. Hence $f \in \mathcal{R}$.

The results in 3 are due to Knapp: Decomposition theorem for bounded uniformly continuous functions on a group, Amer. J. of Math., vol. 88 (1966) 902-914.

CHAPTER 10

THE MINIMAL T-SUBALGEBRAS OF $\mathfrak{C}$

In this chapter I would like to characterize those T-subalgebras $\mathfrak{A}$ of $\mathfrak{C}$ such that $(|\mathfrak{A}|, T)$ is minimal.

Before proceeding let me remind the reader that βT has been identified with $E(\beta T)$ and that if (X,T) is a transformation group, $p \in \beta T$ has been identified with its image in $E(X)$ under the canonical map $(\beta T, e) \to (E(X), e)$ (see 2 of 9.2). Under the above map the minimal right ideals in βT go over into minimal right ideals in $E(X)$.

10.1 DEFINITION. Let $\mathfrak{A}$ be a T-subalgebra of $\mathfrak{C}$. Then $\mathfrak{A}$ is distal, minimal, etc. if $(|\mathfrak{A}|, T)$ is distal, minimal, etc.

For $\emptyset \neq K \subset \beta T$, set $\mathfrak{U}(K) = \{f \mid fp = f (p \in K)\}$. Then it is immediate that $\mathfrak{U}(K)$ is a T-subalgebra of $\mathfrak{C}$.

10.2 PROPOSITION. Let M be a minimal right ideal of βT, J the set of idempotents in M, and $\mathfrak{A}$ a T-subalgebra of $\mathfrak{C}$. Then $\mathfrak{A}$ is minimal iff $\mathfrak{A} \subset \mathfrak{U}(u)$ for some $u \in J$.

PROOF. Let $|\mathfrak{A}|$ be minimal. Then the map $\varphi\colon M \to |\mathfrak{A}|$ such that $\varphi(p) = p|\mathfrak{A}$ is an epimorphism. Hence $\{p \mid \varphi(p) = i_{\mathfrak{A}}\}$ is a non-empty closed subsemigroup of M. Thus there exists $u \in J$ with $\varphi(u) = i_{\mathcal{A}}$, whence $\mathcal{A} \subset \mathfrak{A}(u)$.

Now suppose $\mathcal{A} \subset \mathfrak{A}(u)$ with $u \in J$. Then $i_{\mathcal{A}}u = i_{\mathcal{A}}$ whence $i_{\mathcal{A}}$ is an almost periodic point of $(|\mathcal{A}|,T)$ by 3.7. Since $\overline{i_{\mathcal{A}}T} = |\mathcal{A}|$, $(|\mathcal{A}|,T)$ is minimal.

10.3 <u>REMARKS</u>. 1. Proposition 10.2 shows that we may restrict our attention to one minimal right ideal and its idempotents in order to study the minimal T-subalgebras of $\mathcal{C}$. For this reason we shall fix a minimal right ideal M of βT and its idempotents J for the remainder of the text.

2. The T-subalgebras $\mathfrak{A}(u)$ is just $\mathcal{C}u$ for: let $f \in \mathfrak{A}(u)$, then $fu = f$ whence $f \in \mathcal{C}u$. On the other hand if $f = gu$ for some $g \in \mathcal{C}$, then $fu = gu^2 = gu = f$ whence $f \in \mathfrak{A}(u)$.

10.4 <u>PROPOSITION</u>. Let $\varphi\colon (\beta T,e) \rightrightarrows (X,x_o)$ and $x_o v = x_o$ with $v \in J$. Then $\mathrm{im}\varphi^* \subset \mathfrak{A}(v)$.

<u>PROOF</u>. Let $f = \varphi^* g$. Then $\langle fv,e\rangle = \langle f,v\rangle = \langle \varphi^* g,v\rangle = \langle g,\varphi(v)\rangle = \langle g,\varphi(e)\psi(v)\rangle = \langle g,x_o v\rangle = \langle g,x_o\rangle = \langle g,\varphi(e)\rangle = \langle f,e\rangle$.

Now replace f by tf. Then $\langle fv,t\rangle = \langle tfv,e\rangle = \langle tf,e\rangle = \langle f,t\rangle$ whence $fv = f$.

10.5 <u>COROLLARY</u>. Let (X,T) be minimal and $u \in J$. Then there exists a T-subalgebra $\mathcal{A}$ of $\mathfrak{A}(u)$ such that $(X,T) \cong (|\mathcal{A}|,T)$.

<u>PROOF</u>. Let $x \in X$ and $x_o = xu$. Then $x_o u = x_o$ and $\overline{x_o T} = X$. Hence there exists $\varphi\colon (\beta T,e) \rightrightarrows (X,x_o)$ and $\mathcal{A} = \mathrm{im}\varphi^* \subset \mathfrak{A}(u)$ by 10.4. Moreover $(X,T) \cong (|\mathcal{A}|,T)$ by 9.8.

10.6 <u>COROLLARY</u>. Let $\mathcal{A}$ be a T-subalgebra of $\mathcal{C}$. Then

$(|\mathcal{A}|,T)$ is a universal minimal set iff $\mathcal{A} = \mathfrak{A}(u)$ for some $u \in J$.

PROOF. Let $(|\mathcal{A}|,T)$ be a universal minimal set. By 10.2, $\mathcal{A} \subset \mathfrak{A}(u)$ for some $u \in J$. Thus $i_{\mathcal{A}}$ is a monomorphism of $\mathcal{C}(|\mathcal{A}|) = \mathcal{A}$ into $\mathcal{C}(|\mathfrak{A}(u)|) = \mathfrak{A}(u)$. Hence $\overline{i}_{\mathcal{A}}\colon |\mathfrak{A}(u)| \xrightarrow{\sim} |\mathcal{A}|$. By the comments following 9.2, $\overline{i}_{\mathcal{A}}$ is an isomorphism, whence $\overline{i}^{*}_{\mathcal{A}} = i_{\mathcal{A}}$ is onto and $\mathcal{A} = \mathfrak{A}(u)$.

On the other hand $(|\mathfrak{A}(u)|,T)$ is a universal minimal set by 10.5.

Let (X,T) and (Y,T) be minimal sets and $\rho\colon X \xrightarrow{\sim} Y$. Then there are many ways of studying the above situation by means of T-subalgebras of $\mathcal{C}$. I.e. the algebras one associates with X and Y depend upon the base point chosen.

The following proposition shows that we so choose the base points $x_o \in X$ and $y_o \in Y$ that when we take the algebraic "picture" of $\rho\colon X \to Y$, ρ goes over into the inclusion map. Indeed all that is required is that $\rho(x_o) = y_o$.

10.7 PROPOSITION. Let $\rho\colon (X,x_o) \xrightarrow{\sim} (Y,y_o)$, $\varphi\colon (\beta T,e) \xrightarrow{\sim} (X,x_o)$, $\psi\colon (\beta T,e) \xrightarrow{\sim} (Y,y_o)$ and let $x_o u = x_o$ for some $u \in J$. Then

1. $y_o u = y_o$
2. $\operatorname{im}\psi^* \subset \operatorname{im}\varphi^*$
3. The diagram

$$\begin{array}{ccc} |\operatorname{im}\varphi^*| & \xrightarrow{r} & |\operatorname{im}\psi^*| \\ F\downarrow & & \downarrow G \\ X & \xrightarrow{\rho} & Y \end{array}$$

is commutative where F and G are the canonical isomorphisms of 9.8 and r is the restriction map.

PROOF. 1. $y_o = \rho(x_o) = \rho(x_o u) = \rho(x_o)u = y_o u$.

2. Since $\rho\varphi\colon (\beta T, e) \rightrightarrows (Y, y_o)$ and there is only one such map, $\rho\varphi = \psi$ whence $\psi^* = \varphi^*\rho^*$ and $\mathrm{im}\psi^* \subset \mathrm{im}\varphi^*$.

3. Let $\gamma \in |\mathrm{im}\varphi^*|$ and $f \in \mathcal{C}(Y)$. Then $\langle f, \rho F(\gamma)\rangle = \langle \rho^* f, F(\gamma)\rangle = \langle \gamma(\varphi^*\rho^* f), e\rangle = \langle r(\lambda)(\psi^* f), e\rangle = \langle f, G(r(\gamma))\rangle$ whence $\rho F(\gamma) = Gr(\gamma)$.

10.8 LEMMA. Let $\varphi\colon (\beta T, e) \rightrightarrows (X, x_o)$, $\psi\colon \beta T \rightrightarrows X$ and let $x_o u = x_o$, for some $u \in J$. Then there exists $p \in M$ such that $pu = p$ and $\varphi L_p = \psi$.

PROOF. Since $x_o u = x_o$ and $\overline{x_o T} = X$, (X,T) is minimal. Hence there exists $r \in M$ with $\psi(r) = x_o$. If $q = ru$, then $qu = q$ and $\psi(q) = \psi(ru) = \psi(r)u = x_o u = x_o$. There exists $p \in M$ with $pu = p$ and $u = pq = qp$ (3.5). Then $\varphi L_p(q) = \varphi(pq) = \varphi(u) = \varphi(e\,u) = \varphi(e)u = x_o u = x_o = \psi(q)$. Hence $\varphi L_p = \psi$ since (X,T) is minimal.

10.9 PROPOSITION. Let $\varphi\colon (\beta T, e) \rightrightarrows (X, x_o)$, $\mathcal{A} = \mathrm{im}\varphi^*$ and ρ a homomorphism of (X,T) into (X,T). Then there exists $p \in M$ with $pu = p$, $\mathcal{A}p \subset \mathcal{A}$, and such that the following diagram is commutative:

$$\begin{array}{ccc} \beta T & \xrightarrow{L_p} & \beta T \\ \varphi \downarrow & & \downarrow \varphi \\ X & \xrightarrow{\rho} & X \end{array}$$

PROOF. 10.9 follows from 10.8 with $\psi = \rho\varphi$.

10.10 REMARKS. 1. With the same notation as in 10.9 let $\pi: \beta T \to |\mathcal{A}|$ be the restriction mapping. Then $\varphi = F\pi$ and L_p induces a homomorphism $\overline{L}_p: |\mathcal{A}| \to |\mathcal{A}|$ (since $\mathcal{A}p \subset \mathcal{A}$) such that the diagram

$$\begin{array}{ccc} |\mathcal{A}| & \xrightarrow{\overline{L}_p} & |\mathcal{A}| \\ F\downarrow & & \downarrow F \\ X & \xrightarrow{\rho} & X \end{array}$$

is commutative.

Thus if $|\mathcal{A}|$ is identified with X by means of F, then the T-endomorphisms of X are induced by those $p \in M$ with $\mathcal{A}p \subset \mathcal{A}$.

NOTES

1. A further discussion of the material contained in this chapter may be found in

(a) Robert Ellis, Point transitive transformation groups, Trans. A.M.S., vol. 101, (1961) 384-395.

(b) Brindell Horelick, An algebraic approach to the study of minimal sets in topological dynamics, thesis, Wesleyan University, 1967.

In the above works real-valued functions are used rather than complex-valued ones. There is of course no difference in the results. The reason for using complex-valued functions in the text is for convenience in discussing group representations.

2. Let $\mathcal{L}'$ be the category whose objects are the T-subalgebras of $\mathfrak{A}(u)$ and whose morphisms are inclusion maps, and let $\mathcal{K}'$ be the category whose objects are pointed transformation groups, (X,x_o) with $x_o u = x_o$ and where $\text{mor}((X,x_o), (Y,y_o)) = \{\varphi \mid \varphi: (X,x_o) \xrightarrow{\sim} (Y,y_o)\}$. Then $\mathcal{L}'$ and $\mathcal{K}'$ are full subcategories respectively of the categories $\mathcal{L}$ and $\mathcal{K}$ considered in 1 of the notes to chapter 9. Moreover the functors S and G there defined are such that $S(\mathcal{L}') \subset \mathcal{K}'$ and $G(\mathcal{K}') \subset \mathcal{L}'$.

Thus the properties of $\mathcal{K}'$ are faithfully reflected by $\mathcal{L}'$ and in order to study the class of minimal sets we may restrict ourselves to the class of T-subalgebras of $\mathfrak{A}(u)$.

3. Let $\mathfrak{T}$ be a topology on T making it into a topological group. Then 3 of the notes to chapter 9 and 10.5 show that $|\mathfrak{R} \cap \mathfrak{A}(u)|$ is a universal minimal set for the collection of minimal transformation groups (X,T) where T is provided with the topology $\mathfrak{T}$. Here $u \in J$ and $\mathfrak{R} = \{f \mid f: (T,\mathfrak{T}) \to C \text{ is bounded and right uniformly continuous}\}$.

4. The T-subalgebras of $\mathcal{C}$ of the form $\mathfrak{A}(K) = \{f \mid fp = f \ (p \in K)\}$ where $\emptyset \neq K \subset \beta T$ seem to have special properties. In this note I would like to indicate some of them. They are considered again in chapter 11 for special K.

4.1 <u>DEFINITIONS AND NOTATION</u>. Let $\mathcal{A}$ be a T-subalgebra of $\mathcal{C}$. Then $\varphi_{\mathcal{A}}: T \to |\mathcal{A}|$ will denote the map such that $\varphi_{\mathcal{A}}(t) = i_{\mathcal{A}}t \ (t \in T)$ and $\mathfrak{I}_{\mathcal{A}}$ the topology induced on T by $\varphi_{\mathcal{A}}$. When $\mathcal{A} = \mathfrak{A}(K)$ these will be abbreviated φ_K and $\mathfrak{I}_K$.

Again let $\mathcal{A}$ be a T-subalgebra of $\mathcal{C}$. Then $\delta(\mathcal{A}) = \{p \mid fp = f \ (f \in \mathcal{A})\}$. Then $\delta(\mathcal{A})$ is a closed subsemigroup of βT containing e.

4.2 <u>PROPOSITION</u>. Let $\mathcal{A}$ be a T-subalgebra of $\mathcal{C}$, and $K = \delta(\mathcal{A})$. Then for $f \in \mathcal{C}$, $f \in \mathfrak{A}(K)$ iff $f: (T, \mathfrak{I}_{\mathcal{A}}) \to C$ is continuous.

<u>PROOF</u>. Let $f \in \mathfrak{A}(K)$ and $t_n \to t$ with respect to $\mathfrak{I}_{\mathcal{A}}$. Then we may assume that $t_n \to p$ in βT.

Now let $g \in \mathcal{A}$. Then $\langle f, t_n \rangle \to \langle g, t \rangle$ and $\langle g, t_n \rangle \to \langle g, p \rangle$. Hence $\langle g, t \rangle = \langle g, p \rangle$. Since $sg \in \mathcal{A}$ $(s \in T)$ the above implies that $\langle g, s \rangle = \langle t^{-1}sg, t \rangle = \langle t^{-1}sg, p \rangle = \langle sg, pt^{-1} \rangle = \langle gpt^{-1}, s \rangle$ $(s \in T)$, whence $g = gpt^{-1}$ and $pt^{-1} \in K$.

Hence $\langle f, t_n \rangle \to \langle f, p \rangle = \langle fpt^{-1}, t \rangle = \langle f, t \rangle$ whence f is continuous on $(T, \mathfrak{I}_{\mathcal{A}})$.

Now let $f \in \mathcal{C}$ be continuous on $(T, \mathfrak{I}_{\mathcal{A}})$ and let $p \in K$. Choose a net (t_n) in T with $t_n \to p$ in βT. Then $\langle sg, \varphi_{\mathcal{A}}(t_n) \rangle = \langle sg, i_{\mathcal{A}}t_n \rangle = \langle g, t_n s \rangle \to \langle g, ps \rangle = \langle gp, s \rangle = \langle g, s \rangle$ $(g \in \mathcal{A}, s \in T)$. Thus $i_{\mathcal{A}}t_n s \to i_{\mathcal{A}}s$ in $|\mathcal{A}|$.

4.3 COROLLARY. Let $\mathcal{A} = \mathfrak{A}(K)$ and $L = \delta(\mathcal{A})$. Then $\mathfrak{A}(L) = \mathfrak{A}(K)$, i.e. $\mathfrak{A}\delta\mathfrak{A} = \mathfrak{A}$.

PROOF. Clearly $K \subset L$ whence $\mathfrak{A}(L) \subset \mathfrak{A}(K)$.

Let $f \in \mathfrak{A}(K)$. Then $f\colon (T,\mathfrak{J}_K) \to C$ is continuous whence $f \in \mathfrak{A}(L)$ by 4.2.

The proof of the following two results are left to the reader.

4.4 COROLLARY. Let $\mathcal{A}$ and $\mathcal{B}$ be T-subalgebras of $\mathcal{C}$. Then $\mathfrak{J}_{\mathcal{A}} \subset \mathfrak{J}_{\mathcal{B}}$ iff $\mathfrak{A}(\delta(\mathcal{A})) \subset \mathfrak{A}(\delta(\mathcal{B}))$.

4.5 COROLLARY. Let $\mathcal{A}$ be a T-subalgebra of $\mathcal{C}$, $f \in \mathfrak{A}(\delta(\mathcal{A}))$ and ψ a bounded continuous function from $f(T)$ into C. Then $\psi f \in \mathfrak{A}(\delta(\mathcal{A}))$.

4.6 PROPOSITION. Let $\emptyset \neq K \subset \beta T$. Then the pair $(|\mathfrak{A}(K)|, \varphi_K)$ is the β-compactification of $(T,\mathfrak{J}_K)$. (I assume the map φ_K is injective; if it isn't replace T by $T/\ker\varphi_K$).

PROOF. Let $\psi\colon (T,\mathfrak{J}_K) \to X$ be a continuous function such that $\overline{\psi(T)} = X$, where X is a compact Hausdorff space.

Then there exists a continuous map $\rho\colon \beta T \to X$ such that $\rho(t) = \psi(t)$ $(t \in T)$.

Let $g \in \mathcal{C}(X)$. Then $\langle \rho^* g, t\rangle = \langle g, \rho(t)\rangle = \langle g, \psi(t)\rangle$ $(t \in T)$. Hence $\rho^* g\colon (T,\mathfrak{J}_K) \to C$ is continuous so that $\rho^* g \in \mathfrak{A}(K)$ (4.2 and 4.3). Consequently ρ induces $\gamma\colon |\mathfrak{A}(K)| \to X$ with $\gamma(\varphi_K(t)) = \psi(t)$ $(t \in T)$.

Thus the universal minimal set $|\mathfrak{A}(u)|$ is the β-compactification of $(T,\mathfrak{J}_u)$. (Recall that T acts freely on $|\mathfrak{A}(u)|$ (8.14) whence φ_u is injective). Of course $\mathfrak{J}_u$ is in general not discrete.

Let $\mathfrak{J}$ be a topology on T making it into a topological group and $\mathfrak{R}$ the set of bounded right uniformly continuous functions on $(T,\mathfrak{J})$. (See the notes to chapter 9.) One might ask is $\mathfrak{R}$ of the form $\mathfrak{A}(K)$? When $\mathfrak{J}$ is locally compact the answer is yes.

4.7 <u>PROPOSITION</u>. With the above notation let $\mathfrak{J}$ be locally compact and $R = \delta(\mathfrak{R})$. Then $\mathfrak{R} = \mathfrak{A}(R)$ i.e. $\mathfrak{R} = \mathfrak{A}(\delta(\mathfrak{R}))$.

<u>PROOF</u>. Clearly $\mathfrak{R} \subset \mathfrak{A}(R)$.

By 3.3 of the notes to chapter 9 in order to show that $\mathfrak{A}(R) \subset \mathfrak{R}$ it suffices to prove that the map Π: $|\mathfrak{A}(R)| \times (T,\mathfrak{J}) \to |\mathfrak{A}(R)|$ such that $\Pi(x,t) = xt$ $(x \in |\mathfrak{A}(R)|, t \in T)$ is continuous.

Since $\mathfrak{J}$ is locally compact it suffices to show the Π is unilaterally continuous. (See Robert Ellis, <u>Locally compact transformation groups</u>, Duke Math, Journal, vol. 24 (1957), 119-125.)

Now the map $x \to \Pi(x,t)$ $(x \in |\mathfrak{A}(R)|)$ is continuous $(t \in T)$.

To show that the map $t \to \Pi(x,t)$ of $(T,\mathfrak{J})$ into $|\mathfrak{A}(R)|$ is continuous $(x \in |\mathfrak{A}(R)|)$ it suffices to show that the map $t \to \langle f,xt \rangle$ of $(T,\mathfrak{J})$ into C is continuous $(f \in \mathfrak{A}(R))$ or in other words that fx: $(T,\mathfrak{J}) \to C$ is continuous.

Since the map φ_R: $(T,\mathfrak{J}) \to |\mathfrak{R}|$ is continuous, $\mathfrak{J} \supset \mathfrak{J}_R$ and the proof can be completed by showing that $fx \in \mathfrak{A}(R)$. But this is clear from the definition of $\mathfrak{A}(R)$.

Many of the results in 4 in particular 4.2, 4.5, and 4.6 are due to Knapp and Veech. For more details see:

A. W. Knapp, <u>Functions behaving like almost automorphic functions</u>, Topological dynamics, an international symposium, Benjamin Inc. 1968 edited by Joseph Auslander and

Walter H. Gottschalk 299-317.

W. A. Veech, *Almost automorphic functions on groups*, Amer. J. Math. Vol. 87(1965) 719-751.

CHAPTER 11

A GROUP ASSOCIATED WITH A MINIMAL SET

In this chapter I associate with every minimal set (X,T) a group, $\mathfrak{g}(X)$. This group reflects the dynamical properties of (X,T) in much the same manner that the subgroup H of G reflects those of $(G/H,G)$. Thus it bears some relation to Mackey's virtual groups [1].

These groups will also be used to give a unified presentation of Furstenberg's structure theorem for distal flows, Knapp's work on generalized almost periodic functions and Furstenberg's theory of disjointness.

11.1 STANDING NOTATION. Let me remind the reader that for the rest of this work M denotes a fixed minimal right ideal of βT and J the set of its idempotents. Henceforth u will denote a fixed element of J and G the set Mu. Recall that by 3.5, G is a subgroup of M with identity u. In order to distinguish them from the other elements of βT, the elements of G other than u will be denoted by lower case greek letters, $\alpha,\beta,\gamma\ldots$.

11.2 DEFINITION. Let $\mathcal{A}$ be a T-subalgebra of $\mathfrak{A}(u)$. Then the group $\mathfrak{g}(\mathcal{A})$ of $\mathcal{A}$ is the subgroup $\{\alpha \mid \alpha \in G,\ f\alpha =$

$f\ (f \in \mathfrak{A})\}$ of G.

11.3 <u>REMARKS</u>. 1. The T-subalgebra $\mathfrak{A}$ is required to be in $\mathfrak{U}(u)$ in order that $\mathfrak{g}(\mathfrak{A})$ be non-null.

2. By 10.5, 11.2 assigns a subgroup of G to every pointed transformation group (X, x_o) with $x_o u = x_o$. We shall see in a moment how this group depends upon the base point x_o.

3. The reader is cautioned that if $\alpha \in G$, $\alpha\alpha^{-1} = u$, not e. Of course $u = e$ on $\mathfrak{U}(u)$.

4. The group $\mathfrak{g}(\mathfrak{A})$ is just $\delta(\mathfrak{A}) \cap G$ (see notes to chapter 10).

11.4 <u>PROPOSITION</u>. Let $\mathfrak{A}$, $\mathfrak{B}$, and $(\mathfrak{A}_i \mid i \in I)$ be T-subalgebras of $\mathfrak{U}(u)$. Then:

1. $\mathfrak{A} \subset \mathfrak{B}$ implies $\mathfrak{g}(\mathfrak{B}) \subset \mathfrak{g}(\mathfrak{A})$.

2. $\mathfrak{g}(\mathfrak{A}\alpha) = \alpha^{-1}\mathfrak{g}(\mathfrak{A})\alpha\ (\alpha \in G)$.

3. $\mathfrak{g}([\cup \mathfrak{A}_i]) = \cap\, \mathfrak{g}(\mathfrak{A}_i)$ where $[\cup \mathfrak{A}_i]$ is the T-subalgebra of $\mathfrak{U}(u)$ generated by $\{\cup \mathfrak{A}_i \mid i \in I\}$.

<u>PROOF</u>. 1 and 2 are immediate from definition 11.2.

3. Since $\mathfrak{A}_j \subset [\cup \mathfrak{A}_i]\ (j \in I)$, $\mathfrak{g}([\cup \mathfrak{A}_i]) \subset \cap\, \mathfrak{g}(\mathfrak{A}_i)$ by 1.

Let $\alpha \in \cap\, \mathfrak{g}(\mathfrak{A}_i)$ and $\mathfrak{L} = \{f \mid f\alpha = f\} \cap \mathfrak{U}(u)$. Then $\mathfrak{L}$ is a T-subalgebra of $\mathfrak{U}(u)$ with $\cup\, \mathfrak{A}_i \subset \mathfrak{L}$. Hence $[\cup \mathfrak{A}_i] \subset \mathfrak{L}$ and $\alpha \in \mathfrak{g}([\cup \mathfrak{A}_i])$.

11.5 <u>REMARKS</u>. 1. Let (X,T) be minimal, $x_o, x_1 \in X$ with $x_o u = x_o$ and $x_1 u = x_1$. Let $\varphi: (\beta T, e) \rightrightarrows (X, x_o)$, $\psi: (\beta T, e) \rightrightarrows (X, x_1)$, $\mathfrak{A} = \text{im}\varphi^*$ and $\mathfrak{B} = \text{im}\psi^*$. Then by 10.8 there exists $\alpha \in G$ such that $\psi L_\alpha = \varphi$. Hence $\mathfrak{A} = \mathfrak{B}\alpha$ and so by 2 of 11.4 $\mathfrak{g}(\mathfrak{C}) = \alpha^{-1}\mathfrak{g}(\mathfrak{B})\alpha$.

This shows how the group assigned to a minimal set depends upon the base point; namely if $(|\mathfrak{B}|, i_{\mathfrak{B}}) \cong (X, x_0)$ and $(|\mathfrak{C}|, i_{\mathfrak{C}}) \cong (X, x_1)$, then $\mathfrak{C} = \mathfrak{B}\alpha$ and $\mathfrak{g}(\mathfrak{C}) = \alpha^{-1}\mathfrak{g}(\mathfrak{B})\alpha$.

2. Henceforth I shall restrict my attention to T-subalgebras of $\mathfrak{A}(u)$. Using the last two chapters the reader should be able to translate any statement about minimal sets into one about T-subalgebras of $\mathfrak{A}(u)$ and vice-versa.

3. Let $(I, \leq)$ be a directed set, $(\mathfrak{C}_i \mid i \in I)$ a family of T-subalgebras of $\mathfrak{A}(u)$ such that $\mathfrak{C}_i \subset \mathfrak{C}_j$ $(i \leq j \in I)$, and $\mathfrak{B} = \overline{\cup \mathfrak{C}_i}$. Then $\mathfrak{B} = [\cup \mathfrak{C}_i]$. It is left as an exercise for the reader to show that $|\mathfrak{B}|$ is the inverse limit of the system $((|\mathfrak{C}_j|, \varphi_i^j) \mid j \geq i,\ i,j \in I)$ where $\varphi_i^j\colon |\mathfrak{C}_j| \to |\mathfrak{C}_i|$ is the restriction mapping for $i \leq j$. Thus the inverse limit of a system of minimal sets is again a minimal set.

The question now arises: given a subgroup A of G does there exist a T-subalgebra $\mathfrak{C}$ such that $\mathfrak{g}(\mathfrak{C}) = A$? In general the answer is no. In order to characterize those subgroups A for which the answer is yes I must introduce various topologies on G. These topologies will also be used later in connection with other dynamical questions.

11.6 <u>DEFINITION AND NOTATION</u>. Let $\mathfrak{C}$ be a T-subalgebra of C. Then $\mathfrak{C}_R$ will denote the set of real-valued functions in $\mathfrak{C}$.

Let $f \in C_R$, $\emptyset \neq K \subset \beta T$ and $t \in T$. Set $\langle f^K, t\rangle = \sup\{\langle f, kt\rangle \mid k \in K\}$ and $\langle f_K, t\rangle = \inf\{\langle f, kt\rangle \mid k \in K\}$. Then f^K and f_K are bounded functions on T. Hence they give continuous extensions to all of βT. These extensions will also be denoted f^K and f_K respectively.

Let $p \in \beta T$, (t_i) a net in T with $t_i \to p$. Then $\langle f^K, p\rangle = \lim \langle f^K, t_i\rangle$. Since $\lim \langle f, kt_i\rangle = \langle f, kp\rangle$ and $\langle f^K, t_i\rangle \geq \langle f, kt_i\rangle$ $(k \in K)$, $\langle f^K, p\rangle \geq \sup \{\langle f, kp\rangle \mid k \in K\}$. The reader is cautioned that in general $\langle f^K, p\rangle = \sup \{\langle f, kp\rangle \mid k \in K\}$ only when $p \in T$.

Similarly $\langle f_K, p\rangle \leq \inf \{\langle f, kp\rangle \mid k \in K\}$.

The proof of the following is straightforward and is left to the reader.

11.7 <u>LEMMA</u>. Let $f \in C_R$, $x \in \beta T$, $t \in T$ and $\emptyset \neq K \subset \beta T$. Then:

1. $(-f)^K = -(f_K)$.
2. $(tf)^K = t(f^K)$.

2'. $(tf)_K = t(f_K)$.

3. $(fx)^K = f^{xK}$.

3'. $(fx)_K = f_{xK}$.

4. $f^{Kx} \leq f^K x$.

4'. $f_{Kx} \geq f_K x$.

11.8 <u>LEMMA</u>. Let $f \in C_R$ and K,L non-empty subsets of βT. Then $f^{K \cup L} = f^K \vee f^L$ where $\vee$ denotes supremum.

<u>PROOF</u>. Since $\langle f^{K \cup L}, t\rangle = \langle f^K, t\rangle \vee \langle f^L, t\rangle$ $(t \in T)$, 11.8 follows by continuity.

11.9 <u>DEFINITION</u>. Let $f \in C_R$, and $\emptyset \neq K \subset G$. Then $K^f = \{\alpha \mid \alpha \in G,\ f\alpha \leq f^K u\}$, $K_f = \{\alpha \mid \alpha \in G,\ f_K u \leq f\alpha\}$, and $K(f) = K^f \cap K_f$.

11.10 PROPOSITION. Let $\mathcal{G}$ be a T-subalgebra of C. Then the mapping $K \to \mathrm{cls}_{\mathcal{G}} K = \bigcap \{K(f) \mid f \in \mathcal{G}_R\}$ $(\emptyset \neq K \subset G)$ and $\mathrm{cls}_{\mathcal{G}} \emptyset = \emptyset$ defines a closure operator on G. That is,

(i) $K \subset \mathrm{cls}_{\mathcal{G}} K$.

(ii) $K \subset L$ implies $\mathrm{cls}_{\mathcal{G}} K \subset \mathrm{cls}_{\mathcal{G}} L$.

(iii) $\mathrm{cls}_{\mathcal{G}}(\mathrm{cls}_{\mathcal{G}} K) = \mathrm{cls}_{\mathcal{G}} K$.

(iv) $\mathrm{cls}_{\mathcal{G}}(K \cup L) = \mathrm{cls}_{\mathcal{G}} K \cup \mathrm{cls}_{\mathcal{G}} L$.

(Note that since $\mathcal{G}$ is an algebra and $(-f)^K = (-f_K)$ then $K^{(-f)} = K_f$ and so $\bigcap \{K(f) \mid f \in \mathcal{G}_R\} = \bigcap \{K^f \mid f \in \mathcal{G}_R\} = \bigcap\{K_f \mid f \in \mathcal{G}_R\}$).

PROOF. (i) and (ii) are immediate.

(iii) Let $L = \mathrm{cls}_{\mathcal{G}} K$. Then by (i) and (ii) $\mathrm{cls}_{\mathcal{G}} K \subset \mathrm{cls}_{\mathcal{G}} L$.

Let $\beta \in L$, $f \in \mathcal{G}_R$. Then $\beta \in K^f$ implies that $\langle f, \beta t\rangle \leq \langle f^K u, t\rangle$ $(t \in T)$. Hence $f^L \leq f^K u$ whence $f^L u \leq f^K u^2 = f^K u$.

Now let $\alpha \in \mathrm{cls}_{\mathcal{G}} L$ and $f \in \mathcal{G}_R$. Then $f\alpha \leq f^L u \leq f^K u$. Hence $\alpha \in K^f$ and so $\alpha \in \mathrm{cls}_{\mathcal{G}} K$.

(iv) Since both K and L are contained in $K \cup L$, $\mathrm{cls}_{\mathcal{G}} K \cup \mathrm{cls}_{\mathcal{G}} L \subset \mathrm{cls}_{\mathcal{G}}(K \cup L)$ by (ii).

Now suppose $\alpha \notin \mathrm{cls}_{\mathcal{G}} K \cup \mathrm{cls}_{\mathcal{G}} L$. Then there exist $f, g \in \mathcal{G}_R$ such that $\alpha \notin K^f \cup L^g$. This implies that there exist $t, s \in T$ with $\langle f, \alpha t\rangle > \langle f^K, ut\rangle$ and $\langle f, \alpha s\rangle > \langle g^L, us\rangle$. adding a constant function if necessary we may assume $\langle f, \alpha t\rangle = \langle g, \alpha s\rangle$. Set $h = tf \wedge sg \in \mathcal{G}_R$. Then $\langle h, \alpha\rangle = \langle ft, \alpha\rangle \wedge \langle sg, \alpha\rangle = \langle f, \alpha t\rangle = \langle g, \alpha t\rangle$ whence $\langle h, \alpha\rangle > \langle f^K, ut\rangle =$

$<(tf)^K,u>$ and $<h,\alpha> > <g^L,us> = <(sg)^L,u>$.

On the other hand $<(tf)^K \vee (sg)^L,u> \geq <h^{K \cup L},u>$ by 11.8 ($h^{K \cup L} = h^K \vee h^L \leq (tf)^K \vee (sg)^L$). Thus $<h,\alpha> > <h^{K \cup L},u>$ whence $\alpha \notin (K \cup L)^h$. Hence $\alpha \notin cls_{\mathfrak{A}}(K \cup L)$.

11.11 <u>REMARKS AND NOTATION</u>. 1. The topology defined on G by the closure operator $K \to cls_{\mathfrak{A}}K$ will be denoted by $\tau(\mathfrak{A})$, and $\tau(C)$ simply by τ.

2. Let $\emptyset \neq K \subset \beta T$ and $p \in \beta T$. If $p \in \overline{K}$ (the closure of K in the original topology in βT) and $f \in C_R$ then it is clear that $fp \leq f^K$.

On the other hand if $p \notin \overline{K}$ there exists $f \in C_R$ such that $<f,p> = 1$ and $<f,k> = 0$ $(k \in K)$. Thus $<fp,e> = 1 > 0 = <f^K,e>$ whence $fp \not\leq f^K$.

Consequently $p \in \overline{K}$ iff $fp \leq f^K$ $(f \in C_R)$. This shows that if we were to drop the 'u' in the definition of K^f the τ topology on G would coincide with that induced by βT.

3. Let $\mathfrak{A}$ and $\mathfrak{B}$ be T-subalgebras with $\mathfrak{A} \subset \mathfrak{B}$. Then $\tau(\mathfrak{A}) \subset \tau(\mathfrak{B})$.

4. Let $\mathfrak{A}$ be a T-subalgebra, $f \in \mathfrak{A}_R$, $\emptyset \neq K \subset G$ and $g = fu$. Then $g^K = (fu)^K = f^{uK} = f^K$ by 11.7 and the fact that $uK = K$. Thus $K^f = K^{fu}$ $(f \in \mathfrak{A})$ whence $cls_{\mathfrak{A}}K = cls_{\mathfrak{A}u}K$. Consequently $\tau(\mathfrak{A}) = \tau(\mathfrak{A}u)$.

This means that we need only consider T-subalgebras of $\mathfrak{A}(u)$ in defining the various τ-topologies on G.

11.12 <u>PROPOSITION</u>. 1. Let $\mathfrak{A}$ be a T-subalgebra of $\mathfrak{A}(u)$. Then $\mathfrak{g}(\mathfrak{A})$ is a $\tau(\mathfrak{A})$ (and hence τ)-closed subgroup of G.

2. Let H be a τ-closed subgroup of G. Then $\mathfrak{A}(H)$ is

a T-subalgebra of $\mathfrak{A}(u)$ with $H = \mathfrak{g}(\mathfrak{A}(H))$.

PROOF. 1. Let $A = \mathfrak{g}(\mathfrak{a})$, $\alpha \in \text{cls}_C A$ and $f \in \mathfrak{a}$. Then $f_A u \leq f\alpha \leq f^A u$. But in this case $f_A \doteq f^A = f = fu$. Hence $f\alpha = f$ and $\alpha \in A$.

2. It has already been noted (10.1) that $\mathfrak{A}(H)$ is a T-subalgebra of C. Since $u \in H$, $\mathfrak{A}(H) \subset \mathfrak{A}(u)$.

Now let $K = \mathfrak{g}(\mathfrak{A}(H))$. Then clearly $H \subset K$.

Let $\gamma \in K$. I shall show that $\gamma \in \text{cls}_C H = H$.

Let $f \in C$ and $g = f^H u$. If $\alpha \in H$ then $g = f^{H\alpha} u \leq f^H \alpha = g\alpha$ (4 of 11.7). Since H is a group, $g\alpha = g$ $(\alpha \in H)$ whence $g \in \mathfrak{A}(H)$.

Since $\gamma \in K$, $g\gamma = g$ whence $f\gamma \leq f^H \gamma = f^H u$ and so $\gamma \in H^f$. The proof is completed.

The various "τ-topologies" introduced above will play an important role in subsequent chapters. Here I should like to describe $\tau(\mathfrak{a})$ in terms of the original topology on βT and to derive some of its elementary properties.

11.13 DEFINITION. Let $\mathfrak{a}$ be a T-subalgebra of C and $\Gamma \subset \beta T$. Then Γ is $\mathfrak{a}$-saturated if whenever $p \in \beta T$ and there exists $q \in \Gamma$ with $fp = fq$ $(f \in \mathfrak{a})$ then $p \in \Gamma$.

Now let $U \subset T$ and $p \in h(U)$ (i.e. $U \in p$). Then $h(U)$ is an $\mathfrak{a}$-neighborhood of p if there exists a saturated neighborhood Γ of p with $\Gamma \subset h(U)$.

Finally let $U, V \subset T$. Then $(U,V) = \{\alpha \mid \alpha \in G \text{ and } U\alpha \cap V \neq \emptyset\}$. (Recall we are using the ultra-filter interpretation of βT, see chapter 7.)

11.14 REMARKS. 1. Notice that every subset of βT is C-saturated and that $h(U)$, where $U \subset T$, is a C-neighborhood of p for all p with $U \in p$.

2. Let $\Gamma \subset \beta T$. Then Γ is $\mathcal{G}$-saturated iff $\pi^{-1}\pi(\Gamma) = \Gamma$ where $\pi: \beta T \to |\mathcal{G}|$ is the restriction mapping.

Let $p \in \beta T$, $x = \pi(p) \in |\mathcal{G}|$ and N a neighborhood of x in $|\mathcal{G}|$. Choose an open neighborhood S of x in $|\mathcal{G}|$ with $\overline{S} \subset N$. Then $\pi^{-1}(S) = \Gamma$ is an $\mathcal{G}$-saturated open neighborhood of p. There exists $U \subset T$ with $h(U) = \overline{\Gamma}$ (8.6 and 8.7). Then h(U) is an $\mathcal{G}$-neighborhood of p such that $\pi(h(U)) = \pi(\overline{\Gamma}) \subset \overline{\pi(\Gamma)} = \overline{S} \subset N$.

Thus the set $\{\pi(h(U)) \mid h(U)$ an $\mathcal{G}$-neighborhood of $p\}$ is a neighborhood base of $\pi(p)$.

3. Let $U \subset T$, $p \in \beta T$ and $U \in p$. Then h(U) is an $\mathcal{G}$-neighborhood of p iff there exist $\varepsilon > 0$ and a finite subset F of $\mathcal{G}$ such that $\{q \mid |\langle f,q\rangle - \langle f,p\rangle| < \varepsilon, (f \in F)\} \subset h(U)$.

11.14.1 PROPOSITION. Let $\mathcal{G}$ be a T-subalgebra of $\mathcal{C}$ and $\alpha \in G$. Then $\{(U,N) \mid h(U)$ an $\mathcal{G}$-neighborhood of α, $N \in u\}$ is a neighborhood base at α in the $\tau(\mathcal{G})$-topology. The elements N of u may be taken such that Nu = N.

PROOF. Let W be a $\tau(\mathcal{G})$-open subset of G with $\alpha \in W$. Then $\alpha \notin K = G - W = \mathrm{cls}_{\mathcal{G}}K$. Hence there exists $f \in \mathcal{G}_R$ with $\langle f,\alpha\rangle > \langle f^K,u\rangle = c$.

Set $x = \alpha|\mathcal{G}$. Then $\langle fx,e\rangle > c + \varepsilon$ for some $\varepsilon > 0$ and there exists a closed neighborhood V of x in $|\mathcal{G}|$ such that $\langle fy,e\rangle > c + \varepsilon$ $(y \in V)$ (i).

Let $\Gamma = \pi^{-1}(\text{int } V)$ where $\pi: \beta T \to |\mathcal{G}|$ is the restriction mapping. Then Γ is an $\mathcal{G}$-saturated open neighborhood of α (2 of 11.14). By 8.6 and 8.7, $\overline{\Gamma} = h(U)$ for some subset U of T. Then h(U) is an $\mathcal{G}$-neighborhood of α with $\pi(h(U)) \subset V$ (ii).

Now $\langle f^K,u\rangle = c$ implies that there exists $L \in u$ such that $\langle f^K,p\rangle < c + \varepsilon$ $(p \in h(L))$.

Set $N = Lu$. Then $Nu = N$ and $e \in N$ implies $N \in u$. Moreover if $t \in N$ then $Lt^{-1} \in u$ whence $L \in ut$ and so $\langle f^K, ut\rangle < c + \varepsilon$ (iii).

Finally let $\beta \in (U,N)$. This means that there exists $t \in N$ with $U \in \beta t$. Then $\langle tf,\beta\rangle = \langle f,\beta t\rangle > c + \varepsilon$ by (ii) and (i) and $\langle (tf)^K, u\rangle = \langle f^K, ut\rangle < c + \varepsilon$ by (iii). Hence $\beta \notin \mathrm{cls}_{\mathcal{A}}K = K$ so that $(U,N) \subset W$.

Now let $h(U)$ be an $\mathcal{A}$-neighborhood of α and $N \in u$. I show that (U,N) is a $\tau(\mathcal{A})$-neighborhood of α.

To this end let Γ be an $\mathcal{A}$-saturated neighborhood of α with $\Gamma \subset h(U)$. Let $f \in \mathcal{A}$ and Δ an open $\mathcal{A}$-saturated neighborhood of α with $\langle f,p\rangle = 1$ $(p \in \Delta)$ and $\langle f,p\rangle = 0$ $(p \notin \Gamma)$.

Let $\beta \in G - (U,N) = K$. Then $U \notin \beta t$ $(t \in N)$. Hence $\langle f\beta, t\rangle = \langle f,\beta t\rangle = 0$ $(\beta \in K,\ t \in N)$. Thus $\langle f^K, t\rangle = 0$ $(t \in N)$ whence $\langle f^K, u\rangle = 0$.

Consequently $\alpha \in \mathrm{cls}_{\mathcal{A}}K$ implies that $\langle f,\alpha\rangle = 0$ and so $\alpha \notin \Delta$. Hence $\Delta \subset (\mathrm{cls}_{\mathcal{A}}K)' = \mathrm{int}(U,N)$.

11.15 <u>COROLLARY</u>. Let $\mathcal{A}$ be a T-subalgebra of $\mathcal{C}$ and $\mathcal{F}$ a filter base on G such that $\mathcal{F} \to p \in M$ on $|\mathcal{A}|$. Then $\mathcal{F} \to pu \in G$ with respect to $\tau(\mathcal{A})$.

<u>PROOF</u>. Let $h(U)$ be an $\mathcal{A}$-neighborhood of pu and $N \in u$. Then $pu \in \Gamma \subset h(U)$ where Γ is an $\mathcal{A}$-saturated open subset of βT.

Let W be a subset of U with $pu \in h(W) \subset \Gamma$. Then $W \in pu$ whence $Wp \in u$ and there exists $t \in Wp \cap N$. This implies that $pt \in h(W) \subset \Gamma$ and so there exists $F \in \mathcal{F}$ with $Ft \subset \Gamma \subset h(U)$. (Recall that $\mathcal{F} \to pt$ on $|\mathcal{A}|$).

If $\alpha \in F$ then $U \in \alpha t$ and so $\alpha \in (U,N)$.

11.16 <u>COROLLARY</u>. Let $\mathcal{A}$ be a T-subalgebra of $\mathcal{C}$. Then:

1. $(G,\tau(\mathcal{A}))$ is compact.
2. $(G/A,\tau(\mathcal{A}))$ is T_1 where $A = \mathfrak{g}(\mathcal{A})$. (Thus (G,τ) is

T_1).

PROOF. 1. Let $\mathcal{F}$ be an ultra-filter on G. Since $|\mathcal{A}|$ is compact, $\mathcal{F} \to p \in M$ on $|\mathcal{A}|$. Then $\mathcal{F} \to pu \in G$ with respect to $\tau(\mathcal{A})$.

2. Let $\alpha, \beta \in G$ with $\beta \notin A\alpha$. There exists $f \in \mathcal{A}$ with $\langle f,\alpha\rangle \neq \langle f,\beta\rangle$. Hence there exists an $\mathcal{A}$-neighborhood $h(U)$ of α with $\beta \notin h(U)$.

If $\alpha \in (U,N)$ $(N \in u)$, then $U\alpha \cap N \neq \emptyset$ $(N \in u)$ whence $U\alpha \in u$ and so $U \in \alpha u = \alpha$. Thus $\bigcap\{(U,N) \mid N \in u\} \subset h(U)$ and so there exists $N \in u$ with $\beta \notin (U,N)$.

11.17 PROPOSITION. Let H be a subgroup of G and $\mathcal{A}$ a T-subalgebra of $\mathcal{C}$. Then:

1. The map $R_\alpha: (H,\tau(\mathcal{A})) \to (H,\tau(\mathcal{A}))$ such that $R_\alpha(\beta) = \beta\alpha$ $(\beta \in H)$ is continuous $(\alpha \in H)$.

2. Let $\mathcal{A}\alpha \subset \mathcal{A}$ with $\alpha \in H$. Then the map $L_\alpha: (H,\tau(\mathcal{A})) \to (H,\tau(\mathcal{A}))$ such that $L_\alpha(\beta) = \alpha\beta$ $(\beta \in H)$ is continuous.

3. The map $\varphi: (H,\tau) \to (H,\tau)$ such that $\varphi(\alpha) = \alpha^{-1}$ is continuous.

PROOF. 1. Let $K \subset H$, $\beta \in \mathrm{cls}_{\mathcal{A}} K$ and $f \in \mathcal{A}$. Then $f\beta \leq f^K u$ implies $f\beta\alpha \leq f^K\alpha = f^{K\alpha\alpha^{-1}}\alpha \leq f^{K\alpha}u$ (4 of 11.7). Thus $R_\alpha(\mathrm{cls}_{\mathcal{A}} K) \subset \mathrm{cls}_{\mathcal{A}} R_\alpha(K)$.

2. Again let $K \subset H$, $\beta \in \mathrm{cls}_{\mathcal{A}} K$ and $f \in \mathcal{A}$. Since $\mathcal{A}H \subset \mathcal{A}$, $f\alpha \in \mathcal{A}$ whence $f\alpha\beta \leq (f\alpha)^K u = f^{\alpha K}u$ (3 of 11.7). Thus $L_\alpha(\mathrm{cls}_{\mathcal{A}} K) \subset \mathrm{cls}_{\mathcal{A}}(L_\alpha(K))$.

3. This follows from 1 and 2 and the fact that $(U,N)^{-1} = (N,U)$ $(U,N \in u)$.

Let me conclude this chapter with some results

relating the endomorphisms of $|\mathfrak{A}|$ with G and $\mathfrak{g}(\mathfrak{A})$.

Let $\varphi: |\mathfrak{A}| \rightrightarrows |\mathfrak{A}|$. Then $\varphi^*: \mathfrak{A} \to \mathfrak{A}$ is a T-homomorphism whence by 9.6 there exists $p \in \beta T$ such that $fp = \varphi^*(f)$ $(f \in \mathfrak{A})$. If $\mathfrak{A} \subset \mathfrak{U}(u)$ then $up = p$ on $\mathfrak{A}$. Moreover since $\mathfrak{A}p \subset \mathfrak{A}$, $pu = p$ on $\mathfrak{A}$. Thus $f\alpha = \varphi^*(f)$ $(f \in \mathfrak{A})$ where $\alpha = upu \in G$.

11.18 DEFINITION. Let $\mathfrak{A}$ be a T-subalgebra of $\mathfrak{U}(u)$ and $A = \mathfrak{g}(\mathfrak{A})$. Then:

$\Sigma(A) = \{\alpha \mid A \subset \alpha^{-1}A\alpha\}$.

$N(A) = \{\alpha \mid A = \alpha^{-1}A\alpha\}$.

$\mathrm{End}(\mathfrak{A})$ = endomorphisms of $|\mathfrak{A}|$.

$\mathrm{Aut}(\mathfrak{A})$ = automorphisms of $|\mathfrak{A}|$.

11.19 REMARKS. 1. $N(A)$ is just the normalizer of A in G and $N(A) = \Sigma(A) \cap \Sigma(A)^{-1}$.

In general $\mathrm{End}(\mathfrak{A}) \neq \Sigma(A)/A$ because if $\alpha \in \Sigma(A)$, $A\alpha$ need not be contained in $\mathfrak{A}$. However if $\mathfrak{A} = \mathfrak{U}(A)$ and $\alpha \in \Sigma(A)$ then since $f\alpha\beta = f\alpha$ $(f \in \mathfrak{A}, \beta \in A)$, $\mathfrak{A}\alpha \subset \mathfrak{A}$. Thus $\mathrm{End}(\mathfrak{U}(A)) = \Sigma(A)/A$, and the identification preserves the semigroup structures.

2. Let $\alpha \in G$ with $\mathfrak{A}\alpha \subset \mathfrak{A}$. Then $A = \mathfrak{g}(\mathfrak{A}) \subset \mathfrak{g}(\mathfrak{A}\alpha) = \alpha^{-1}A\alpha$ by 2 of 11.4. Hence $\alpha \in \Sigma(A)$ and by the remarks preceding 11.18, $\mathrm{End}(\mathfrak{A})$ may be identified with a subset of $\Sigma(A)/A = \{A\alpha \mid \alpha \in \Sigma(A)\}$.

3. Let $\alpha \in G$ with $\mathfrak{A}\alpha = \mathfrak{A}$. Then $\alpha \in N(A)$ and $\mathrm{Aut}(\mathfrak{A}) \subset N(A)/A$. Just as in 2 above, one sees easily that $\mathrm{Aut}(\mathfrak{U}(A)) = N(A)/A$.

4. Of course $N(A) \subset \Sigma(A)$. It is not hard to show that $N(A) = \Sigma(A)$ if $\mathfrak{A}$ is equicontinuous. However, it is not known whether $N(A) = \Sigma(A)$ when $\mathfrak{A}$ is distal. In general $N(A) \neq \Sigma(A)$ (see [2]).

11.19.1 DEFINITION. Let $\mathcal{A}$ be a T-subalgebra of $\mathfrak{A}(u)$. Then the regularizer, $r(\mathcal{A})$ of $\mathcal{A}$ is the T-subalgebra of $\mathfrak{A}(u)$ generated by $\{\mathcal{A}\alpha \mid \alpha \in G\}$. The algebra $\mathcal{A}$ is regular if $\mathcal{A} = r(\mathcal{A})$.

Notice that $r(\mathcal{A})$ is again minimal.

11.20 REMARKS. 1. It is clear from 11.19 that $\mathcal{A}$ is regular iff $\mathcal{A}G \subset \mathcal{A}$. Thus in this case $\Sigma(A) = N(A) = G$ and $\mathrm{End}(\mathcal{A}) = \mathrm{Aut}(\mathcal{A}) = G/A$ where $A = \mathfrak{g}(\mathcal{A})$.

2. It is easy to see that if A is a τ-closed subgroup of G, then $\mathfrak{A}(A)$ is regular iff A is a normal subgroup.

3. If $A = \mathfrak{g}(\mathcal{A})$, then by 2 and 3 of 11.4, $\mathfrak{g}(r(\mathcal{A})) = \cap \{\alpha A \alpha^{-1} \mid \alpha \in G\}$.

11.21 PROPOSITION. Let $\mathcal{A}$ be a T-subalgebra of $\mathfrak{A}(u)$, $A = \mathfrak{g}(\mathcal{A})$ and $E(\mathcal{A})$ the enveloping semigroup of $\mathcal{A}$. Then $r(\mathcal{A}) = E(\mathcal{A}) \cap \mathfrak{A}(u) = E(\mathcal{A})u \cong$ minimal right ideals of $E(\mathcal{A})$.

PROOF. Recall that $E(\mathcal{A})$ is the T-subalgebra of C generated by $\{\mathcal{A}p \mid p \in \beta T\}$ (9.9). Hence $r(\mathcal{A}) \subset E(\mathcal{A}) \cap \mathfrak{A}(u)$.

If $f \in E(\mathcal{A}) \cap \mathfrak{A}(u)$ then $fu = f$ and $f \in E(\mathcal{A})u$. Thus $r(\mathcal{A}) \subset E(\mathcal{A}) \cap \mathfrak{A}(u) \subset E(\mathcal{A})u$.

Now let $\mathcal{B} = \{f \mid f \in E(\mathcal{A}),\ fu \in r(\mathcal{A})\}$ and let $f = gp$ with $g \in \mathcal{A}$ and $p \in \beta T$. Then $gu = g$ implies that $fu = gupu \in \mathcal{A}\alpha \subset r(\mathcal{A})$ where $\alpha = upu \in G$. Thus $\mathcal{B}$ is a T-subalgebra of $E(\mathcal{A})$ with $\mathcal{A}p \subset \mathcal{B}$ $(p \in \beta T)$. Hence $\mathcal{B} = E(\mathcal{A})$ and so $E(\mathcal{A})u \subset r(\mathcal{A})$.

Now consider the homomorphism $L_u\colon |E(\mathcal{A})| \to |E(\mathcal{A})|$ such that $L_u(x) = ux$ $(x \in E(\mathcal{A}))$ induced by u. Then $\mathrm{im}L_u$ is a closed invariant subset of $|E(\mathcal{A})|$ which corresponds to the T-subalgebra $L_u^*(E(\mathcal{A})) = E(\mathcal{A})u$ of $E(\mathcal{A})$. Hence $\mathrm{im}L_u$ is a minimal right ideal of $E(\mathcal{A})$.

It thus follows from 11.21 and 1 of 11.20 that $\mathcal{A}$ is regular iff $\mathfrak{A}$ is isomorphic to the minimal right ideals of its enveloping semigroup. This was the way Auslander first defined the notion of regularity (see [3]).

NOTES

1. George W. Mackey, *Virtual groups*, Topological dynamics, an international symposium edited by J. Auslander and W. H. Gottschalk, 335-364.

2. Joseph Auslander, *Endomorphisms of minimal sets*, Duke Math. Journal, vol.30 (1963), 605-614.

3. Joseph Auslander, *Regular minimal sets*, Trans. A.M.S., vol.123 (1966), 469-479.

4. Many times it is of interest to know what the T-subalgebra $\mathfrak{A}(G)$ is. When T is abelian $\mathfrak{A}(G) = \mathbf{C}$ as follows:

Let $f \in \mathfrak{A}(G)$ and $t \in T$. Since T is abelian $tu = ut = utu \in G$. Hence $\langle f,t\rangle = \langle fu,t\rangle = \langle futu,e\rangle = \langle f,e\rangle$.

We shall see presently that $\mathfrak{A}(G)$ need not be $\mathbf{C}$ when T is not abelian.

CHAPTER 12

DISTAL EXTENSIONS OF MINIMAL SETS

The groups defined in chapter 11 will be used to study the dynamical properties of the algebra with which they are associated. But first I should like to study the extent to which the group determines the algebra. Thus it may very well be the case that $\mathfrak{A} \subsetneqq \mathfrak{B}$ but $\mathfrak{g}(\mathfrak{B}) = \mathfrak{g}(\mathfrak{A})$. (For instance let $A = \mathfrak{g}(\mathfrak{A})$ and $\mathfrak{B} = \mathfrak{U}(A)$. Then $\mathfrak{g}(\mathfrak{B}) = \mathfrak{g}(\mathfrak{A})$, $\mathfrak{A} \subset \mathfrak{B}$ but in general $\mathfrak{A} \neq \mathfrak{B}$.)

In this chapter I would like to impose sufficient conditions on pairs of T-subalgebras $(\mathfrak{A},\mathfrak{B})$ with $\mathfrak{A} \subset \mathfrak{B}$ such that $\mathfrak{A} = \mathfrak{B}$ iff $\mathfrak{g}(\mathfrak{A}) = \mathfrak{g}(\mathfrak{B})$.

12.1 <u>STANDING NOTATION</u>. Unless specified otherwise all the T-subalgebras considered in this and subsequent chapters are assumed to be contained in $\mathfrak{U}(u)$.

12.2 <u>LEMMA</u>. Let $\mathfrak{A}$ and $\mathfrak{B}$ be T-subalgebras with $\mathfrak{A} \subsetneqq \mathfrak{B}$. Then there exist $p,y \in M$ with $\mathfrak{A}p \subset \mathfrak{U}(y)$ and $\mathfrak{B}p \not\subset \mathfrak{U}(y)$.

<u>PROOF</u>. Since $\mathfrak{A} \neq \mathfrak{B}$, the restriction map of $|\mathfrak{B}|$ onto $|\mathfrak{A}|$ is not one-one. Hence there exist $p,q \in \beta T$ such that $p|\mathfrak{A} = q|\mathfrak{A}$ but $p|\mathfrak{B} \neq q|\mathfrak{B}$. Since $up|\mathfrak{B} = p|\mathfrak{B}$ and $uq|\mathfrak{B} = q|\mathfrak{B}$

we may assume $up = p$ and $uq = q$. Thus $p, q \in M$.

Let $h \in \mathfrak{B}$ with $hp \neq hq$ and let $y \in M$ with $py = q$. Then $fpy = fq = fp$ $(f \in \mathfrak{A})$ and $hpy = hq \neq hp$. Thus $\mathfrak{A}p \subset \mathfrak{U}(y)$ but $\mathfrak{B}p \not\subset \mathfrak{U}(y)$.

12.3 PROPOSITION. Let $\mathfrak{A}$ and $\mathfrak{B}$ be T-subalgebras with $\mathfrak{A} \subsetneqq \mathfrak{B}$. Then either:

1. $\mathfrak{g}(\mathfrak{A}) \neq \mathfrak{g}(\mathfrak{B})$, or
2. There exist $x \in M$ and $w^2 = w \in M$ with $\mathfrak{A}x \subset \mathfrak{U}(w)$ and $\mathfrak{B}x \not\subset \mathfrak{U}(w)$.

PROOF. Assume 2 does not hold and let $p, y \in M$ be as in 12.2, i.e. $\mathfrak{A}p \subset \mathfrak{U}(y)$, $\mathfrak{B}p \not\subset \mathfrak{U}(y)$.

Let $w^2 = w \in M$ with $yw = y$. Then $\mathfrak{A}p \subset \mathfrak{U}(y) \subset \mathfrak{U}(w)$ and so because 2 does not hold, $\mathfrak{B}p \subset \mathfrak{U}(w)$. Thus $p|\mathfrak{B} = pw|\mathfrak{B}$ and we may assume $p = pw$.

Now let $pyr = u$ with $r \in M$. Then $\alpha = pru \in G$.

Let $f \in \mathfrak{A}$. Then $fpy = fp$ and $f = fu = fpyru = fpru = f\alpha$. Hence $\alpha \in \mathfrak{g}(\mathfrak{A})$.

If α were in $\mathfrak{g}(\mathfrak{B})$ then we would have $g = gu = gpyru = g\alpha = gpru$ $(g \in \mathfrak{B})$. Let $rux = w$. Then $gpy = gpyw = gpyrux = grux = gpw = gp$. This, however, contradicts $\mathfrak{B}p \not\subset \mathfrak{U}(y)$. Hence $\alpha \notin \mathfrak{g}(\mathfrak{B})$.

12.4 DEFINITION. Let $\mathfrak{A}$ be a T-subalgebra of $\mathfrak{B}$. Then $\mathfrak{B}$ is a distal extension of $\mathfrak{A}$ (denoted $\mathfrak{A} \leq \mathfrak{B}$) if $\mathfrak{A}p \subset \mathfrak{U}(w)$ implies $\mathfrak{B}p \subset \mathfrak{U}(w)$ $(p \in M, w \in J)$, where J is the set of idempotents of the minimal right ideal M. Thus if $\mathfrak{A} \leq \mathfrak{B}$, then $\mathfrak{A} = \mathfrak{B}$ iff $\mathfrak{g}(\mathfrak{A}) = \mathfrak{g}(\mathfrak{B})$.

In [1] and [2] what is here termed a distal extension was called a group-like extension. The present terminology is much more suggestive (see for example 12.8).

The following T-subalgebras are relevant for the study

of the collection of distal extensions of $\mathcal{A}$.

Let $\mathfrak{A}(p,w) = \{f | fp \in \mathfrak{A}(w)\}$ and $\mathcal{A}^* = \cap \{\mathfrak{A}(p,w) \mid \mathcal{A} \subset \mathfrak{A}(p,w),\ p \in M,\ w \in J\}$.

Observe that $\mathcal{A} \subset \mathfrak{A}(p,w)$ iff $\mathcal{A}p \subset \mathfrak{A}(w)$.

Let I be another minimal right ideal in βT, K the idempotents in I, and $k \in K$. Then there exists $w \in J$ with $kw = k$ and $wk = w$, whence $\mathfrak{A}(w) = \mathfrak{A}(k)$. Thus the notion of a distal extension is idependent of the minimal right ideal used.

12.5 <u>PROPOSITION</u>. Let $\mathcal{A}$ and $\mathcal{B}$ be T-subalgebras. Then

1. $\mathcal{A}^*$ is a T-subalgebra of $\mathfrak{A}(u)$ with $\mathcal{A} \subset \mathcal{A}^*$.
2. $\mathcal{A} \leq \mathcal{B}$ iff $\mathcal{A} \subset \mathcal{B} \subset \mathcal{A}^*$.

Thus $\mathcal{A}^*$ is the maximum distal extension of $\mathcal{A}$.

<u>PROOF</u>. 1. Since p, pw are T-homomorphisms, $\mathfrak{A}(p,w)$ is a T-subalgebra of $\mathfrak{A}(u)$ $(p \in M,\ w \in J)$. Clearly $\mathcal{A} \subset \mathcal{A}^*$.

2. Let $\mathcal{A} \leq \mathcal{B}$, $p \in M$, $w \in J$ and $\mathcal{A} \subset \mathfrak{A}(p,w)$. Then $\mathcal{A}p \subset \mathfrak{A}(w)$ whence $\mathcal{B}p \subset \mathfrak{A}(w)$ or equivalently $\mathcal{B} \subset \mathfrak{A}(p,w)$. Thus $\mathcal{B} \subset \mathcal{A}^*$.

Now let $\mathcal{A} \subset \mathcal{B} \subset \mathcal{A}^*$ and $p \in M$, $w \in J$ with $\mathcal{A}p \subset \mathfrak{A}(w)$. Then $\mathcal{A} \subset \mathfrak{A}(p,w)$ whence $\mathcal{A}^* \subset \mathfrak{A}(p,w)$. Thus $\mathcal{B} \subset \mathfrak{A}(p,w)$ or $\mathcal{B}p \subset \mathfrak{A}(w)$. Hence $\mathcal{A} \leq \mathcal{B}$.

12.6 <u>PROPOSITION</u>. Let $\mathcal{A}, \mathcal{B}$ be T-subalgebras. Then:

1. $\mathcal{A} \subset \mathcal{B}$ implies $\mathcal{A}^* \subset \mathcal{B}^*$.

2. $(\mathcal{A}\alpha)^* = \mathcal{A}^*\alpha$ $(\alpha \in G)$.

3. $\mathcal{A}^{**} = \mathcal{A}^*$.

4. $[\mathcal{A}^* \cup \mathcal{B}^*] \subset [\mathcal{A} \cup \mathcal{B}]^*$ (where $[\mathcal{N}]$ denotes the T-subalgebra generated by $\mathcal{N}$ for all subsets $\mathcal{N}$ of C).

5. $(\mathcal{A} \cap \mathcal{B})^* \subset \mathcal{A}^* \cap \mathcal{B}^*$.

PROOF. The proofs of 1, 3, 4, and 5 are straightforward and I omit them.

2. Let $\alpha \in G$, $p \in M$, $w \in J$ with $\mathcal{A}\alpha \subset \mathfrak{A}(p,w)$. Then $\mathcal{A} \subset \mathfrak{A}(p,w)\alpha^{-1} = \mathfrak{A}(\alpha p,w)$ ($f \in \mathfrak{A}(p,w)\alpha^{-1}$ iff $f\alpha \in \mathfrak{A}(p,w)$ iff $f\alpha p = f\alpha pw$ iff $f \in \mathfrak{A}(\alpha p,w)$). Consequently $\mathcal{A}^* \subset \mathfrak{A}(\alpha p,w)$ or $\mathcal{A}^*\alpha \subset \mathfrak{A}(p,w)$. Thus $\mathcal{A}^*\alpha \subset (\mathcal{A}\alpha)^*$.

Replacing α by α^{-1} and $\mathcal{A}$ by $\mathcal{A}\alpha$ in the above argument yields $(\mathcal{A}\alpha)^*\alpha^{-1} \subset \mathcal{A}^*$ or $(\mathcal{A}\alpha)^* \subset \mathcal{A}^*\alpha$.

12.7 PROPOSITION. Let $\mathcal{A}, \mathcal{B}$, and $\mathcal{F}$ be T-subalgebras. Then:

1. $\mathcal{A} \leq \mathcal{B}$ iff $\mathcal{A}\alpha \leq \mathcal{B}\alpha$ $(\alpha \in G)$.
2. If $\mathcal{A} \subset \mathcal{B} \subset \mathcal{F}$, then $\mathcal{A} \leq \mathcal{F}$ iff $\mathcal{A} \leq \mathcal{B}$ and $\mathcal{B} \leq \mathcal{F}$.
3. Let $\mathcal{A} \leq \mathcal{B}$ and $\mathcal{L} = [\mathcal{B}\alpha \mid \mathcal{A}\alpha \subset \mathcal{A}]$. Then $\mathcal{A} \leq \mathcal{L}$.

Thus by 3, $\mathcal{A} \leq \mathcal{S} = [\mathcal{B}\alpha \mid \alpha \in \mathfrak{g}(\mathcal{A})]$.

PROOF. 1. $\mathcal{A} \leq \mathcal{B}$ iff $\mathcal{A} \subset \mathcal{B} \subset \mathcal{A}^*$ iff $\mathcal{A}\alpha \subset \mathcal{B}\alpha \subset \mathcal{A}^*\alpha = (\mathcal{A}\alpha)^*$ iff $\mathcal{A}\alpha \leq \mathcal{B}\alpha$.

2. Let $\mathcal{A} \subset \mathcal{B} \subset \mathcal{F}$ and $\mathcal{A} \leq \mathcal{F}$. Then $\mathcal{A} \subset \mathcal{B} \subset \mathcal{F} \subset \mathcal{A}^* \subset \mathcal{B}^*$ (12.6) whence $\mathcal{A} \leq \mathcal{B}$ and $\mathcal{B} \leq \mathcal{F}$.

Now suppose $\mathcal{A} \subset \mathcal{B} \subset \mathcal{F}$ and $\mathcal{A} \leq \mathcal{B}$ and $\mathcal{B} \leq \mathcal{F}$. Then $\mathcal{F} \subset \mathcal{B}^*$ and $\mathcal{B} \subset \mathcal{A}^*$. This implies $\mathcal{B}^* \subset \mathcal{A}^{**} = \mathcal{A}^*$. Thus $\mathcal{F} \subset \mathcal{A}^*$.

3. Let $\alpha \in G$ with $\mathcal{A}\alpha \subset \mathcal{A}$. Then $\mathcal{A} \leq \mathcal{B}$ implies that $\mathcal{B} \subset \mathcal{A}^*$ and $\mathcal{B}\alpha \subset \mathcal{A}^*\alpha = (\mathcal{A}\alpha)^* \subset \mathcal{A}^*$. Thus $\mathcal{A} \subset \mathcal{L} \subset \mathcal{A}^*$ whence $\mathcal{A} \leq \mathcal{L}$.

12.8 PROPOSITION. Let $\mathcal{A}$ be a T-subalgebra. Then $\mathcal{A}$ is distal iff $\mathbb{C} \leq \mathcal{A}$.

PROOF. Recall that $\mathcal{A}$ is distal iff its enveloping semigroup $E(\mathfrak{A}) = [\mathfrak{A}p \mid p \in M]$ is minimal (5.3). Since $E(\mathfrak{A})p \subset E(\mathfrak{A})$ $(p \in \beta T)$ (9.9), this is equivalent to $E(\mathfrak{A}) \subset \mathfrak{U}(u)$ (10.2).

Thus if $\mathfrak{A}$ is distal $\mathfrak{A}p \subset \mathfrak{U}(u)$ $(p \in \beta T)$. Let $p \in M$, $w \in J$, $f \in \mathfrak{A}$. Then in this case $fp = fpu = fpwu = fpw$ (since $pw \in \beta T$) and so $f \in \mathfrak{U}(p,w)$. Thus $\mathfrak{A} \subset \cap\{\mathfrak{U}(p,w) \mid p \in M, w \in J\} = \mathfrak{C}^*$ whence $\mathfrak{C} \leq \mathfrak{A}$.

On the other hand if $\mathfrak{A} \subset \mathfrak{C}^*$ then $\mathfrak{A} \subset \mathfrak{U}(p,w)$ $(p \in M, w \in J)$. This implies $\mathfrak{A}p = \mathfrak{A}up \subset \mathfrak{U}(u)$ $(p \in \beta T)$, whence $E(\mathfrak{A}) \subset \mathfrak{U}(u)$ and so $\mathfrak{A}$ is distal.

12.9 <u>COROLLARY</u>. If $\mathfrak{D} = \{f \mid [f] \text{ is distal}\}$, then $\mathfrak{D} = \mathfrak{C}^*$.

<u>PROOF</u>. This follows immediately from 12.8.

I would now like to give a topological interpretation of what it means for $\mathfrak{B}$ to be a distal extension of $\mathfrak{A}$.

If A and B are subgroups of G I shall denote the fact that B is a normal subgroup of A by $B \triangleleft A$.

12.10 <u>LEMMA</u>. Let $\mathfrak{A} \leq \mathfrak{B}$, $A = \mathfrak{g}(\mathfrak{A})$ and $B = \mathfrak{g}(\mathfrak{B})$. Then $B \triangleleft A$ iff $\mathfrak{B}A \subset \mathfrak{B}$.

<u>PROOF</u>. If $\mathfrak{B}A \subset \mathfrak{B}$ Then $B \triangleleft A$ by 2 of 11.4 .

Now let $B \triangleleft A$ and $\alpha \in A$. Then $\mathfrak{B} \subset \mathfrak{A}^*$ implies that $\mathfrak{B}\alpha \subset \mathfrak{A}^*\alpha = (\mathfrak{A}\alpha)^* = \mathfrak{A}^*$. Hence $\mathfrak{A} \subset \mathfrak{B} \subset [\mathfrak{B} \cup \mathfrak{B}\alpha] \subset \mathfrak{A}^*$. Moreover $\mathfrak{g}[\mathfrak{B} \cup \mathfrak{B}\alpha] = B \cap \alpha^{-1}B\alpha = B$ (11.4). Since $\mathfrak{B} \leq [\mathfrak{B} \cup \mathfrak{B}\alpha]$ (12.7) then $\mathfrak{B} = [\mathfrak{B} \cup \mathfrak{B}\alpha]$ so that $\mathfrak{B}\alpha \subset \mathfrak{B}$.

12.11 <u>LEMMA</u>. Let $\mathfrak{A} \leq \mathfrak{B}$, $p,q \in \beta T$ with $p = q$ on $\mathfrak{A}$. Then there exists $\alpha \in \mathfrak{g}(\mathfrak{A})$ with $\alpha p = q$ on $\mathfrak{B}$.

<u>PROOF</u>. Since $\mathfrak{A} \subset \mathfrak{B} \subset \mathfrak{U}(u)$ we may assume $p,q \in M$.

Let $p = pv$ for some $v \in J$. Then $q = qv$ on $\mathfrak{A}$, whence $q = qv$ on $\mathfrak{B}$.

Let $r \in M$ with $rp = qv$ (3 of 3.5). Set $\alpha = ru \in G$.

Then $\alpha p = qv$.

Let $f \in \mathcal{A}$. Then $fp = fq$ implies that $f\alpha p = fqv = fq = fp$. Let $m \in M$ with $pm = u$. Then $f = fu = fpm = f\alpha pm = f\alpha u = f\alpha$. Thus $\alpha \in \mathfrak{g}(\mathcal{A})$.

Now let $g \in \mathcal{B}$. Then $g\alpha p = gqv = gq$.

12.12 <u>PROPOSITION</u>. Let $\mathcal{A}, \mathcal{B}$ be T-subalgebras, $A = \mathfrak{g}(\mathcal{A})$ and $B = \mathfrak{g}(\mathcal{B})$. Then $\mathcal{A} \leq \mathcal{B}$ with $B \lhd A$ iff $\mathcal{A} \subset \mathcal{B}$ and there exists a group H of automorphisms of $(|\mathcal{B}|, T)$ such that the restriction mapping $r\colon |\mathcal{B}| \to |\mathcal{A}|$ induces an isomorphism of $(|\mathcal{B}|/H, T)$ onto $(|\mathcal{A}|, T)$. (In other words $(H, |\mathcal{B}|, T)$ is a bitransformation group with $(|\mathcal{B}|/H, T) \cong (|\mathcal{A}|, T)$.)

The group H is isomorphic to A/B.

<u>PROOF</u>. Let $\mathcal{A} \leq \mathcal{B}$ with $B \lhd A$. Then $\mathcal{B}A \subset \mathcal{B}$ (12.10) and A/B may be identified with a subgroup H of Aut($\mathcal{B}$) (3 of 11.19). The automorphism $\bar{\alpha}$ corresponding to the class $B\alpha$ is just the map such that $\bar{\alpha}(x) = \alpha x|\mathcal{B}$ $(x \in |\mathcal{B}|)$.

Then $r(\alpha x) = \alpha x|\mathcal{A} = x|\mathcal{A} = r(x)$ $(x \in |\mathcal{B}|, \alpha \in A)$. On the other hand if $x, y \in |\mathcal{B}|$ with $r(x) = r(y)$ then $y = \alpha x|\mathcal{B}$ (i.e. $y = \alpha x$) for some $\alpha \in A$ by 12.11. Thus r induces an isomorphism of $|\mathcal{B}|/H$ into $|\mathcal{A}|$.

Conversely suppose H is a group of automorphisms of $(|\mathcal{B}|, T)$ such that r induces an isomrophism of $|\mathcal{B}|/H$ onto $|\mathcal{A}|$.

By 11.19 every automorphism of $|\mathcal{B}|$ is of the form $\bar{\alpha}(x) = \alpha x|\mathcal{B}$ $(x \in |\mathcal{B}|)$ where $\alpha \in G$ with $\mathcal{B}\alpha = \mathcal{B}$. Thus given $x, y \in |\mathcal{B}|$ with $r(x) = r(y)$ there exists $\alpha \in G$ with $\mathcal{B}\alpha = \mathcal{B}$ and $y = \alpha x|\mathcal{B}$.

Let $p = pv$ on $\mathcal{A}$ with $v \in J$. Then there exists $\alpha \in G$ with $\alpha p = pv$ on $\mathcal{B}$ and $\mathcal{B}\alpha^{-1} = \mathcal{B}$. Hence $\alpha^{-1}pv = p$ whence $pv = \alpha^{-1}pv^2 = \alpha^{-1}pv = p$ on $\mathcal{B}$. Thus $\mathcal{A} \leq \mathcal{B}$.

Now let $\alpha \in A$ and $x = \alpha|\mathfrak{B}$. Then $r(x) = r(i_{\mathfrak{B}})$ and so $\alpha|\mathfrak{B} = \beta i_{\mathfrak{B}}|\mathfrak{B}$ with $\mathfrak{B}\beta = \mathfrak{B}$. Since $\beta i_{\mathfrak{B}} = \beta$ this implies that $\mathfrak{B}\alpha = \mathfrak{B}$. Thus $\mathfrak{B}A \subset \mathfrak{B}$, and $B \lhd A$ by 12.10.

Finally let $\varphi: A \to \mathrm{Aut}(|\mathfrak{B}|)$ be the map such that $\varphi(\alpha) = \bar{\alpha}$. Since $r(\bar{\alpha}(i_{\mathfrak{B}})) = \alpha i_{\mathfrak{B}}|\mathfrak{A} = i_{\mathfrak{B}}|\mathfrak{A} = r(i_{\mathfrak{B}})$, there exists $h \in H$ with $h(i_{\mathfrak{B}}) = \bar{\alpha}(i_{\mathfrak{B}})$. Since $(|\mathfrak{B}|,T)$ is minimal and h and $\bar{\alpha}$ are automorphisms, $h = \bar{\alpha}$. Thus the image of φ is contained in H.

I leave the proof that φ is a homomorphism with $\mathrm{Im}\varphi =$ H and kernel of $\varphi = B$ to the reader.

12.13 PROPOSITION. Let $\mathfrak{A} \leq \mathfrak{B}$ and $\mathfrak{S} = [\mathfrak{B}\alpha \mid \alpha \in \mathfrak{g}(\mathfrak{A})]$. Then:

1. $\mathfrak{A} \leq \mathfrak{B} \leq \mathfrak{S}$.
2. $\mathfrak{g}(\mathfrak{S}) \lhd \mathfrak{g}(\mathfrak{A})$.
3. $|\mathfrak{A}| \cong |\mathfrak{S}|/H$ and $|\mathfrak{B}| \cong |\mathfrak{S}|/K$,

where $H \cong \mathfrak{g}(\mathfrak{A})/\mathfrak{g}(\mathfrak{S})$ and $K \cong \mathfrak{g}(\mathfrak{B})/\mathfrak{g}(\mathfrak{S})$.

PROOF. 1 is just 3 of 12.7.

2. follows from the fact that $\mathfrak{g}(\mathfrak{S}) = \bigcap \{\alpha\mathfrak{g}(\mathfrak{B})\alpha^{-1} \mid \alpha \in \mathfrak{g}(\mathfrak{A})\}$ (2 and 3 of 11.4).

3. follows from 1, 2, and 12.12.

12.14 REMARKS. With the same notation as in 12.13 let $A = \mathfrak{g}(\mathfrak{A})$, $B = \mathfrak{g}(\mathfrak{B})$ and $S = \mathfrak{g}(\mathfrak{S})$. Then one may draw an analogy between the situation discussed in 12.13 and what occurs in the theory of fiber spaces.

Thus let $F = A/B = \{B\alpha \mid \alpha \in A\}$. Then F is a typical fiber of $|\mathfrak{B}|$ over $|\mathfrak{A}|$.

Since $S \subset B$, the group A/S acts on F via the relation $(S\alpha)(B\beta) = B\alpha\beta$ $(\alpha,\beta \in A)$, and of course A/S acts on $|\mathfrak{S}|$ $((\alpha S,x) \to \alpha x)$.

Let T act on $|\mathbb{S}| \times F$ via the relation $(x,f)t = (xt,f)$ $(x \in |\mathbb{S}|,\ f \in F,\ t \in T)$. Then $(A/S, |\mathbb{S}| \times F, T) = (H, |\mathbb{S}| \times F, T)$ is a bitransformation group and so we can form the orbit transformation group $(|\mathbb{S}| \underset{H}{\times} F, T)$.

Let $\psi\colon |\mathbb{S}| \to |\mathbb{S}| \underset{H}{\times} F$ be the map such that $\psi(x) = \kappa(x,B)$ $(x \in |\mathbb{S}|)$ where $\kappa\colon |\mathbb{S}| \times F \to |\mathbb{S}| \underset{H}{\times} F$ is the canonical map. Then it is easy to verify that ψ is a continuous surjective homomorphism such that $\psi(x) = \psi(y)$ iff $y = \alpha x|\mathbb{S}$ for some $\alpha \in B$. Thus ψ induces a continuous bijective homomorphism φ of $|\mathbb{B}| = |\mathbb{S}|/K$ onto $|\mathbb{S}| \underset{H}{\times} F$. Unfortunately φ is in general not a homeomorphism because $|\mathbb{S}| \underset{H}{\times} F$ need not be Hausdorff.

NOTES

1. Robert Ellis, Group-like extensions of minimal sets, Trans. A. M. S. Vol.127 (1967), 125-135.

2. Robert Ellis, The structure of group-like extensions of minimal sets, Trans. A.M.S. Vol.135 (1968), 261-287.

3. Let $\mathcal{A},\mathcal{B}$ be T-subalgebras with $\mathcal{A} \subset \mathfrak{C}^*$. Then $[\mathcal{A} \cup \mathcal{B}]^* \subset [\mathfrak{C}^* \cup \mathcal{B}^*]^* = [\mathcal{B}^*]^* = \mathcal{B}^{**} = \mathcal{B}^*$. Hence $\mathcal{B} \leq [\mathcal{A} \cup \mathcal{B}]^*$.

It might be conjectured that all distal extensions of $\mathcal{B}$ arise in this way, i.e. by the addition of distal functions. The following example shows that this is not the case in general.

Let X be the set of complex numbers of modules 1 (i.e. the circle) and $\sigma: X \to X$ such that $\sigma(x) = -x$ $(x \in X)$. Let T be the homeomorphisms t of X such that $t\sigma = \sigma t$. Then T is a group and (H,X,T) is a bitransformation group such that (X,T) is minimal, where $H = \{e,\sigma\}$.

It is easy to verify that $\overline{P(X,T)} = X \times X$. Thus the algebra $\mathcal{F}$ corresponding to X has no distal functions. However, $\mathcal{B} \leq \mathcal{F}$ where $(|\mathcal{B}|,T) \cong (X/H,T)$ by 12.12.

4. Proposition 12.8 shows that the collection of distal functions is a T-subalgebra of $\mathcal{C}$ namely $\mathfrak{C}^*$. This is not true in general of the collection $\mathfrak{M}$ of minimal functions (A function $f \in \mathcal{C}$ is minimal if the T-subalgebra [f] generated by f is minimal.) The reason for this is that $f \in \mathfrak{M}$ iff $fv = f$ for some $v \in J$ and it may happen that $fv = f$ and $gw = g$ with $v,w \in J$, $v \neq w$ but $[f,g] \not\subset \mathfrak{A}(\eta)$ $(\eta \in J)$.

Notice, however, that if $f \in \mathfrak{C}^*$ and $gw = g$ then $[f,g] \subset \mathfrak{A}(w)$ since $fv = f$ $(v \in J)$.

5. Let $\mathcal{A},\mathcal{B}$ be T-subalgebras of $\mathcal{C}$. Then in general

$|\mathcal{A}| \times |\mathcal{B}|$ is not point transitive and so there is no T-subalgebra of C which corresponds to it. However, if $x \in |\mathcal{A}|$ and $y \in |\mathcal{B}|$ the transformation group $(\overline{(x,y)T},T)$ is point transitive. What is the T-subalgebra $\mathcal{G}$ of C that corresponds to it?

Let $p,q \in \beta T$ with $x = p|\mathcal{A}$ and $y = q|\mathcal{B}$, and let $\mathcal{F}$ be the T-subalgebra of C generated by $\{\mathcal{A}p \cup \mathcal{B}q\}$, i.e. $\mathcal{F} = [\mathcal{A}p \cup \mathcal{B}q]$.

First observe that the T-subalgebras corresponding to $(\overline{xT},x)$ and $(\overline{yT},y)$ are $\mathcal{A}p$ and $\mathcal{B}q$ respectively. Then $\mathcal{G}$ must contain $\mathcal{A}p$ and $\mathcal{B}q$. Hence $\mathcal{G} \supset \mathcal{F}$.

On the other hand the restriction map r maps $(|\mathcal{F}|,i_{\mathcal{F}})$ onto both $(|\mathcal{A}p|,i_{\mathcal{A}p}) \cong (\overline{xT},x)$, $(|\mathcal{B}q|,i_{\mathcal{B}q}) \cong (\overline{yT},y)$. Hence r maps $(|\mathcal{F}|,i_{\mathcal{F}})$ onto $(|\mathcal{G}|,i_{\mathcal{G}}) \cong (\overline{(x,y)T}, (x,y))$ whence $\mathcal{G} \subset \mathcal{F}$. Thus $\mathcal{G} = \mathcal{F}$.

Notice that even if $\mathcal{A}$ and $\mathcal{B}$ are contained in $\mathfrak{U}(u)$, $[\mathcal{A}p \cup \mathcal{B}q]$ need not be minimal. However if $\mathcal{A}$ is distal, $\mathcal{A} \subset \mathfrak{U}(v)$ $(v \in J)$ and so if $\mathcal{B}$ is minimal $\mathcal{B}q$ is minimal and $[\mathcal{A}p \cup \mathcal{B}q] = [\mathcal{A} \cup \mathcal{B}q]$ is again minimal. Thus the product of a minimal distal transformation group and a minimal one is pointwise almost periodic.

CHAPTER 13

THE GALOIS THEORY OF DISTAL EXTENSIONS

In order to study the notion of a distal extension more deeply we must "relativize" the various concepts studied previously. Thus if $\mathcal{A}$ and $\mathcal{B}$ are T-subalgebras of C with $\mathcal{A} \subset \mathcal{B}$, $\mathcal{B}$ may be viewed as an algebra over $\mathcal{A}$ rather than one over $\mathbb{C}$. Then one might define such notions as "distal over $\mathcal{A}$" or "almost periodic over $\mathcal{A}$", etc. Indeed it turns out that $\mathcal{B}$ is distal over $\mathcal{A}$ iff $\mathcal{A} \leq \mathcal{B}$.

Recall that all the T-subalgebras are assumed to be contained in $\mathfrak{U}(u)$.

13.1 <u>DEFINITION</u>. Let $\mathcal{A}, \mathcal{F}$ be T-subalgebras. Then $R(\mathcal{A}:\mathcal{F}) = \{(x,y) \mid x,y \in |\mathcal{A}|$ and there exist $p,q \in M$ with $p|\mathcal{A} = x,\ q|\mathcal{A} = y$ and $p|\mathcal{F} = q|\mathcal{F}\}$.

If $\mathcal{F} \subset \mathcal{A}$ then $R(\mathcal{A}:\mathcal{F}) = \{(p|\mathcal{A},\ q|\mathcal{A}) \mid p,q \in M$ with $p|\mathcal{F} = q|\mathcal{F}\}$.

$P(\mathcal{A}:\mathcal{F}) = P(\mathcal{A}) \cap R(\mathcal{A}:\mathcal{F})$ where $P(\mathcal{A})$ is the proximal relation on $|\mathcal{A}|$.

Thus $P(\mathcal{A}:\mathcal{F}) = \cap \{\eta T \cap R(\mathcal{A}:\mathcal{F}) \mid \eta \in \mathcal{U}\}$ where $\mathcal{U}$ is the set of indices on $|\mathcal{A}|$.

The regionally proximal relation $Q(\mathcal{A})$ is "relativized" as follows:

$$Q(\mathcal{A}:\mathcal{F}) = \cap \{\overline{\eta T \cap R(\mathcal{A}:\mathcal{F})} \mid \eta \in \mathcal{U}\}.$$

Notice that $Q(\mathcal{A}:\mathcal{F}) \subset Q(\mathcal{A}) \cap R(\mathcal{A}:\mathcal{F})$ but that in general they are not equal. The reason for the present choice for $Q(\mathcal{A}:\mathcal{F})$ will become clear in chapter 14.

Let $\mathcal{F} \subset \mathcal{A}$. Then $\mathcal{A}$ is <u>distal over</u> $\mathcal{F}$ if $P(\mathcal{A}:\mathcal{F}) = \Delta$, the diagonal of $|\mathcal{A}| \times |\mathcal{A}|$, and it is <u>almost periodic</u> (or <u>equicontinuous) over</u> $\mathcal{F}$ if $Q(\mathcal{A}:\mathcal{F}) = \Delta$.

13.2 <u>REMARKS</u>. 1. Notice that in the definition of $R(\mathcal{A}:\mathcal{F})$, $\mathcal{F}$ need not be contained in $\mathcal{A}$. Thus $R(\mathcal{A}:\mathcal{F})$ is a closed invariant, reflexive and symmetric relation on $|\mathcal{A}|$, but it need not be transitive.

2. If $\mathcal{A} \subset \mathcal{F}$, then $R(\mathcal{A}:\mathcal{F})$ is just the diagonal of $|\mathcal{A}|$.

3. When $\mathcal{F} \subset \mathcal{A}$, $R(\mathcal{A}:\mathcal{F}) = \{(x,y) \mid x,y \in |\mathcal{A}|, r(x) = r(y)\}$ where $r: |\mathcal{A}| \to |\mathcal{F}|$ is the restriction mapping. Thus in this case $R(\mathcal{A}:\mathcal{F})$ is a closed equivalence relation on $|\mathcal{A}|$.

4. When $\mathcal{F} = \mathbb{C}$, $R(\mathcal{A}:\mathcal{F}) = |\mathcal{A}| \times |\mathcal{A}|$ and the notions of distal over $\mathcal{F}$ and equicontinuous over $\mathcal{F}$ coincide with distal and equicontinuous (5.3 and 4.12).

5. Let $\mathcal{F} \subset \mathcal{A}$. Then $P(\mathcal{A}:\mathcal{F})$ is reflexive and symmetric. Also if $x,y \in |\mathcal{A}|$, then $(x,y) \in P(\mathcal{A}:\mathcal{F})$ iff $x|\mathcal{F} = y|\mathcal{F}$ and $xp = yp$ $(p \in I)$ where I is a minimal right ideal in βT.

The proof of the following purely topological lemma is left to the reader.

13.3 <u>LEMMA</u>. Let X be a compact T_2 space, N a closed equivalence relation on X and $\mathcal{N} = \{f \mid f \in C(X), f(x) = f(y)$ $((x,y) \in N)$. Then $(x,y) \in N$ iff $f(x) = f(y)$ $(f \in \mathcal{N})$.

13.4 <u>LEMMA</u>. Let $\mathcal{A}, \mathcal{F}$ be T-subalgebras of $\mathfrak{U}(u)$. Then $R(\mathcal{A}:\mathcal{A} \cap \mathcal{F})$ is the smallest closed invariant equivalence relation on $|\mathcal{A}|$ which contains $R(\mathcal{A}:\mathcal{F})$.

PROOF. Let $x,y \in |\mathcal{A}|$ with $(x,y) \in R(\mathcal{A}:\mathcal{F})$. Then there exist $p,q \in \beta T$ with $p|\mathcal{A} = x$, $q|\mathcal{A} = y$ and $p|\mathcal{F} = q|\mathcal{F}$. Then $x|\mathcal{A} \cap \mathcal{F} = p|\mathcal{A} \cap \mathcal{F} = q|\mathcal{A} \cap \mathcal{F} = y|\mathcal{A} \cap \mathcal{F}$ whence $(x,y) \in R(\mathcal{A}:\mathcal{A} \cap \mathcal{F})$.

Now let S be a closed invariant equivalence relation on $|\mathcal{A}|$ with $R(\mathcal{A}:\mathcal{F}) \subset S$, and $\mathcal{K} = \{f \mid f \in \mathcal{A}, \langle fx,e\rangle = \langle fy,e\rangle \ ((x,y) \in S)\}$. Since S is invariant, $\mathcal{K} = \{f \mid f \in \mathcal{A}, fx = fy \ ((x,y) \in S)\}$.

I claim $\mathcal{K} \subset \mathcal{A} \cap \mathcal{F}$. Let $f \in \mathcal{K}$. Then of course $f \in \mathcal{A}$. Let $p,q \in M$ with $p|\mathcal{F} = q|\mathcal{F}$. It suffices to show that $fp = fq$.

Set $x = p|\mathcal{A}$, $y = q|\mathcal{A}$. Then $(x,y) \in R(\mathcal{A}:\mathcal{F}) \subset S$ whence $fp = fx = fy = fq$.

Finally $\mathcal{K} \subset \mathcal{F}$ implies that $R(\mathcal{A}:\mathcal{A} \cap \mathcal{F}) \subset S$ by 13.3, and 3 of 13.2 implies that $R(\mathcal{A}:\mathcal{A} \cap \mathcal{F})$ is a closed equivalence relation.

13.5 PROPOSITION. Let $\mathcal{F},\mathcal{A}$ be T-subalgebras with $\mathcal{F} \subset \mathcal{A}$. Then the following statements are pairwise equivalent:

1. $\mathcal{F} \leq \mathcal{A}$.
2. $P(\mathcal{B}:\mathcal{F}) \subset R(\mathcal{B}:\mathcal{A})$ for all T-subalgebras $\mathcal{B}$ with $\mathcal{A} \subset \mathcal{B}$.
3. $P(\mathcal{B}:\mathcal{F}) \subset R(\mathcal{B}:\mathcal{A})$ for some T-subalgebra, $\mathcal{B}$ with $\mathcal{A} \subset \mathcal{B}$.
4. $\mathcal{A}$ is distal over $\mathcal{F}$.

PROOF. 1. implies 2. Let $\mathcal{A} \subset \mathcal{B}$, $x,y \in |\mathcal{B}|$ with $(x,y) \in P(\mathcal{B}:\mathcal{F})$. Then $x|\mathcal{F} = y|\mathcal{F}$ and $xp = yp \ (p \in I)$ where I is a minimal right ideal in βT. Let $w^2 = w \in I$ with $yw = y$. Then $xw = x$ on $\mathcal{F}$ whence $xw = x$ on $\mathcal{A}$ $(\mathcal{F} \leq \mathcal{A})$. Thus $x|\mathcal{A} = y|\mathcal{A}$ and so $(x,y) \in R(\mathcal{B}:\mathcal{A})$. 2. implies 3. is obvious.

3. implies 4. Let $\mathcal{B}$ be a T-subalgebra with $\mathcal{A} \subset \mathcal{B}$

and $P(\mathcal{B}:\mathcal{F}) \subset P(\mathcal{B}:\mathcal{A})$. Let $x,y \in |\mathcal{A}|$ with $(x,y) \in P(\mathcal{A}:\mathcal{F})$. Then $x|\mathcal{F} = y|\mathcal{F}$ and $xp = yp$ $(p \in I)$ where I is a minimal right ideal in βT.

Since $|\mathcal{A}|$ is minimal there exists an idempotent $w \in I$ with $yw = y$. Let $q \in M$ with $q|\mathcal{A} = x$. Then $qw|\mathcal{A} = xw = yw = y$, and $q|\mathcal{F} = x|\mathcal{F} = y|\mathcal{F} = qw|\mathcal{F}$. Hence $(q|\mathcal{B}, qw|\mathcal{B}) \in P(\mathcal{B}:\mathcal{F}) \subset P(\mathcal{B}:\mathcal{A})$ whence $x = q|\mathcal{A} = qw|\mathcal{A} = y$.

4. implies 1. Let $p \in M$, $w \in J$ with $p|\mathcal{F} = pw|\mathcal{F}$. Since $(p)w = (pw)w$, $(p|\mathcal{A}, pw|\mathcal{A}) \in P(\mathcal{A}:\mathcal{F})$. Hence $p|\mathcal{A} = pw|\mathcal{A}$.

13.6 <u>PROPOSITION</u>. Let $\mathcal{A},\mathcal{F}$ be T-subalgebras with $\mathcal{F} \subset \mathcal{A}$. Then $R(\mathcal{A}:\mathcal{A} \cap \mathcal{F}^*)$ is the smallest closed invariant equivalence relation, S on $|\mathcal{A}|$ such that $|\mathcal{A}|/S \geq |\mathcal{F}|$.

<u>PROOF</u>. Let S be a closed invariant equivalence relation on $|\mathcal{A}|$ and $\mathcal{S} = \{f \mid f \in \mathcal{A},\ fx = fy\ ((x,y) \in S)\}$, the T-subalgebra of $\mathcal{A}$ corresponding to it. Then $|\mathcal{S}| \cong |\mathcal{A}|/S$ (13.3) and $|\mathcal{A}|/S \geq |\mathcal{F}|$ iff $\mathcal{F} \subset \mathcal{S} \subset \mathcal{F}^*$ (12.5).

Since the algebra corresponding to $R(\mathcal{A}:\mathcal{A} \cap \mathcal{F}^*)$ is $\mathcal{A} \cap \mathcal{F}^*$, 13.6 follows from the above.

13.7 <u>PROPOSITION</u>. Let $\mathcal{A},\mathcal{F}$ be T-subalgebras with $\mathcal{F} \subset \mathcal{A}$. Then $R(\mathcal{A}:\mathcal{A} \cap \mathcal{F}^*)$ is the smallest closed invariant equivalence relation S on $|\mathcal{A}|$ with $P(\mathcal{A}:\mathcal{F}) \subset S \subset R(\mathcal{A}:\mathcal{F})$.

<u>PROOF</u>. Since $\mathcal{F} \leq \mathcal{A} \cap \mathcal{F}^* \subset \mathcal{A}$, $P(\mathcal{A}:\mathcal{F}) \subset R(\mathcal{A}:\mathcal{A} \cap \mathcal{F}^*)$ by 13.5. That $R(\mathcal{A}:\mathcal{A} \cap \mathcal{F}^*) \subset R(\mathcal{A}:\mathcal{F})$ follows from $\mathcal{F} \subset \mathcal{A} \cap \mathcal{F}^*$.

Now let S be a closed invariant equivalence relation on $|\mathcal{A}|$ with $P(\mathcal{A}:\mathcal{F}) \subset S \subset R(\mathcal{A}:\mathcal{F})$ and $\mathcal{S}$ the T-subalgebra of $\mathcal{A}$ corresponding to it (see proof of 13.6). Then $\mathcal{F} \subset \mathcal{S}$ since $S \subset R(\mathcal{A}:\mathcal{F})$ and $R(\mathcal{A}:\mathcal{S}) = S \supset P(\mathcal{A}:\mathcal{F})$ implies $\mathcal{F} \leq \mathcal{S}$ by 13.5. Hence $\mathcal{F} \subset \mathcal{S} \subset \mathcal{F}^*$ whence $\mathcal{S} \subset \mathcal{A} \cap \mathcal{F}^*$ and $R(\mathcal{A}:\mathcal{A} \cap \mathcal{F}^*) \subset R(\mathcal{A}:\mathcal{S}) = S$.

13.8 <u>REMARKS</u>. Proposition 13.7 suggests that $R(\mathcal{A}:\mathcal{A} \cap \mathcal{F}^*)$ be called the <u>$\mathcal{F}$-distal structure relation</u> on $|\mathcal{A}|$ in analogy with the case $\mathcal{F} = \mathfrak{C}$. Thus the distal structure relation on $|\mathcal{A}|$ is just $R(\mathcal{A}:\mathcal{A} \cap \mathfrak{D})$ where $\mathfrak{D} = \mathfrak{C}^*$, the T-subalgebra of distal functions.

The next few results are aimed at computing the group of $\mathcal{A} \cap \mathcal{F}^*$.

13.9 <u>LEMMA</u>. Let $\mathcal{A}$ and $\mathfrak{B}$ be T-subalgebras such that $R(\mathcal{A}:\mathfrak{B}) = R(\mathcal{A}:\mathcal{A} \cap \mathfrak{B})$. Then $\mathfrak{g}(\mathcal{A} \cap \mathfrak{B}) = ABA$ where $A = \mathfrak{g}(\mathcal{A})$ and $B = \mathfrak{g}(\mathfrak{B})$. If in addition $\mathcal{A}B \subset \mathcal{A}$ or $\mathfrak{B}A \subset \mathfrak{B}$, $\mathfrak{g}(\mathcal{A} \cap \mathfrak{B}) = AB = BA$.

<u>PROOF</u>. Since $\mathcal{A} \cap \mathfrak{B} \subset \mathcal{A}$ and $\mathcal{A} \cap \mathfrak{B} \subset \mathfrak{B}$, $A \cup B \subset \mathfrak{g}(\mathcal{A} \cap \mathfrak{B})$. Hence $ABA \subset \mathfrak{g}(\mathcal{A} \cap \mathfrak{B})$ since the latter is a group.

Let $\alpha \in \mathfrak{g}(\mathcal{A} \cap \mathfrak{B})$. Then $(\alpha|\mathcal{A}, u|\mathcal{A}) \in R(\mathcal{A}:\mathcal{A} \cap \mathfrak{B}) = R(\mathcal{A}:\mathfrak{B})$. Hence there exist $p,q \in M$ with $p|\mathcal{A} = \alpha|\mathcal{A}$, $q|\mathcal{A} = u|\mathcal{A}$ and $p|\mathfrak{B} = q|\mathfrak{B}$. Set $\beta = pu$ and $\alpha = qu$. Then $\beta,\alpha \in G$ and the above relations hold with p and q replaced by β and α respectively. Then $\alpha \in A$, $\alpha\beta^{-1} \in A$, and $\beta\alpha^{-1} \in B$, whence $\alpha = \alpha\beta^{-1}\beta\alpha^{-1}\alpha \in ABA$.

If in addition $\mathcal{A}B \subset \mathcal{A}$ or $\mathfrak{B}A \subset \mathfrak{B}$, $AB = BA$ and $\mathfrak{g}(\mathcal{A} \cap \mathfrak{B}) = AB$. (2 of 11.19.)

13.10 <u>PROPOSITION</u>. Let $\mathcal{A},\mathfrak{B}$ be T-subalgebras such that $\mathcal{A} \leq [\mathcal{A} \cup \mathfrak{B}]$ and $\mathfrak{B}A \subset \mathfrak{B}$ where $A = \mathfrak{g}(\mathcal{A})$. Then $R(\mathcal{A}:\mathfrak{B}) = R(\mathcal{A}:\mathcal{A} \cap \mathfrak{B})$ and so $\mathfrak{g}(\mathcal{A} \cap \mathfrak{B}) = AB = BA$ where $B = \mathfrak{g}(\mathfrak{B})$.

<u>PROOF</u>. By 13.4 and 1 of 13.2 it suffices to show that $R(\mathcal{A}:\mathfrak{B})$ is transitive. To this end let $x,y,z \in |\mathcal{A}|$ with (x,y), $(y,z) \in R(\mathcal{A}:\mathfrak{B})$. Let $p,q,r,s \in M$ be such that $p|\mathcal{A} = x$, $q|\mathcal{A} = y = r|\mathcal{A}$, $s|\mathcal{A} = z$, $p|\mathfrak{B} = q|\mathfrak{B}$ and $r|\mathfrak{B} = s|\mathfrak{B}$. Let $q = qv$ with $v \in J$, and $\alpha \in G$ with $q = \alpha rv$. Since $q|\mathcal{A} = r|\mathcal{A}$,

$r|\mathcal{A} = rv|\mathcal{A}$ whence $\beta \in A$. Since $\mathcal{A} \leq \{\mathcal{A} \cup \mathcal{B}\}$ and $\mathcal{B}\alpha \subset \mathcal{B}$, $r|\mathcal{B} = rv|\mathcal{B}$ and $\alpha s|\mathcal{B} = \alpha rv|\mathcal{B}$. Thus $p|\mathcal{A} = x$, $\alpha s|\mathcal{A} = s|\mathcal{A} = z$, and $p|\mathcal{B} = q|\mathcal{B} = \alpha rv|\mathcal{B} = \alpha s|\mathcal{B}$, whence $(x,z) \in R(\mathcal{A}:\mathcal{B})$.

13.11 <u>COROLLARY</u>. Let $\mathcal{A},\mathcal{F}$ be T-subalgebras with $\mathcal{F} \subset \mathcal{A}$. Then $\mathfrak{g}(\mathcal{A} \cap \mathcal{F}^*) = AF^*$ where $A = \mathfrak{g}(\mathcal{A})$ and $F^* = \mathfrak{g}(\mathcal{F}^*)$.

<u>PROOF</u>. Let $p \in M$, $w \in J$ with $p|\mathcal{A} = pw|\mathcal{A}$. Then $p|\mathcal{F} = pw|\mathcal{F}$ whence $p|\mathcal{F}^* = pw|\mathcal{F}^*$ and so $p|[\mathcal{A} \cup \mathcal{F}^*] = pw|[\mathcal{A} \cup \mathcal{F}^*]$. Thus $\mathcal{A} \leq [\mathcal{A} \cup \mathcal{F}^*]$.

Moreover if $\alpha \in A$ then $f\alpha = f$ $(\alpha \in \mathcal{F})$ so that $\mathcal{F}\alpha = \mathcal{F}$ and $\mathcal{F}^*\alpha = \mathcal{F}^*$ (2 of 12.6).

Corollary 13.11 now follows from 13.10.

13.12 <u>PROPOSITION</u>. Let $\mathcal{A},\mathcal{F}$ be T-subalgebras with $\mathcal{F} \subset \mathcal{A}$, and let $p,q \in M$. Then $(p|\mathcal{A}, q|\mathcal{A}) \in R(\mathcal{A}:\mathcal{A} \cap \mathcal{F}^*)$ iff $(p|\mathcal{A},q|\mathcal{A}) \in R(\mathcal{A}:\mathcal{F})$ and $(pu)(qu)^{-1} \in AF^*$ where again $A = \mathfrak{g}(\mathcal{A})$ and $F^* = \mathfrak{g}(\mathcal{F}^*)$.

<u>PROOF</u>. Let $(p|\mathcal{A},q|\mathcal{A}) \in R(\mathcal{A}:\mathcal{A} \cap \mathcal{F}^*)$. Then $(p|\mathcal{A},q|\mathcal{A}) \in R(\mathcal{A}:\mathcal{F})$ because $\mathcal{F} \subset \mathcal{F}^*$.

Also $(pu|\mathcal{A},qu|\mathcal{A}) \in R(\mathcal{A}:\mathcal{A} \cap \mathcal{F}^*)$ since the latter is closed and invariant. Hence $(pu)(qu)^{-1} \in \mathfrak{g}(\mathcal{A} \cap \mathcal{F}^*) = AF^*$.

Now let $(p|\mathcal{A},q|\mathcal{A}) \in R(\mathcal{A}:\mathcal{F})$ and $(pu)(qu)^{-1} \in AF^*$. Then $(pu|\mathcal{A},qu|\mathcal{A}) \in R(\mathcal{A}:\mathcal{A} \cap \mathcal{F}^*)$.

Let $v \in J$ with $pv = p$. Then $(p|\mathcal{A},qv|\mathcal{A}) = (puv|\mathcal{A}, quv|\mathcal{A}) \in R(\mathcal{A}:\mathcal{A} \cap \mathcal{F}^*)$. Also $p|\mathcal{F} = q|\mathcal{F}$ implies $q|\mathcal{F} = qv|\mathcal{F}$, whence $(p|\mathcal{A},qv|\mathcal{A}) \in P(\mathcal{A}:\mathcal{F}) \subset R(\mathcal{A}:\mathcal{A} \cap \mathcal{F}^*)$. Hence $(p|\mathcal{A},q|\mathcal{A}) \in R(\mathcal{A}:\mathcal{A} \cap \mathcal{F}^*)$.

13.13 <u>PROPOSITION</u>. Let $\mathcal{A},\mathcal{F}$ be T-subalgebras with $\mathcal{F} \subset \mathcal{A}$. Then $P(\mathcal{A}:\mathcal{F})$ is a closed equivalence relation iff $F^* = \mathfrak{g}(\mathcal{F}^*) \subset \mathfrak{g}(\mathcal{A}) = A$.

<u>PROOF</u>. By 13.7 $P(\mathcal{A}:\mathcal{F})$ is a closed equivalence re-

lation iff $P(\mathfrak{A}:\mathfrak{F}) = R(\mathfrak{A}:\mathfrak{A} \cap \mathfrak{F}^*)$.

Let $P(\mathfrak{A}:\mathfrak{F}) = R(\mathfrak{A}:\mathfrak{A} \cap \mathfrak{F}^*)$ and $\alpha \in F^*$. Then $(\alpha|\mathfrak{A}, u|\mathfrak{A}) \in R(\mathfrak{A}:\mathfrak{A} \cap \mathfrak{F}^*)$ implies $\alpha p|\mathfrak{A} = up|\mathfrak{A}$ $(p \in I)$ where I is some minimal right ideal in βT (5 of 13.2). Let $w^2 = w \in I$ with $uw = u$. Then $\alpha|\mathfrak{A} = \alpha w|\mathfrak{A} = uw|\mathfrak{A} = u|\mathfrak{A}$ whence $\alpha \in A$.

Now suppose $F^* \subset A$. Let $p,q \in M$ with $(p|\mathfrak{A}, q|\mathfrak{A}) \in R(\mathfrak{A}:\mathfrak{A} \cap \mathfrak{F}^*)$. Then by 13.12 $(pu)(qu)^{-1} \in AF^* = A$. Hence $pu|\mathfrak{A} = qu|\mathfrak{A}$, and so $(p|\mathfrak{A}, q|\mathfrak{A}) \in P(\mathfrak{A})$. Since $p|\mathfrak{F} = q|\mathfrak{F}$ $(p|\mathfrak{A}, q|\mathfrak{A}) \in P(\mathfrak{A}:\mathfrak{F})$.

If one sets $\mathfrak{F} = \mathbf{C}$ in 13.13 one obtains:

13.14 <u>COROLLARY</u>. Let $\mathfrak{A}$ be a T-subalgebra of $\mathfrak{U}(u)$. Then proximal is a closed equivalence relation on $\mathfrak{A}$ iff $\mathfrak{g}(\mathfrak{A}) \supset D = \mathfrak{g}(\mathfrak{D})$ where $\mathfrak{D} = \mathbf{C}^*$ is the T-subalgebra of distal functions.

13.15 <u>COROLLARY</u>. Let $\mathfrak{A}$, $\mathfrak{B}$, $\mathfrak{F}$ be T-subalgebras such that $\mathfrak{F} \subset \mathfrak{A} \subset \mathfrak{B}$ and $P(\mathfrak{B}:\mathfrak{F})$ is a closed equivalence relation on $|\mathfrak{B}|$. Then $P(\mathfrak{A}:\mathfrak{F})$ is a closed equivalence relation on $|\mathfrak{A}|$.

13.16 <u>PROPOSITION.</u> Let $\mathfrak{A}$, $\mathfrak{B}$, $\mathfrak{F}$ be T-subalgebras with $\mathfrak{F} \subset \mathfrak{A} \cap \mathfrak{B}$. Then $A \subset B$ iff $R(\mathfrak{B}:\mathfrak{A}) \subset P(\mathfrak{B}:\mathfrak{F})$ where $A = \mathfrak{g}(\mathfrak{A})$ and $B = \mathfrak{g}(\mathfrak{B})$.

Thus $A \subset B$ iff $R(\mathfrak{B}:\mathfrak{A}) = P(\mathfrak{B}:\mathfrak{A} \cap \mathfrak{B})$.

<u>PROOF</u>. Let $A \subset B$ and $p,q \in M$ with $p|\mathfrak{A} = q|\mathfrak{A}$. Then $pu|\mathfrak{A} = qu|\mathfrak{A}$ whence $(pu)(pu)^{-1} \in A \subset B$. Hence $pu|\mathfrak{B} = qu|\mathfrak{B}$. Since $\mathfrak{F} \subset \mathfrak{A}$, $p|\mathfrak{F} = q|\mathfrak{F}$ whence $(p|\mathfrak{B}, q|\mathfrak{B}) \in P(\mathfrak{B}:\mathfrak{F})$.

Let $R(\mathfrak{B}:\mathfrak{A}) \subset P(\mathfrak{B}:\mathfrak{F})$ and $\alpha \in A$. Then $(\alpha|\mathfrak{B}, u|\mathfrak{B}) \in R(\mathfrak{B}:\mathfrak{A})$ implies that $\alpha p|\mathfrak{B} = up|\mathfrak{B}$ $(p \in I)$ for some minimal right ideal I in βT. Let $w^2 = w \in I$ be such that $uw = u$. Then $\alpha|\mathfrak{B} = \alpha w|\mathfrak{B} = uw|\mathfrak{B} = u|\mathfrak{B}$ whence $\alpha \in B$.

13.17 <u>REMARKS</u>. 1. Let $\mathfrak{B}$ be the roving circle (5.6) Then we know that $P(\mathfrak{B}:\mathfrak{C}) = P(\mathfrak{B}) = |\mathfrak{B}| \times |\mathfrak{B}|$. Thus by 13.16 with $\mathfrak{F} = \mathfrak{A} = \mathfrak{C}$, $B \supset \mathfrak{g}(\mathfrak{C}) = G$. Consequently $B = G$ and $\mathfrak{B} \subset \mathfrak{U}(G)$. Thus when T is the group of homeomorphisms of the circle, $\mathfrak{U}(G) \neq \mathfrak{C}$.

13.18 <u>COROLLARY</u>. With the same notation as in 13.16, if $\mathfrak{A} \subset \mathfrak{B}$ and $R(\mathfrak{B}:\mathfrak{A}) = P(\mathfrak{B}:\mathfrak{F})$ then $A = B$ and $\mathfrak{F} \leq \mathfrak{A}$.

<u>PROOF</u>. Since $\mathfrak{A} \subset \mathfrak{B}$, $B \subset A$ whence $B = A$. That $\mathfrak{F} \leq \mathfrak{A}$ follows from 13.5.

13.19 <u>PROPOSITION</u>. Let $\mathfrak{F}$ be a T-subalgebra of $\mathfrak{U}(u)$, H a τ-closed subgroup of G and $\Omega_H(\mathfrak{F})$ the collection of all T-subalgebras $\mathfrak{A}$ of $\mathfrak{U}(u)$ with $\mathfrak{F} \subset \mathfrak{A}$ and $\mathfrak{g}(\mathfrak{A}) = H$. Then the following are pairwise equivalent:

1. $F^* \subset H \subset F$ (where $F^* = \mathfrak{g}(\mathfrak{F}^*)$).

2. $\mathfrak{F}^* \cap \mathfrak{U}(H) \in \Omega_H(\mathfrak{F})$.

3. There exists $\mathfrak{A} \in \Omega_H(\mathfrak{F})$ with $\mathfrak{F} \leq \mathfrak{A}$.

<u>PROOF</u>. 1 implies 2. Since H is a τ-closed subgroup of G, $\mathfrak{g}(\mathfrak{U}(H)) = H$ (2 of 11.12). Also $\mathfrak{F} \subset \mathfrak{U}(F) \subset \mathfrak{U}(H)$ and $\mathfrak{g}(\mathfrak{F}^* \cap \mathfrak{U}(H)) = HF^*$ (13.11). Thus $\mathfrak{F}^* \cap \mathfrak{U}(H) \in \Omega_H(\mathfrak{F})$.

2 implies 3. Since $\mathfrak{F} \subset \mathfrak{F}^* \cap \mathfrak{U}(H) \subset \mathfrak{F}^*$, $\mathfrak{F} \leq \mathfrak{F}^* \cap \mathfrak{U}(H) \in \Omega_H(\mathfrak{F})$.

3 implies 1. Let $\mathfrak{A} \in \Omega_H(\mathfrak{F})$ with $\mathfrak{F} \leq \mathfrak{A}$. Then $\mathfrak{F} \subset \mathfrak{A} \subset \mathfrak{F}^*$ whence $F^* \subset H \subset F$.

13.20 <u>REMARKS</u>. 1. Since $\mathfrak{g}(\mathfrak{U}(H)) = H, \Omega_H(\mathfrak{F}) \neq \emptyset$ if $H \subset F$.

2. Proposition 13.19 settles the question as to when there is a T-subalgebra $\mathfrak{A} \supset \mathfrak{F}$ with $\mathfrak{F} \leq \mathfrak{A}$ and $\mathfrak{g}(\mathfrak{A}) = H$, namely when $F^* \subset H$.

13.21 PROPOSITION. With the same notation as in 13.19, let $F^* \subset H \subset F$. Then:

1. $\mathfrak{A}(H) \cap \mathcal{F}^*$ is the only element, $\mathcal{A}$ of $\Omega_H(\mathcal{F})$ with $\mathcal{F} \leq \mathcal{A}$.

2. $\mathfrak{A}(H) \cap \mathcal{F}^* \subset \mathcal{A} \quad (\mathcal{A} \in \Omega_H(\mathcal{F}))$.

PROOF. Let $\mathcal{A} \in \Omega_H(\mathcal{F})$ with $\mathcal{F} \leq \mathcal{A}$ and let $\mathcal{B} \in \Omega_H(\mathcal{F})$. Then $\mathcal{A} \subset \mathcal{F}^*$ implies that $\mathcal{A}^* \subset \mathcal{F}^{**} = \mathcal{F}^*$ (12.6). Also $\mathcal{F} \subset \mathcal{B}$ implies that $\mathcal{F}^* \subset \mathcal{B}^*$. Thus $[\mathcal{A} \cup \mathcal{B}]^* \subset [\mathcal{A}^* \cup \mathcal{B}^*]^* = [\mathcal{B}^*]^* = \mathcal{B}^*$ (12.6) whence $\mathcal{B} \leq [\mathcal{A} \cup \mathcal{B}]$. Since $\mathfrak{g}[\mathcal{A} \cup \mathcal{B}] = \mathfrak{g}(\mathcal{A}) \cap \mathfrak{g}(\mathcal{B}) = H = \mathfrak{g}(\mathcal{B})$, $\mathcal{B} = [\mathcal{A} \cup \mathcal{B}]$, whence $\mathcal{A} \subset \mathcal{B}$.

Thus the element $\mathcal{A}$ of $\Omega_H(\mathcal{F})$ with $\mathcal{F} \leq \mathcal{A}$ is the smallest element of $\Omega_H(\mathcal{F})$. Hence there can be at most one such. Since $\mathcal{F} \leq \mathfrak{A}(H) \cap \mathcal{F}^* \in \Omega_H(\mathcal{F})$, the proof is completed.

13.22 PROPOSITION. Let $\mathcal{A} \in \Omega_H(\mathcal{F})$. Then $P(\mathcal{A}:\mathcal{F})$ is a closed invariant equivalence relation on $|\mathcal{A}|$ iff there exists $\mathcal{L} \in \Omega_H(\mathcal{F})$ with $\mathcal{F} \leq \mathcal{L}$.

PROOF. This follows from 13.13 and 13.19.

13.23 PROPOSITION. Let $\mathcal{A}$, $\mathcal{B}$ be T-subalgebras with $\mathcal{A} \leq \mathcal{B}$, $A = \mathfrak{g}(\mathcal{A})$ and $B = \mathfrak{g}(\mathcal{B})$. Let $(\mathcal{A},\mathcal{B}) = \{\mathcal{L} \mid \mathcal{L}$ a T-subalgebra with $\mathcal{A} \subset \mathcal{L} \subset \mathcal{B}\}$ and $(B,A) = \{H \mid H$ a τ-closed subgroup of G with $B \subset H \subset A\}$. Let $\varphi\colon (\mathcal{A},\mathcal{B}) \to (B,A)$; $\psi\colon (B,A) \to (\mathcal{A},\mathcal{B})$ be such that $\varphi(\mathcal{L}) = \mathfrak{g}(\mathcal{L}) \quad (\mathcal{L} \in (\mathcal{A},\mathcal{B}))$ and $\psi(H) = \mathfrak{A}(H) \cap \mathcal{B}$ $(H \in (B,A))$. Then $\psi\varphi$ = identity on $(\mathcal{A},\mathcal{B})$ and $\varphi\psi$ = identity on (B,A). Thus φ, ψ establish a Galois connection between $(\mathcal{A},\mathcal{B})$ and (B,A).

PROOF. Let $\mathcal{L} \in (\mathcal{A},\mathcal{B})$ and $L = \mathfrak{g}(\mathcal{L})$. Then $\mathcal{A} \leq \mathcal{L} \leq \mathcal{B}$ and $B \subset L \subset A$. Moreover $\mathcal{A} \leq \mathcal{B}$ implies that $\mathcal{B} \subset \mathcal{A}^*$ whence

$A^* \subset B \subset L \subset A$. By 13.21, $\mathcal{L} = \mathfrak{A}(L) \cap \mathcal{A}^*$. Thus $\psi\varphi(\mathcal{L}) = \psi(L) = \mathfrak{A}(L) \cap \mathcal{B} = \mathfrak{A}(L) \cap \mathcal{A}^* \cap \mathcal{B} = \mathcal{L} \cap \mathcal{B} = \mathcal{L}$.

Let $H \in (B,A)$, and $\mathcal{L} = \psi(H) = \mathcal{B} \cap \mathfrak{A}(H)$. Then $\mathcal{A} \subset \mathcal{L} \subset \mathcal{B}$ whence $\mathcal{A} \leq \mathcal{L} \leq \mathcal{B}$.

By 13.21, $\mathcal{B} = \mathfrak{A}(B) \cap \mathcal{A}^*$. Hence $\mathcal{L} = \mathfrak{A}(B) \cap \mathcal{A}^* \cap \mathfrak{A}(H) = \mathfrak{A}(H) \cap \mathcal{A}^*$. Since $A^* \subset H$, $\mathfrak{g}(\mathcal{L}) = H$ (13.21). Thus $\varphi\psi(H) = H$.

NOTES

1. For a slightly different approach to many of the results in this chapter see: Brindell Horelick, <u>An algebraic approach to the study of minimal sets in topological dynamics</u>, thesis, Wesleyan University, 1967.

2. Let $\mathfrak{A}$, $\mathfrak{F}$ be T-subalgebras with $\mathfrak{F} \subset \mathfrak{A}$. Then one might ask when does there exist a T-subalgebra $\mathfrak{B}$ with $\mathfrak{F} \leq \mathfrak{B} \subset \mathfrak{A}$ and $\mathfrak{F} \neq \mathfrak{B}$? In terms of the groups involved a necessary and sufficient condition for the existence of such a $\mathfrak{B}$ is that $AF^* \neq F$ (Apply 13.11 and note that $\mathfrak{A} \cap \mathfrak{F}^* \neq \mathfrak{F}$ when such a $\mathfrak{B}$ exists.) It would be interesting to have "dynamical" conditions which would insure that $AF^* \neq F$.

CHAPTER 14

ALMOST PERIODIC EXTENSIONS

In this chapter I continue the study of the situation given by two T-subalgebras of $\mathfrak{U}(u)$, $\mathcal{A}$ and $\mathcal{F}$, with $\mathcal{F} \subset \mathcal{A}$. Now the emphasis is on $Q(\mathcal{A}:\mathcal{F})$ rather than $P(\mathcal{A}:\mathcal{F})$. The analysis of $Q(\mathcal{A}:\mathcal{F})$ requires a deeper study of the various τ-topologies on G so that this chapter is sommewhat technical in nature.

14.1 <u>NOTATION</u>. Throughout this chapter $\mathcal{F}$ will denote a fixed T-subalgebra, F its group, and F^* the group of $\mathcal{F}^*$.

Again all T-subalgebras are assumed in $\mathfrak{U}(u)$.

Recall that $Q(\mathcal{A}:\mathcal{F}) = \cap \{cls(\eta T \cap R(\mathcal{A}:\mathcal{F})) \mid \eta$ an index on $|\mathcal{A}|\}$ for all T-subalgebras $\mathcal{A}$.

14.2 <u>LEMMA</u>. Let $\mathcal{A}, \mathcal{B}$ be T-subalgebras of $\mathfrak{U}(u)$ with $\mathcal{F} \subset \mathcal{A} \subset \mathcal{B}$ and $\varphi: |\mathcal{B}| \to |\mathcal{A}|$ the restriction mapping. Then $\varphi \times \varphi\ (Q(\mathcal{B}:\mathcal{F})) = Q(\mathcal{A}:\mathcal{F})$.

<u>PROOF</u>. Let η be an index on $|\mathcal{A}|$. Since φ is uniformly continuous, there exists an index α on $\mathcal{B}$ with $\varphi \times \varphi\ (\alpha) \subset \eta$. Then $\varphi \times \varphi\ (Q(\mathcal{B}:\mathcal{F})) \subset \varphi \times \varphi\ (cls(\alpha T \cap R(\mathcal{B}:\mathcal{F}))=$ $cls(\varphi \times \varphi\ (\alpha T \cap R(\mathcal{B}:\mathcal{F})) \subset cls(\eta T \cap R(\mathcal{A}:\mathcal{F}))$. Hence $\varphi \times \varphi\ (Q(\mathcal{B}:\mathcal{F})) \subset Q(\mathcal{A}:\mathcal{F})$.

Now let α be an index on $|\mathfrak{B}|$. Let $x \in |\mathfrak{B}|$ and V a closed neighborhood of x with $V \times V \subset \alpha$. There exists a finite subset K of T with $|\mathfrak{B}| = VK$. Then $\varphi(V)K = Q(VK) = |\mathfrak{A}|$. Hence $\text{int}\varphi(V) \neq \emptyset$.

Let $\eta = (\text{int}\varphi(V) \times \text{int}\varphi(V))T$. Then η is an open invariant subset of $|\mathfrak{A}|$ which meets the diagonal of $|\mathfrak{A}| \times |\mathfrak{A}|$. Since the latter is a minimal subset, η contains it. Hence η is an index on $|\mathfrak{A}|$.

Then $\varphi \times \varphi\ \text{cls}(\alpha T \cap R(\mathfrak{B}:\mathfrak{F})) = \text{cls}(\varphi \times \varphi\ (\alpha T \cap R(\mathfrak{B}:\mathfrak{F}))= \text{cls}(\varphi \times \varphi\ (\alpha T \cap R(\mathfrak{A}:\mathfrak{F})) \supset \text{cls}(\eta T \cap R(\mathfrak{A}:\mathfrak{F})) \supset Q(\mathfrak{A}:\mathfrak{F})$.

Let $z \in Q(\mathfrak{A}:\mathfrak{F})$. For each index α on $|\mathfrak{B}|$ set $E_\alpha = (\varphi \times \varphi)^{-1}(z) \cap \text{cls}(\alpha T \cap R(\mathfrak{B}:\mathfrak{F}))$. Then $\{E_\alpha \mid \alpha \text{ index on } |\mathfrak{B}|\}$ is a collection of closed subsets of $|\mathfrak{B}| \times |\mathfrak{B}|$ having the finite intersection property. If $y \in E_\alpha$ for all indices α, then $y \in Q(\mathfrak{B}:\mathfrak{F})$ and $\varphi \times \varphi\ (y) = z$. Thus $Q(\mathfrak{A}:\mathfrak{F}) \subset \varphi \times \varphi\ (Q(\mathfrak{B}:\mathfrak{F}))$.

In chapter 13 it was seen that $P(\mathfrak{A}:\mathfrak{F})$ is intimately related to the T-subalgebra $\mathfrak{F}^*$. I would now like to introduce and study the T-subalgebra $\mathfrak{F}^\#$ which plays a corresponding role with respect to $Q(\mathfrak{A}:\mathfrak{F})$.

14.3 <u>DEFINITION</u>. Let $g \in \mathfrak{C}$. Then g is <u>almost periodic</u> <u>over</u> $\mathfrak{F}$ if $g \in \mathfrak{F}^*$ and the map $\alpha \to \langle g,\alpha p\rangle$ $(\alpha \in F)$ of $(F,\tau(\mathfrak{F}^*))$ into $\mathbb{C}$ is continuous $(p \in M)$.

The collection of all almost periodic functions over $\mathfrak{F}$ will be denoted $\mathfrak{F}^\#$.

(This terminology anticipates the result that $\mathfrak{A}$ is almost periodic over $\mathfrak{F}$, i.e. $Q(\mathfrak{A}:\mathfrak{F})$ = the diagonal iff $\mathfrak{A} \subset \mathfrak{F}^\#$.)

It is immediate that $\mathfrak{F}^\#$ is a T-subalgebra of $\mathfrak{C}$ with $\mathfrak{F} \subset \mathfrak{F}^\# \subset \mathfrak{F}^*$. The group $\mathfrak{g}(\mathfrak{F}^\#)$ of $\mathfrak{F}^\#$ will be denoted $F^\#$.

If $\mathcal{A}$ is a T-subalgebra with $\mathcal{F} \subset \mathcal{A} \subset \mathcal{F}^{\#}$, I shall say that $\mathcal{A}$ is an <u>almost periodic extension</u> of $\mathcal{F}$ ($\mathcal{F} \leq_p \mathcal{A}$).

14.1 <u>REMARKS</u>. 1. If $\alpha \in F$, then $f\alpha \in \mathcal{F}^{\#}$ ($f \in \mathcal{F}^{\#}$) by 11.17 and 3 of 12.7. Thus $F^{\#} \lhd F$.

2. If $\mathcal{F} \subset \mathcal{A} \subset \mathcal{F}^{\#}$ and $\mathcal{L} = [\mathcal{A}\alpha \mid \alpha \in F]$, then $\mathcal{L} \subset \mathcal{F}^{\#}$ and $\mathcal{g}(\mathcal{L}) \lhd F$.

In order to characterize the almost periodic extensions of $\mathcal{F}$ it will be necessary to study the topological space $(F, \tau(\mathcal{F}^*))$. It will be convenient to do this by abstracting the essentials of the situation.

To this end for the next few results S will denote a compact (not necessarily Hausdorff) space with a group structure such that multiplication is continuous in each variable separately. Let $\mathfrak{n}$ denote the neighborhoods of the identity, e of S and $H = \cap \{\overline{V} \mid V \in \mathfrak{n}\}$.

14.5 <u>LEMMA</u>. Let $\emptyset \neq A \subset S$. Then $\overline{A} = \cap \{AV^{-1} \mid V \in \mathfrak{n}\}$.

<u>PROOF</u>. Let $x \in \overline{A}$ and $V \in \mathfrak{n}$. Since left multiplication by x is a homeomorphism, xV is a neighborhood of x. Hence $xV \cap A \neq \emptyset$, whence $x \in AV^{-1}$.

Now suppose $x \in AV^{-1}$ ($V \in \mathfrak{n}$), and let N be a neighborhood of x. Then there exists $V \in \mathfrak{n}$ with $xV \subset N$. Since $x \in AV^{-1}$, $xV \cap A \neq \emptyset$, whence $N \cap A \neq \emptyset$. Thus $x \in \overline{A}$.

14.6 <u>PROPOSITION</u>. H is a closed normal subgroup of S.

<u>PROOF</u>. That H is closed is clear from its definition.

Now let $x, y \in H$, $V, W \in \mathfrak{n}$. Since $y \in \overline{\text{int}V}$, $yW \cap \text{int}V \neq \emptyset$. Let $a \in W$ with $ya \in \text{int}V$. Then there exists $U \in \mathfrak{n}$ with $Uya \subset V$ whence $\overline{U}ya = \overline{Uya} \subset \overline{V}$.

Now $x \in H$ implies $x \in \overline{U}$. Hence $xya \in \overline{V}$ whence $xy \in \overline{V}W^{-1}$. Since W was an arbitrary element of $\mathfrak{n}$, $xy \in \overline{\overline{V}} = $

$\overline{V}$ by 14.5. Thus $xy \in H$ and so H is a closed non-null ($e \in H$) semigroup. Hence H is a subgroup of S (2.11).

Now let $a \in S$ and $f: S \to S$ the map such that $f(x) = axa^{-1}$ ($x \in S$). Then f is a homeomorphism and $f(e) = e$. Hence for each $V \in \mathfrak{n}$ there exists $W \in \mathfrak{n}$ with $f(W) \subset V \subset \overline{V}$. Then $a\overline{W}a^{-1} = f(\overline{W}) \subset \overline{V}$ whence $aHa^{-1} \subset \overline{V}$ ($V \in \mathfrak{n}$). Thus $aHa^{-1} \subset H$.

14.7 <u>LEMMA</u>. Let V be open with $V \in \mathfrak{n}$. Then $H\overline{V} = \overline{V}$.

<u>PROOF</u>. Let $y \in V$. Since V is open there exists $W \in \mathfrak{n}$ with $Wy \subset V$. Then $Hy \subset \overline{W}y = \overline{Wy} \subset \overline{V}$.

Thus $HV \subset \overline{V}$ and by the continuity of left multiplication $H\overline{V} \subset \overline{V}$.

14.8 <u>PROPOSITION</u>. 1. S/H is a compact T_2 topological group.

2. Let K be a subgroup of S. Then $S/K = \{Kx \mid x \in S\}$ is T_2 iff K is closed and $H \subset K$.

<u>PROOF</u>. 1. Let $\pi: S \to S/H$ be the canonical map, $A \subset S$. Then $\pi^{-1}\pi(A) = AH = HA$.

Now let $x, y \in S$ with $\pi(x) \neq \pi(y)$. Then $xy^{-1} \notin H$ and so there exists V open with $V \in \mathfrak{n}$ and $xy^{-1} \notin \overline{V}$. Hence there exists W open with $W \in \mathfrak{n}$ and $Wxy^{-1} \cap \overline{V} = \emptyset$. By 14.7 this implies that $Wxy^{-1} \cap HV = \emptyset$. Hence $HWxy^{-1} \cap HV = \emptyset$ and so $HWx \cap HVy = \emptyset$. Thus $\pi(Wx)$ and $\pi(Vy)$ are disjoint neighborhoods of $\pi(x)$ and $\pi(y)$ respectively.

It is easy to see that the multiplication in S/H is continuous in each variable separately. Hence S/H is a topological group by [1].

2. Let K be a subgroup of S such that S/K is T_2. Let $\delta: S \to S/K$ be the canonical map. Since $\{K\}$ is closed in S/K, $K = \delta^{-1}(\{K\})$ is closed in S.

Now let N be a closed neighborhood of $\{K\}$ in S/K. Then there exists $V \in \mathfrak{n}$ with $\delta(V) \subset N$. Since N is closed, $\delta(H) \subset \delta(\overline{V}) \subset N$. The intersection of all the closed neighborhoods of $\{K\}$ is just $\{K\}$ itself. Hence $\delta(H) = \{K\}$ where $H \subset K$.

On the other hand if K is a closed subgroup of S with $H \subset K$, $\pi(K)$ is a closed subgroup of S/H and $S/K \cong (S/H)/\pi(K)$; where $\pi: S \to S/H$ is the canonical map.

Now let us apply the above considerations to the situation described at the beginning of this chapter. Since $\mathcal{F}^*F = \mathcal{F}^*$ (3 of 12.7), the pair $(F,\tau(\mathcal{F}^*))$ satisfies the condition imposed on S (11.16, 11.17). Hence we have the following:

14.9 COROLLARY. 1. $(F/H(F,\mathcal{F}^*),\tau(\mathcal{F}^*))$ is a compact T_2 topological group.

2. Let K be a subgroup of F. Then $(F/K,\tau(\mathcal{F}^*))$ is T_2 iff K is $\tau(\mathcal{F}^*)$-closed and $H(F,\mathcal{F}^*) \subset K$.

Here $H(F,\mathcal{F}^*) = \cap \{\text{cls}_{\mathcal{F}^*}V \mid V \text{ a } \tau(\mathcal{F}^*)\text{-neighborhood of } u \text{ in } F\}$.

14.10 REMARKS AND NOTATION. 1. Now let $\mathcal{A}$ be an arbitrary T-subalgebra of $\mathfrak{U}(u)$. Since $\mathcal{A}F$ need not be contained in $\mathcal{A}$, the preceding results do not apply to the topological space $(F,\tau(\mathcal{A}))$. Nevertheless, we may still form $H(F,\mathcal{A}) = \cap \{\text{cls}_{\mathcal{A}}V \mid V \text{ a } \tau(\mathcal{A})\text{-neighborhood of } u \text{ in } F\}$. Then $H(F,\mathcal{A})$ is a closed subset of F with respect to $\tau(\mathcal{B})$ for every T-subalgebra $\mathcal{B}$ with $\mathcal{A} \subset \mathcal{B}$ since $\tau(\mathcal{A}) \subset \tau(\mathcal{B})$, but it is not clear that it is a subgroup of F.

2. Notice that if K is any $\tau(\mathcal{A})$-closed subset of G, then $AK = K$. Thus $AH(F,\mathcal{A}) = H(F,\mathcal{A})$.

3. Again suppose $\mathcal{F} \subset \mathcal{A}$ and form $\mathcal{L} = [\mathcal{A}\alpha \mid \alpha \in F]$. Then $\mathcal{L}F \subset \mathcal{L}$ and the general considerations may be applied to

the space $(F,\tau(\mathcal{L}))$. Let $A = g(\mathcal{A})$ and π the canonical map of F onto $F/H(F,\mathcal{L})$. Since $\mathcal{A} \subset \mathcal{L}$ implies that A is a $\tau(\mathcal{L})$-closed subset of F, it is $\tau(\mathcal{L})$-compact. Hence $\pi(A)$ is compact, whence closed. Thus $AH(F,\mathcal{L}) = \pi^{-1}\pi(A) = H(F,\mathcal{L})A$ is a $\tau(\mathcal{L})$-closed subgroup of F.

Since $\mathcal{A} \subset \mathcal{L}$, $H(F,\mathcal{L}) \subset H(F,\mathcal{A})$ whence by 2 above $AH(F,\mathcal{L}) \subset H(F,\mathcal{A})$. It turns out that in many cases $AH(F,\mathcal{L}) = H(F,\mathcal{A})$.

14.11 PROPOSITION. Let $H = H(F,\mathcal{F}^*)$. Then $H \subset F^\#$ and the map $\varphi\colon (F/H,\tau(\mathcal{F}^*)) \times |\mathcal{F}^\#| \to |\mathcal{F}^\#|$ such that $\varphi(H\alpha,x) = (\alpha|\mathcal{F}^\#)x$ $(\alpha \in F,\ x \in |\mathcal{F}^\#|)$ is continuous. Thus the map $(\alpha,x) \to \alpha x\colon (F,\tau(\mathcal{F}^*)) \times |\mathcal{F}^\#| \to |\mathcal{F}^\#|$ is continuous.

PROOF. Let $\alpha \in H$, $f \in \mathcal{F}^\#$ and $\varepsilon > 0$. Then by 14.3 with $p = u$ there exists a $\tau(\mathcal{F}^*)$-neighborhood V of u such that $|\langle f,\beta\rangle - \langle f,u\rangle| < \varepsilon$ $(\beta \in \mathrm{cls}_{\mathcal{F}^*}V)$. Hence $|\langle f,\alpha\rangle - \langle f,u\rangle| < \varepsilon$. Thus $\langle f,\alpha\rangle = \langle f,u\rangle$ $(f \in \mathcal{F}^\#)$ whence $\alpha \in F^\#$.

The map φ is thus well defined. From the definition of $\mathcal{F}^\#$ it follows that φ is continuous in the first variable. It is continuous in the second variable because left multiplication is continuous on βT. Since $(F/H,\tau(\mathcal{F}^*))$ is a compact T_2 topological group by 14.8, 14.11 follows from [1].

14.12 LEMMA. Let $\mathcal{A}$ be a T-subalgebra with $\mathcal{F} \subset \mathcal{A} \subset \mathcal{F}^\#$ and let $f \in \mathcal{A}$. Then f is continuous on $(F,\tau(\mathcal{A}))$.

PROOF. It suffices to prove 14.12 for real-valued functions.

Let $b \in \mathbb{R}$ and $K = f^{-1}(-\infty,b] \cap F$. I claim $\langle f^K,u\rangle \le b$ if $\emptyset \ne K$. Suppose $\langle f^K,u\rangle = b + \varepsilon$ with $\varepsilon > 0$. Then for each $N \in u$ there exist $\alpha_N \in K$, $t_N \in N$ with $\langle f\alpha_N,t_N\rangle \ge b + \varepsilon/2$. Since $f\colon (F,\tau(\mathcal{F}^*)) \to \mathbb{R}$ is continuous, K is $\tau(\mathcal{F}^*)$ closed.

Hence we may assume $\alpha_N \to \alpha \in K$ with respect to $\tau(\mathcal{F}^*)$. Also Also $t_N \to u$ implies $ut_N \to u$ on $|\mathcal{F}^{\#}|$. By 14.11 and the fact that $f \in \mathcal{F}^{\#}$, $\langle f, \alpha_N t_N\rangle \to \langle f,\alpha\rangle$. This however contradicts the fact that $\alpha \in K$.

Now let $\beta \in \mathrm{cls}_{\mathfrak{A}} K$. Then $\langle f,\beta\rangle \leq \langle f^K, u\rangle \leq b$ whence $\beta \in K$. Hence K is $\tau(\mathfrak{A})$-closed.

Similarly $L = f^{-1}[a,\infty) \cap F$ is closed, whence f $f^{-1}(b,a) \cap F = (K \cup L)'$ is open.

14.13 <u>LEMMA</u>. Let L be a subgroup of G, $\mathfrak{A}$ a T-subalgebra of $\mathfrak{U}(u)$, and $(\alpha_n | n \in I)$ a net of elements in L such that $\alpha_n \to \alpha \in L$ with respect to $\tau(\mathfrak{A})$ and $\alpha_n p \to p$ on $|\mathfrak{A}|$ for some $p \in M$. Then $\alpha \in H(L,\mathfrak{A})$.

<u>PROOF</u>. Let V be a $\tau(\mathfrak{A})$-neighborhood of α. I shall show that $u \in \mathrm{cls}_{\mathfrak{A}} V$.

Let $K = \{\alpha_n \mid \alpha_n \in V\}$ and $J = \{n \mid \alpha_n \in V\}$. Then J is cofinal in I so that $\lim_{n\in J} \alpha_n p = \alpha p$.

Let $f \in \mathfrak{A}$, and $t \in T$. Then $tf \in \mathfrak{A}$ and $\langle tf,p\rangle =$ $\lim \langle tf,\alpha_n p\rangle$ and so $\langle fp,t\rangle = \langle tf,p\rangle \leq \langle (tf)^{Kp}, e\rangle = \langle f^{Kp},t\rangle$. Hence $fp \leq f^{Kp} \leq f^K p$ (4 of 11.7). Let $q \in M$ be such that $pq = u$. Then $fu = fpq \leq f^K pq = f^K u$. Thus $u \in \mathrm{cls}_{\mathfrak{A}} K \subset \mathrm{cls}_{\mathfrak{A}} V$.

14.14 <u>PROPOSITION</u>. $\mathcal{F}^{\#} = \mathfrak{U}(H) \cap \mathcal{F}^*$ and $F^{\#} = H$ where $H = H(F,\mathcal{F}^*)$.

<u>PROOF</u>. By 14.11 $H \subset F^{\#}$.

Now let $f \in \mathfrak{U}(H) \cap \mathcal{F}^*$, (α_n) a net on F with $\alpha_n \to \alpha \in F$ with respect to $\tau(\mathcal{F}^*)$ and $p \in M$. Then we may assume that $\alpha_n p \to q$ in M.

Since $\alpha_n p \mid \mathfrak{F} = p|\mathfrak{F}$, $p|\mathfrak{F} = q|\mathfrak{F}$ whence by 12.11 $p|\mathfrak{F}^* = \beta q|\mathfrak{F}^*$ for some $\beta \in F$.

Then $\beta\alpha_n p \to p$ on $|\mathfrak{F}^*|$ and $\beta\alpha_n \to \beta\alpha$ with respect to $\tau(\mathfrak{F}^*)$. Hence by 14.13, $\beta\alpha \in H$. Since $H \triangleleft F$, $\alpha\beta \in H$.

Finally $\langle f,\alpha_n p\rangle \to \langle f,q\rangle = \langle f,\beta^{-1}p\rangle = \langle f,\alpha\beta\beta^{-1}p\rangle = \langle f,\alpha p\rangle$ whence $f \in \mathfrak{F}^{\#}$.

Thus $\mathfrak{U}(H) \cap \mathfrak{F}^* \subset \mathfrak{F}^{\#}$, whence $F^{\#} = \mathfrak{g}(\mathfrak{U}(H) \cap \mathfrak{F}^*) = H$ (2 of 13.19).

Hence $H = F^{\#}$. That $\mathfrak{F}^{\#} = \mathfrak{U}(H) \cap \mathfrak{F}^*$ now follows from 13.23.

14.15 <u>PROPOSITION</u>. Let $\mathfrak{A}$ be a T-subalgebra with $\mathfrak{F} \subset \mathfrak{A} \subset \mathfrak{F}^*$. Then $\mathfrak{F} \leq_p \mathfrak{A}$ iff $A = H(F,\mathfrak{A})$, where $A = \mathfrak{g}(\mathfrak{A})$.

<u>PROOF</u>. Let $\mathfrak{F} \leq_p \mathfrak{A}$. Then $H(F,\mathfrak{A}) \subset A$ as in the proof of 14.11 with $\mathfrak{F}^{\#}$ replaced by $\mathfrak{A}$ (see 14.12). Since $A \subset H(F,\mathfrak{A})$, $A = H(F,\mathfrak{A})$ in this case.

Now suppose $A = H(F,\mathfrak{A})$. Since $\mathfrak{A} \subset \mathfrak{F}^*$, $F^{\#} = H(F,\mathfrak{F}^*) \subset H(F,\mathfrak{A}) = A$. Then $\mathfrak{A} \subset \mathfrak{F}^{\#}$ by 13.23.

14.16 <u>PROPOSITION</u>. Let $\mathfrak{A}$ be a T-subalgebra of $\mathfrak{U}(u)$ with $\mathfrak{F} \subset \mathfrak{A}$. Then $\mathfrak{g}(\mathfrak{A} \cap \mathfrak{F}^{\#}) = AF^{\#} = F^{\#}A$.

<u>PROOF</u>. Since $\mathfrak{F}^{\#} \subset \mathfrak{F}^*$, $\mathfrak{A} \leq [\mathfrak{A} \cup \mathfrak{F}^{\#}]$. Moreover $\mathfrak{F}^{\#}F \subset \mathfrak{F}^{\#}$ and $A \subset F$ imply $\mathfrak{F}^{\#}A \subset \mathfrak{F}^{\#}$. 14.16 now follows from 13.10.

14.17 <u>LEMMA</u>. Let $\mathfrak{A}$ be a T-subalgebra with $\mathfrak{F} \subset \mathfrak{A}$. Then $Q(\mathfrak{A}:\mathfrak{F})$ is a closed invariant subset of $R(\mathfrak{A}:\mathfrak{A} \cap \mathfrak{F}^{\#})$.

<u>PROOF</u>. The proof that $Q(\mathfrak{A}:\mathfrak{F})$ is closed and invariant is straightforward and will be omitted.

Now let $(x,y) \in Q(\mathfrak{A}:\mathfrak{F})$. Then just as in the case of $Q(\mathcal{Q})$ (see 4.1) there exist nets (x_n) (y_n) on $|\mathcal{Q}|$ and (t_n) on T such that $x_n|\mathcal{F} = y_n|\mathcal{F}$, $x_n \to x$, $y_n \to y$ and $\lim x_n t_n = z = \lim y_n t_n$.

Let $p_n, q_n \in M$ with $p_n|\mathcal{Q} = x_n$ and $q_n|\mathcal{Q} = y_n$. We may suppose $p_n \to p$ and $q_n \to q$ in M.

Since $p_n|\mathcal{F} = q_n|\mathcal{F}$ and $\mathcal{F} \leq \mathcal{Q} \cap \mathcal{F}^\#$, $p_n = \alpha_n q_n$ on $\mathcal{Q} \cap \mathcal{F}^\#$ where $\alpha_n \in F$. We may suppose $\alpha_n \to \alpha \in F$ with respect to $\tau(\mathcal{F}^*)$.

Finally we may assume that $q_n t_n \to r$ on M.

Since the map $(\gamma F^\#, w) \to \gamma w$ of $(F/F^\#, \tau(\mathcal{F}^*)) \times |\mathcal{F}^\#| \to |\mathcal{F}^\#|$ is continuous, $p_n t_n = \alpha_n q_n t_n \to \alpha r$ on $\mathcal{F}^\#$. But $p_n t_n|\mathcal{Q} = x_n t_n \to z$ and $q_n t_n|\mathcal{Q} = y_n t_n \to z$, whence $\alpha r = r$ on $\mathcal{Q} \cap \mathcal{F}^\#$. Hence $\alpha = u$ on $\mathcal{Q} \cap \mathcal{F}^\#$.

Again by the continuity of the above map, $p = \lim p_n = \lim \alpha_n q_n = \alpha q$ on $\mathcal{Q} \cap \mathcal{F}^\#$. Thus $x|\mathcal{Q} \cap \mathcal{F}^\# = p|\mathcal{Q} \cap \mathcal{F}^\# = q|\mathcal{Q} \cap \mathcal{F}^\# = y|\mathcal{Q} \cap \mathcal{F}^\#$, whence $(x,y) \in R(\mathcal{Q}:\mathcal{Q} \cap \mathcal{F}^\#)$.

14.18 <u>PROPOSITION</u>. Let $\mathcal{Q}$ be a T-subalgebra with $\mathcal{F} \subset \mathcal{Q}$. Let $A = \mathfrak{g}(\mathcal{Q})$ and $L = \{\alpha | \alpha \in F, (\alpha|\mathcal{Q}, u|\mathcal{Q}) \in Q(\mathcal{Q}:\mathcal{F})\}$. Then $A \subset H(F,\mathcal{Q}) \subset L \subset AF^\#$. Thus if $F^\# \subset L$, $L = AF^\#$ since $AL \subset L$.

<u>PROOF</u>. Let $\alpha \in A$. Then $f\alpha = f = fu$ $(f \in \mathcal{Q})$ shows that $\alpha \in \text{cls}_{\mathcal{Q}} u \subset H(F,\mathcal{Q})$.

Let $\gamma \in H(F,\mathcal{Q})$, $h(U)$ an $\mathcal{Q}$-neighborhood of γ, $h(K)$ an $\mathcal{Q}$-neighborhood of u. Then (U,Ku) and (K,Ku) are $\tau(\mathcal{Q})$ neighborhoods of γ and u respectively (11.14.1). Hence there exists $\beta \in F \cap (U,Ku) \cap (K,Ku)$. This implies the existence of $t,s \in Ku$ with $U \in \beta t$ and $K \in \beta s$. Then $\beta t|\mathscr{F} = ut|\mathscr{F}$, $\beta t \in h(U)$, $ut \in h(K)$ and $K \in (\beta t)(t^{-1}s) \cap (ut)(t^{-1}s)$ i.e. $(\beta t)t^{-1}s$ and $(ut)t^{-1}s$ are both in $h(K)$. Thus $(\gamma|\mathcal{A}, u|\mathcal{A}) \in Q(\mathcal{A}:\mathscr{F})$ whence $\gamma \in L$.

Let $\alpha \in L$. Then by 14.17 $\alpha \in \mathfrak{g}\,(\mathcal{A} \cap \mathscr{F}^{\#})$, whence $\alpha \in AF^{\#}$ by 14.15.

14.19 <u>COROLLARY</u>. With the same notation as in 14.18 let $\mathcal{A} \subset \mathscr{F}^{*}$. Then:

1. $L = AF^{\#} = H(F,\mathcal{A})$.
2. If $\mathcal{S} = [\mathcal{A}\alpha \mid \alpha \in F]$ then $H(F,\mathcal{A}) = AH(F,\mathcal{S})$. (See 3 of 14.10.)

<u>PROOF</u>. 1. In this case $\tau(\mathcal{A}) \subset \tau(\mathscr{F}^{*})$ whence $F^{\#} = H(F,\mathscr{F}^{*}) \subset H(F,\mathcal{A})$. Then $AF^{\#} \subset AH(F,\mathcal{A}) \subset AL \subset AF^{\#}$. Since $AL = L$ and $AH(F,\mathcal{A}) = H(F,\mathcal{A})$ (2 of 14.10), the proof is completed.

2. $\mathcal{S} \subset \mathscr{F}^{*}$ (12.5 and 12.7). Then by 1 above $H(F,\mathcal{S}) = SF^{\#}$ where $S = \mathfrak{g}(\mathcal{S})$. Since $S \subset A$, $H(F,\mathcal{A}) = AF^{\#} = ASF^{\#} = AH(F,\mathcal{S})$.

14.20 <u>COROLLARY</u>. With the notation of 14.18 let $F^{*} \subset A$. Then again $L = AF^{\#} = H(F,\mathcal{A}) = AH(F,\mathcal{S})$.

<u>PROOF</u>. Set $\mathcal{K} = \mathfrak{A}(A) \cap \mathscr{F}^{*}$. Then $\mathscr{F} \leq \mathcal{K}$ and $\mathfrak{g}(\mathcal{K}) = A$ (13.23). Hence by 1 of 14.19, $AF^{\#} = H(F,\mathcal{K})$.

By 2 of 13.21 $\mathcal{K} \subset \mathcal{A}$, whence $H(F,\mathcal{K}) \subset H(F,\mathcal{A})$. Thus $AF^{\#} \subset H(F,\mathcal{A}) \subset L \subset AF^{\#}$, whence $AF^{\#} = L = H(F,\mathcal{A})$.

Since $S = \cap\,\{\alpha A\alpha^{-1} \mid \alpha \in F\}$ (11.4) and $F^{*} \lhd F$ (12.6 and 12.10), $F^{*} \subset S$. Hence the above argument may be used to show that $H(F,\mathcal{S}) = SF^{\#}$. Thus $H(F,\mathcal{A}) = AF^{\#} = ASF^{\#} = AH(F,\mathcal{S})$.

14.21 <u>PROPOSITION</u>. Let $\mathcal{A}$ be a T-subalgebra with $\mathscr{F} \subset \mathcal{A}$. Then $\mathscr{F} \leq_p \mathcal{A}$ iff $Q(\mathcal{A}:\mathscr{F})$ is the diagonal Δ of $|\mathcal{A}| \times |\mathcal{A}|$.

PROOF. Let $Q(\mathcal{A}:\mathcal{F}) = \Delta$. Then $P(\mathcal{A}:\mathcal{F}) = \Delta$ and so $\mathcal{A} \subset \mathcal{F}^*$ by 13.5. By 14.14 $F^\# = H(F,\mathcal{F}^*)$ whence $F^\# \subset H(F,\mathcal{A})$. Thus by 14.18 $L = AF^\#$. But $Q(\mathcal{A}:\mathcal{F}) = \Delta$ implies $L = A$ so that $F^\# \subset A$. Consequently $\mathcal{A} \subset \mathcal{F}^\#$ by 13.23.

Now suppose $\mathcal{A} \subset \mathcal{F}^\#$. Then $R(\mathcal{A}:\mathcal{A} \cap \mathcal{F}^\#) = R(\mathcal{A}:\mathcal{A}) = \Delta$, whence $Q(\mathcal{A}:\mathcal{F}) = \Delta$ by 14.17.

14.22 PROPOSITION. Let $\mathcal{A}$ be a T-subalgebra with $\mathcal{F} \subset \mathcal{A}$. Then $R(\mathcal{A}:\mathcal{A} \cap \mathcal{F}^\#)$ is the smallest closed invariant equivalence relation S on $|\mathcal{A}|$ with $Q(\mathcal{A}:\mathcal{F}) \subset S \subset R(\mathcal{A}:\mathcal{F})$.

PROOF. Since $\mathcal{F} \subset \mathcal{A} \cap \mathcal{F}^\#$, $R(\mathcal{A}:\mathcal{A} \cap \mathcal{F}^\#) \subset R(\mathcal{A}:\mathcal{F})$. Hence by 14.17 $Q(\mathcal{A}:\mathcal{F}) \subset R(\mathcal{A}:\mathcal{A} \cap \mathcal{F}^\#) \subset R(\mathcal{A}:\mathcal{F})$.

Now let S be a closed invariant equivalence relation on $|\mathcal{A}|$ such that $Q(\mathcal{A}:\mathcal{F}) \subset S \subset R(\mathcal{A}:\mathcal{F})$, and let $\mathcal{K}$ be the T-subalgebra of $\mathcal{A}$ induced by S, i.e. $S = R(\mathcal{A}:\mathcal{K})$.

Let $(x,y) \in Q(\mathcal{K}:\mathcal{F})$. Then by 14.2 there exists $(a,b) \in Q(\mathcal{A}:\mathcal{F})$ with $a|\mathcal{K} = x$ and $b|\mathcal{K} = y$. Hence $x = y$. Thus by 14.21 $\mathcal{K} \subset \mathcal{F}^\#$, whence $R(\mathcal{A}:\mathcal{A} \cap \mathcal{F}^\#) \subset R(\mathcal{A}:\mathcal{K}) = S$.

14.23 PROPOSITION. Let $\mathcal{A}$ be a T-subalgebra with $\mathcal{F} \subset \mathcal{A}$ and $F^\# \subset \{\alpha \mid \alpha \in F, (\alpha|\mathcal{A}, u|\mathcal{A}) \in Q(\mathcal{A}:\mathcal{F})\}$ (= L in the notation of 14.18). Then:

1. $R(\mathcal{A}:\mathcal{A} \cap \mathcal{F}^\#) = \{(x,y) \mid (xw,yw) \in Q(\mathcal{A}:\mathcal{F})\ (w \in K)\} \cap R(\mathcal{A}:\mathcal{F})$, where K is the set of minimal idempotents in βT; i.e. $w \in K$ iff $w^2 = w$ and $w \in I$ for some minimal right ideal in βT.

2. If in addition the almost periodic points of $R(\mathcal{A}:\mathcal{A} \cap \mathcal{F}^\#)$ are dense in $R(\mathcal{A}:\mathcal{A} \cap \mathcal{F}^\#)$, then $R(\mathcal{A}:\mathcal{A} \cap \mathcal{F}^\#) = Q(\mathcal{A}:\mathcal{F})$.

PROOF. 1. Let $S = \{(x,y) \mid (xw,yw) \in Q(\mathcal{A}:\mathcal{F})\ (w \in J)\} \cap R(\mathcal{A}:\mathcal{F})$. I shall show that S is a closed invariant equivalence relation with $Q(\mathcal{A}:\mathcal{F}) \subset S \subset R(\mathcal{A}:\mathcal{A} \cap \mathcal{F}^\#)$

whence 1 will follow from 14.22.

Let $(x,y) \in Q(\mathcal{A}:\mathcal{F})$, and $w \in K$. Then $(x,y) \in R(\mathcal{A}:\mathcal{F})$ and $(xw,yw) \in Q(\mathcal{A}:\mathcal{F})$ since the latter is closed and invariant. Thus $Q(\mathcal{A}:\mathcal{F}) \subset S$.

Let $(x,y) \in S$ and $v \in K$ with $xv = x$ (such exist since $(|\mathcal{A}|,T)$ is minimal). Then $(xv,yv) \in Q(\mathcal{A}:\mathcal{F}) \subset R(\mathcal{A}:\mathcal{A} \cap \mathcal{F}^{\#})$ implies $x|\mathcal{A} \cap \mathcal{F}^{\#} = yv|\mathcal{A} \cap \mathcal{F}^{\#}$. Also $x|\mathcal{F} = y|\mathcal{F}$ implies that $yv|\mathcal{F} = xv|\mathcal{F} = x|\mathcal{F} = y|\mathcal{F}$. Since $\mathcal{F} \leq \mathcal{A} \cap \mathcal{F}^{\#}$, $yv|\mathcal{A} \cap \mathcal{F}^{\#} = y|\mathcal{A} \cap \mathcal{F}^{\#}$. Thus $x|\mathcal{A} \cap \mathcal{F}^{\#} = yv|\mathcal{A} \cap \mathcal{F}^{\#} = y|\mathcal{A} \cap \mathcal{F}^{\#}$ whence $(x,y) \in R(\mathcal{A}:\mathcal{A} \cap \mathcal{F}^{\#})$.

S is clearly reflexive and symmetric. Let $(x,y),(y,z) \in S$ and $w \in K$. Since $R(\mathcal{A}:\mathcal{A} \cap \mathcal{F}^{\#})$ is a closed invariant equivalence relation and $S \subset R(\mathcal{A}:\mathcal{A} \cap \mathcal{F}^{\#})$ $(x,z) \in R(\mathcal{A}:\mathcal{A} \cap \mathcal{F}^{\#})$ and $(xwu,ywu) \in R(\mathcal{A}:\mathcal{A} \cap \mathcal{F}^{\#})$. Let $\alpha|\mathcal{A} = xwu$ and $\beta|\mathcal{A} = ywu$. Then $\alpha\beta^{-1} \in AF^{\#}$ and the hypothesis imply $(\alpha\beta^{-1}|\mathcal{A},u|\mathcal{A}) \in Q(\mathcal{A}:\mathcal{F})$ by 14.18. Since $Q(\mathcal{A}:\mathcal{F})$ is closed and invariant this implies that $(\alpha|\mathcal{A},\beta|\mathcal{A}) \in Q(\mathcal{A}:\mathcal{F})$, i.e. $(xwu,ywu) \in Q(\mathcal{A}:\mathcal{F})$. There exists $v \in M \cap K$ with $wv = w$ (1 of 3.6). Thus $(xw,yw) = (xwu,xwu)v \in Q(\mathcal{A}:\mathcal{F})v \subset Q(\mathcal{A}:\mathcal{F})$. Hence S is an equivalence relation.

Let $(x,y) \in S$, $w \in J$ and $t \in T$. Then tM is a minimal subset of βT and twt^{-1} is an idempotent in tM. Hence $(xtwt^{-1},ytwt^{-1}) \in Q(\mathcal{A}:\mathcal{F})$ and so $(xtw,ytw) \in Q(\mathcal{A}:\mathcal{F})t = Q(\mathcal{A}:\mathcal{F})$. Hence S is invariant.

Now let (x_n,y_n) be a net on S with $(x_n,y_n) \to (x,y)$ and let $w \in K$. Then $(x,y) \in R(\mathcal{A}:\mathcal{A} \cap \mathcal{F}^{\#})$ since $S \subset R(\mathcal{A}:\mathcal{A} \cap \mathcal{F}^{\#})$ and the latter is closed. Hence $(xwu,ywu) \in R(\mathcal{A}:\mathcal{A} \cap \mathcal{F}^{\#})$ from which it follows that $(xw,yw) \in Q(\mathcal{A}:\mathcal{F})$ as above.

2. Let $(x,y) \in R(\mathcal{A}:\mathcal{A} \cap \mathcal{F}^{\#})$ be an almost periodic point of $|\mathcal{A}| \times |\mathcal{A}|$. Then there exists an idempotent v in M

with $(x,y) = (xv,yv)$. By 1, $(xv,yv) \in Q(\mathcal{A}:\mathcal{F})$. Statement 2 now follows from the fact that $Q(\mathcal{A}:\mathcal{F})$ is closed.

14.24 PROPOSITION. Let $\mathcal{A}$ be a T-subalgebra with $\mathcal{F} \leq \mathcal{A}$, $\mathcal{F} \neq \mathcal{A}$. Then:

1. $Q(\mathcal{A}:\mathcal{F}) = R(\mathcal{A}:\mathcal{A} \cap \mathcal{F}^{\#})$.

2. If $|\mathcal{A}|$ is metrizable then $\mathcal{F} \neq \mathcal{A} \cap \mathcal{F}^{\#}$. Thus in this case $\mathcal{A} \cap \mathcal{F}^{\#}$ is a proper almost periodic extension of $\mathcal{F}$ which is contained in $\mathcal{A}$.

PROOF. 1. By 14.19 $\mathcal{A}$ satisfies the condition of 14.23.

Now let $(x,y) \in R(\mathcal{A}:\mathcal{A} \cap \mathcal{F}^{\#})$ and v an idempotent with $x = xv$. Then $y|\mathcal{A} \cap \mathcal{F}^{\#} = x|\mathcal{A} \cap \mathcal{F}^{\#} = xv|\mathcal{A} \cap \mathcal{F}^{\#} = yv|\mathcal{A} \cap \mathcal{F}^{\#}$. Since $\mathcal{A} \cap \mathcal{F}^{\#} \leq \mathcal{A}$, $y = yv$. Hence (x,y) is an almost periodic point of $|\mathcal{A}| \times |\mathcal{A}|$ and 1 follows from 2 of 14.23.

2. Let α be a metric on $\mathcal{A}$ and assume $Q(\mathcal{A}:\mathcal{F}) = R(\mathcal{A}:\mathcal{F})$. For each positive integer n set $\alpha_n = \{(x,y) \mid \alpha(x,y) < 1/n\}$. Then the diagonal, $\Delta = P(\mathcal{A}:\mathcal{F}) = \bigcap_{n=1}^{\infty} \alpha_n T \cap R(\mathcal{A}:\mathcal{F})$. But $Q(\mathcal{A}:\mathcal{F}) \subset \overline{\alpha_n T \cap R(\mathcal{A}:\mathcal{F})}$ implies that $P(\mathcal{A}:\mathcal{F})$ is a residual subset of $R(\mathcal{A}:\mathcal{F})$. This would imply that $\Delta = R(\mathcal{A}:\mathcal{F})$ or that $\mathcal{A} = \mathcal{F}$. But it was assumed that $\mathcal{F} \neq \mathcal{A}$.

Thus $R(\mathcal{A}:\mathcal{A} \cap \mathcal{F}^{\#}) = Q(\mathcal{A}:\mathcal{F}) \neq R(\mathcal{A}:\mathcal{F})$ whence $\mathcal{F} \neq \mathcal{A} \cap \mathcal{F}^{\#}$.

14.25 REMARKS. 1. Propositions 14.23 and 14.24 provide an approach to the problem: given $\mathcal{F} \subset \mathcal{A}$ when does there exist $\mathcal{B}$ with $\mathcal{F} \leq_p \mathcal{B} \subset \mathcal{A}$ and $\mathcal{F} \neq \mathcal{B}$ i.e. when does $\mathcal{A}$ contain a proper almost periodic extension of $\mathcal{F}$? Indeed the Furstenberg structure theorem (chapter 15) is essentially a corollary of 14.24.

14.26 PROPOSITION. Let $(K,|\mathcal{B}|,T)$ be a bitransformation group where K is a compact group of homeomorphisms of

$|\mathfrak{B}|$ and let $\mathfrak{A}$ be the T-subalgebra of $\mathfrak{B}$ corresponding to $|\mathfrak{B}|/K$. Then $\mathfrak{B}$ is an almost periodic extension of $\mathfrak{A}$ and $(A/B, \tau(B))$ is homeomorphic with H. (The converse is of course also true (12.12).)

<u>PROOF</u>. Let $(x,y) \in Q(\mathfrak{B}:\mathfrak{A})$. Then there exist nets $(x_n)(y_n)$ on $|\mathfrak{B}|$ and (t_n) on T such that $x_n \to x$, $y_n \to y$, $\lim x_n t_n = \lim y_n t_n = z \in |\mathfrak{B}|$ and $x_n|\mathfrak{A} = y_n|\mathfrak{A}$ for all n. There exists a net (h_n) on K with $y_n = h_n x_n$ for all n and we may suppose that $h_n \to h \in K$. Then $y = hx$ and $hz = z$ whence h is the identity and $y = x$. Thus $Q(\mathfrak{B}:\mathfrak{A})$ is the diagonal of $|\mathfrak{B}| \times |\mathfrak{B}|$ and so $\mathfrak{B}$ is an almost periodic extension of $\mathfrak{A}$ by 14.21.

We know (12.12) that H is isomorphic with A/B as groups. It is easy to see that the map of H onto A/B is continuous. Hence it is a homeomorphism because $B = H(A,\mathfrak{B})$ (14.15) and so $(A/B, \tau(\mathfrak{B}))$ is Hausdorff.

NOTES

1. Robert Ellis, Locally compact transformation groups, Duke Math. Journal, vol.24(1957), 119-125.

CHAPTER 15

THE FURSTENBERG STRUCTURE THEOREM

In this chapter I would like to apply the results of chapter 14 in two directions: first to obtain a slight generalization of Furstenberg's structure theorem for distal flows [1] and second to the case $\mathcal{F} = \mathbb{C}$ to obtain results about the structure group of an arbitrary minimal set.

In order to state the main result in its fullest generality it is convenient to introduce the notion of a quasi-separable T-subalgebra.

15.1 <u>DEFINITION</u>. Let $\mathcal{A}$ be a T-subalgebra of $\mathcal{C}$, and $\mathcal{N} = \{f \mid f \in \mathcal{A}, [f] \text{ is separable}\}$. Then $\mathcal{A}$ is <u>quasi-separable</u> if $\mathcal{A} = [\mathcal{N}]$. (Recall that [f] denotes the T-subalgebra of $\mathcal{C}$ generated by f.)

15.2 <u>REMARKS</u>. 1. Recall that the T-subalgebra $\mathcal{F}$ of $\mathcal{C}$ is just $\mathcal{C}(|\mathcal{F}|)$ whence it is separable iff $|\mathcal{F}|$ is metrizable. Thus if $|\mathcal{F}|$ is metrizable, $\mathcal{F}$ is quasi-separable.

2. If T is countable then since $\{tf \mid t \in T\}$ separates the points of $|[f]|$, [f] is separable $(f \in \mathcal{C})$. Hence in this case every T-subalgebra of $\mathcal{C}$ is quasi-separable.

15.3 <u>LEMMA</u>. Let $\mathcal{F}, \mathcal{A}$ be T-subalgebras of $\mathfrak{A}(u)$ such that $\mathcal{F} \leq \mathcal{A}$, $\mathcal{F} \neq \mathcal{A}$, and $\mathcal{A}$ is quasi-separable. Then there exists a T-subalgebra $\mathcal{B}$ of $\mathcal{A}$ such that $\mathcal{F} \leq_p \mathcal{B}$ and $\mathcal{F} \neq \mathcal{B}$.

<u>PROOF</u>. Since $\mathcal{A}$ is quasi-separable and $\mathcal{F} \neq \mathcal{A}$ there exists $g \in \mathcal{A}$ such that $[g]$ is separable and $g \notin \mathcal{F}$. Set $\mathcal{K} = [\mathcal{F} \cup \{g\}]$. Then $\mathcal{F} \leq \mathcal{K}$ and $\mathcal{F} \neq \mathcal{K}$.

Let $\{g_i \mid i = 1,\ldots\}$ be a countable dense subset of $[g]$. For every pair of positive integers i,k set $\eta(i,k) = \{(x,y) \mid x,y \in |\mathcal{K}|, |g_i(x) - g_i(y)| < 1/k\}$. Then $\eta(i,k)$ is an index on $|\mathcal{K}|$ and it is immediate that

$\cap \{\overline{\eta(i,k)T \cap R(\mathcal{K}:\mathcal{F})} \mid i,k = 1,\ldots\} = \cap \{\overline{\alpha T \cap R(\mathcal{K}:\mathcal{F})} \mid \alpha \in \mathcal{U}\} = Q(\mathcal{K}:\mathcal{F})$, where $\mathcal{U}$ is the collection of all the indices on $|\mathcal{K}|$.

Since $\mathcal{K} \neq \mathcal{F}$, $R(\mathcal{K}:\mathcal{F}) \neq \Delta$, the diagonal of $|\mathcal{K}| \times |\mathcal{K}|$. Moreover $\mathcal{F} \leq \mathcal{K}$ implies $P(\mathcal{K}:\mathcal{F}) = \Delta$ (13.5). Thus $Q(\mathcal{K}:\mathcal{F}) \neq R(\mathcal{K}:\mathcal{F})$. (Otherwise $P(\mathcal{K}:\mathcal{F}) = \cap(\eta(i,k) \cap R(\mathcal{K}:\mathcal{F}))$ would be residual in $R(\mathcal{K}:\mathcal{F})$.) But $Q(\mathcal{K}:\mathcal{F}) = R(\mathcal{K}:\mathcal{K} \cap \mathcal{F}^{\#})$ (14.24). Hence $\mathcal{B} = \mathcal{K} \cap \mathcal{F}^{\#}$ is the required T-subalgebra of $\mathcal{A}$.

15.4 <u>PROPOSITION</u>. (Furstenberg) Let $\mathcal{F}, \mathcal{A}$ be T-subalgebras of $\mathfrak{A}(u)$ such that $\mathcal{F} \leq \mathcal{A}$ and $\mathcal{A}$ is quasi-separable. Then there exists an ordinal ν and a family of T-subalgebras $(\mathcal{F}_\mu \mid 0 \leq \mu \leq \nu)$ such that:

1. $\mathcal{F}_o = \mathcal{F}$, and $\mathcal{F}_\nu = \mathcal{A}$.
2. $\mathcal{F}_\mu \leq_p \mathcal{F}_{\mu+1}$, $\mathcal{F}_\mu \neq \mathcal{F}_{\mu+1}$ $(0 \leq \mu < \nu)$
3. $\mathcal{F}_\mu = \overline{\cup\{\mathcal{F}_\eta \mid \eta < \mu\}}$ for all limit ordinals $\mu \leq \nu$.

<u>PROOF</u>. Set $\mathcal{F}_o = \mathcal{F}$ and assume $\mathcal{F}_\mu$ defined for all ordinals $\mu < \zeta$ satisfying 2 and 3 with ν replaced by ζ.

If ζ is a limit ordinal set $\mathcal{F}_\zeta = \overline{\cup\{\mathcal{F}_\mu \mid \mu < \zeta\}}$.

If $\zeta = \eta + 1$ and $\mathcal{F}_\eta \neq \mathcal{A}$, then by 15.3 there exists $\mathcal{F}_\zeta \subset \mathcal{A}$ with $\mathcal{F}_\eta \leq_p \mathcal{F}_\zeta$, $\mathcal{F}_\eta \neq \mathcal{F}_\zeta$. If $\mathcal{F}_\eta = \mathcal{A}$, set $\nu = \eta$ and stop the induction.

Since $\mathcal{F}_\mu \neq \mathcal{F}_{\mu+1}$ the process must ultimately produce $\mathcal{F}_\nu = \mathcal{A}$.

15.1 REMARKS. 1. An equivalent statement of 15.4 is: let (X,T) be a minimal set and $\mathfrak{M}$ a collection of minimal sets which contains (X,T) and is closed under the formation of inverse limits and almost periodic extensions. Then $\mathfrak{M}$ contains all the quasi-separable distal extensions of (X,T).

2. The family $(\mathcal{F}_\mu \mid \mu \leq \nu)$ of 15.4 is of course in general not unique. However one may specify a family satisfying 15.4 in a natural way if one takes the maximum possible almost periodic extension at each stage. Thus set $\mathcal{A}_o = \mathcal{F}$ and $\mathcal{A}_{\mu+1} = \mathcal{A} \cap \mathcal{A}_\mu^\#$ if $\mathcal{A}_\mu \neq \mathcal{A}$. (If γ is a limit ordinal set $\mathcal{A}_\gamma = \overline{\cup \{\mathcal{A}_\mu \mid \mu < \gamma\}}$.

This will produce a family $(\mathcal{A}_\mu \mid \mu \leq \zeta)$ with the properties required in 15.4 such that the ordinal ζ is the smallest possible. This ordinal might well be called the <u>degree of $\mathcal{A}$ over $\mathcal{F}$</u>.

The maximal algebras $\mathcal{A}_\mu$ may also be described in terms of the subgroups of $F = \mathcal{g}(\mathcal{F})$. Thus set $B_o = F$, $B_{\mu+1} = H(B_\mu, \mathcal{A})$ and $B_\eta = \bigcap_{\gamma<\eta} B_\gamma$ for limit ordinals η. Then I claim that B_μ is a τ-closed subgroup of F and that $\mathcal{A}_\mu = \mathfrak{A}(B_\mu) \cap \mathcal{A}$ $(\mu \leq \zeta)$.

To see this suppose B_μ is a closed subgroup of F and $\mathcal{A}_\mu = \mathfrak{A}(B_\mu) \cap \mathcal{A}$ for some ordinal $\mu < \zeta$. Then $\mathcal{g}(\mathcal{A}_{\mu+1}) =$

$\mathfrak{g}(\mathfrak{a} \cap \mathfrak{a}_\mu^\#) = AA_\mu^\# = H(A_\mu, \mathfrak{a})$ by 14.15 (where $A_\mu = \mathfrak{g}(\mathfrak{a}_\mu)$ and $A_\mu^\# = \mathfrak{g}(\mathfrak{a}_\mu^\#)$). By 13.23 $\mathfrak{g}(\mathfrak{a}_\mu) = B_\mu$. Thus $B_{\mu+1} = H(B_\mu, \mathfrak{a})$ is a closed subgroup of F. Also $\mathfrak{g}(\mathfrak{a}_{\mu+1}) = H(B_\mu, \mathfrak{a}) = B_{\mu+1} = \mathfrak{g}(\mathfrak{U}(B_{\mu+1}) \cap \mathfrak{a})$ whence $\mathfrak{a}_{\mu+1} = \mathfrak{U}(B_{\mu+1}) \cap \mathfrak{a}$ by 13.23.

Now suppose μ is a limit ordinal $\leq \zeta$ and let B_η be a closed subgroup of F and $\mathfrak{a}_\eta = \mathfrak{U}(B_\eta) \cap \mathfrak{a}$ for all ordinals $\eta < \mu$. Then $B_\mu = \cap B_\eta$ is a closed subgroup of F and $\mathfrak{g}(\mathfrak{a}_\mu) = \mathfrak{g}(\overline{\cup \{\mathfrak{a}_\eta | \eta < \mu\}}) = \cap \mathfrak{g}(\mathfrak{a}_\eta)$ (3 of 11.4) $= \cap B_\eta = B_\mu = \mathfrak{g}(\mathfrak{U}(B_\mu) \cap \mathfrak{a})$ whence again $\mathfrak{a}_\mu = \mathfrak{U}(B_\mu) \cap \mathfrak{a}$.

Finally, since $\mathfrak{a}_0 = \mathfrak{F} = \mathfrak{U}(F) \cap \mathfrak{a}$ (13.21) $= \mathfrak{U}(B_0) \cap \mathfrak{a}$, the proof is completed.

I would now like to apply the results of chapter 14 to the case $\mathfrak{F} = \mathbf{C}$.

Henceforth $\mathfrak{D}$ will denote the set of distal functions and $\mathfrak{E}$ those elements of $\mathfrak{D}$ which are almost periodic over $\mathbf{C}$. Thus $\mathfrak{D} = \mathbf{C}^*$ and $\mathfrak{E} = \mathbf{C}^\#$. The groups of $\mathfrak{D}$ and $\mathfrak{E}$ will be denoted D and E respectively. Since $\mathfrak{g}(\mathbf{C}) = G$, D and E are normal subgroups of G and $E = H(G, \mathfrak{D}) = H(G, \mathfrak{E})$ by 14.14.

15.6 <u>PROPOSITION</u>. 1. The map $\psi: T \to G/E$ such that $\psi(t) = Eutu$ is a homomorphism onto a dense subgroup of $(G/E, \tau(\mathfrak{D}))$.

2. The map $\varphi: (G/E, \tau(\mathfrak{D})) \to |\mathfrak{E}|$ such that $\varphi(E\alpha) = \alpha|\mathfrak{E}$ $(\alpha \in G)$ is a homeomorphism onto such that $\varphi(E\alpha utu) = \varphi(E\alpha)t$. Thus if T is allowed to act on G/E via the map $(E\alpha, t) \to E\alpha utu = E\alpha\psi(t)$, φ becomes a transformation group isomorphism.

<u>PROOF</u>. 1. First observe that since $\mathfrak{E} \subset \mathfrak{D}$, $v = u$ on $\mathfrak{E}$ for every idempotent v in M.

Now let $t,s \in T$. Then there exists an idempotent v in M with $utv = ut$ (3.6). Since $\mathcal{E}\alpha \subset \mathcal{E}$ $(\alpha \in G)$ (1 of 14.4), $(utu)(usu) = (utu)(vsu)$ on $\mathcal{E}$ ($v = u$ on $\mathcal{E}$). Hence $(utu)(usu) = utvsu = utsu$ on $\mathcal{E}$, i.e. $Eutu \cdot Eusu = Eutsu$. Thus $\psi(ts) = \psi(t)\psi(s)$.

To see that $\psi(T)$ is dense, let $\alpha \in G$ and $t_n)$ a net in T with $t_n \to \alpha$. Then $ut_n \to u\alpha = \alpha$ and $ut_n u \to \alpha$ with respect to $\tau(\mathcal{D})$ (11.15).

2. Let π: $(G/E,\tau(\mathcal{D})) \times |\mathcal{E}| \to |\mathcal{E}|$ be such that $\pi(E\alpha,x) = \alpha x$ $(\alpha \in G,\ x \in |\mathcal{E}|)$. Then π is continuous by 14.11. Since $\varphi(E\alpha) = \pi(E\alpha,u|\mathcal{E})$, φ is continuous.

Now $\varphi(E\alpha utu) = \alpha tu|\mathcal{E} = \alpha t|\mathcal{E} = (\alpha|\mathcal{E})t = \varphi(E\alpha)t$. Hence φ is a transformation group homomorphism whence φ is onto since $(G/E,\tau(\mathcal{D}))$ is compact and $(|\mathcal{E}|,T)$ is minimal.

Let $\varphi(E\alpha) = \varphi(E\beta)$. Then $\alpha|\mathcal{E} = \beta|\mathcal{E}$ whence $\alpha\beta^{-1} \in E$ and $E\alpha = E\beta$. Thus φ is one-one and the proof is completed.

15.7 <u>PROPOSITION</u>. $\mathcal{E}$ is the set of almost periodic functions in $\mathcal{C}$; i.e. $f \in \mathcal{E}$ iff $\{tf \mid t \in T\}$ is a relatively compact subset of $\mathcal{C}$.

<u>PROOF</u>. By 15.6 $(|\mathcal{E}|,T)$ is equicontinuous since it is isomorphic with the compact topological group $(G/E,T)$ with T a dense subgroup of G/E. Hence if $f \in \mathcal{E}$, $\{tf \mid t \in T\}$ is relatively compact in $\mathcal{E} \subset \mathcal{C}$ by 4.15.

Now let $f \in \mathcal{C}$ with $\{tf \mid t \in T\}$ a relatively compact subset of $\mathcal{C}$. Then $|[f]|$ is equicontinuous and minimal by 4.15. Hence $fv = f$ for all idempotents v in M, and so $fu = f$. By 14.22, the equicontinuous structure relation on $[f]$ is $R([f],\mathcal{E} \cap [f])$. Hence $R([f],\mathcal{E} \cap [f])$ is the diagonal whence $[f] \subset \mathcal{E}$.

15.8 <u>PROPOSITION</u>. Let ψ: $T \to G/E$ be the map such that

$\psi(t) = Eutu$ ($t \in T$). Then $(\psi, G/E)$ is the Bohr compactification of the discrete group T when G/E is provided with the topology $\tau(\mathfrak{D})$. I.e., if K is a compact topological group and $\varphi: T \to K$ a homomorphism with dense image, then there exists a continuous homomorphism $\eta: G/E \to K$ with $\eta\psi = \varphi$.

PROOF. The maps ψ, φ provide G/E and K respectively with a transformation group structure, (e.g. $(x,t) \to x\varphi(t)$ ($x \in K$, $t \in T$)).

Then (G/E,T) and (K,T) are minimal equicontinuous and $(G/E,T) \cong (|\mathcal{E}|,T)$.

Let $F: (\beta T,e) \rightrightarrows (K,e)$ and $\mathfrak{a} = \mathrm{im}F^*$. Then $\mathfrak{a} \subset \mathcal{E}$ by 15.7. The restriction mapping of $|\mathcal{E}|$ onto $|\mathfrak{a}|$ determines a transformation group homomorphism $\eta: (G/E,T) \rightrightarrows (K,T)$. Then $\eta(\psi(t)) = \eta(e\cdot\psi(t)) = \eta(e)\varphi(t) = \varphi(t)$ ($t \in T$). From this it follows that η is a group homomorphism.

I would now like to compute the structure group of a given minimal set $\mathfrak{a}$. To this end let me introduce:

15.9 NOTATION. Let $\mathfrak{a}$ be a T-subalgebra of $\mathfrak{U}(u)$. Then $\Gamma(\mathfrak{a})$ will denote the structure group of $\mathfrak{a}$.

Recall that $r(\mathfrak{a})$ denotes the regularizer, $[\mathfrak{a}\alpha \mid \alpha \in G]$ of $\mathfrak{a}$. If B is a subgroup of G, r(B) will denote $\cap \{\alpha B\alpha^{-1} \mid \alpha \in G\}$.

15.10 PROPOSITION. Let $\mathfrak{a}$ be a T-subalgebra of $\mathfrak{U}(u)$. Then $\Gamma(\mathfrak{a}) \cong G/r(AE)$ where $A = \mathfrak{g}(\mathfrak{a})$ and G/r(AE) is provided with the topology $\tau(\mathfrak{D})$.

PROOF. By 14.22 $R(\mathfrak{a}:\mathfrak{a} \cap \mathcal{E})$ is the equicontinuous structure relation on $\mathfrak{a}$. Hence $\Gamma(\mathfrak{a})$ is the enveloping semigroup $E(\mathfrak{a} \cap \mathcal{E})$ of $\mathfrak{a} \cap \mathcal{E}$ (3 of 4.19). Since $E(\mathfrak{a} \cap \mathcal{E})$ is a group it is minimal, whence $E(\mathfrak{a} \cap \mathcal{E}) = r(\mathfrak{a} \cap \mathcal{E})$ (11.21).

Since $r(\mathcal{A} \cap \mathcal{B}) \subset \mathcal{B}$, 15.6 implies that $\varphi: (G/E, \tau(\mathcal{D})) \to |r(\mathcal{A} \cap \mathcal{B})|$ such that $\varphi(E\alpha) = \alpha|r(\mathcal{A} \cap \mathcal{B})$ $(\alpha \in G)$ is a transformation group homomorphism onto. Hence φ is a topological group epimorphism. Since kernel of $\varphi =$ $\mathfrak{g}(r(\mathcal{A} \cap \mathcal{B})) = r\mathfrak{g}(\mathcal{A} \cap \mathcal{B}) = r(AE)$ (3 of 11.20, 14.16), the proof is completed.

Proposition 14.23 gives a characterization of the equicontinuous structure relation. However, in order to apply it to a T-subalgebra $\mathcal{A}$ of $\mathfrak{U}(u)$ we must verify that $E \subset \{\alpha \mid (\alpha|\mathcal{A}, u|\mathcal{A}) \in Q(\mathcal{A})\}$. By 14.18 it suffices to show that $E \subset H(G,\mathcal{A})$. When T is abelian this presents no problem, because in that case $E = H(G,\mathfrak{U}(u))$ so that $E \subset H(G,\mathcal{A})$ for all $\mathcal{A}$.

Let me now prove:

15.11 <u>LEMMA</u>. If T is abelian, then $H(G,\mathfrak{U}(u)) = E$.

<u>PROOF</u>. Let $H = H(G,\mathfrak{U}(u))$ and $\varphi: T \to G/H$ such that $\varphi(t) = Hutu = Ht$. Then φ is a homomorphism onto a dense subset of the topological group $(G/H,\tau)$ (14.5 and see the proof of 1 of 15.6). Hence by 15.8 there exists a continuous homomorphism $\eta: (G/E,\tau(\mathcal{D})) \to (G/H,T)$ such that $\eta(Et) = Ht$ $(t \in T)$.

Let $\alpha \in E$ and (ut_n) a net such that $ut_n \to \alpha$ in βT. Then $Et_n \to E\alpha$ $(\tau(\mathcal{A}))$ and $Ht_n \to H\alpha(\tau)$. Thus $H\alpha = \lim Ht_n =$ $\lim \eta(Et_n) = \eta(\lim Et_n) = \eta(E\alpha) = \eta(E) = H$, whence $\alpha \in H$. Hence $E \subset H$. That $H \subset E$ follows from the facts that $\mathcal{D} \subset \mathfrak{U}(u)$ and $E = H(G,\mathcal{D})$.

The above argument fails when T is not abelian because then the map φ need not be a homomorphism. Let me now consider the general case.

The proof of the following purely topological lemma

is straightforward and will be omitted.

15.12 LEMMA. Let X,Y be compact T_2 spaces, let A be a dense subset of X and f: X → Y such that $f(\lim a_n) = \lim f(a_n)$ for every net (a_n) on A convergent in X. Then f is continuous.

15.13 PROPOSITION. Let $\mathcal{K} = \{f \mid ft \in \mathfrak{A}(u), (t \in T)\}$. Then $\mathcal{K}$ is a T-subalgebra of $\mathfrak{A}(u)$ and $E = H(G,\mathcal{K})$.

PROOF. It is clear that $\mathcal{K}$ is a T-subalgebra of $\mathfrak{A}(u)$ with $\mathfrak{D} \subset \mathcal{K}$. Hence $H(G,\mathcal{K}) \subset E$.

Let $K = \mathfrak{g}(\mathcal{K})$ and $H = H(G,\mathfrak{A}(u))$. Then $HK = KH$ is a τ-closed subgroup of G and $(G/HK,\tau)$ is a compact T_2 space (14.8).

Let $\psi: |\mathcal{K}| \to (G/HK,\tau)$ be the map such that $\psi(p|\mathcal{K}) = HKpu$ $(p \in M)$. Then ψ is well defined because if $p|\mathcal{K} = q|\mathcal{K}$, $pu|\mathcal{K} = qu|\mathcal{K}$ whence $HKpu = HKqu$.

Now let (α_n) be a net in G with $\alpha_n \to p$ in M, and $\alpha_n \to \alpha(\tau)$. Then $\alpha_n \to pu(\tau)$ (11.15), whence $(pu)\alpha^{-1} \in H$. Thus $\alpha_n \to p$ implies that $\psi(\alpha_n|\mathcal{K}) \to \psi(p|\mathcal{K})$.

Let $p \in M$, $ut_n \to p$. Then $ut_nu|\mathcal{K} = ut_n|\mathcal{K} \to p|\mathcal{K}$. Thus the set $\{\alpha|\mathcal{K} \mid \alpha \in G\}$ is dense in $|\mathcal{K}|$ so that ψ is continuous by 15.12.

Since G/HK is a quotient of the compact topological group G/H, $\{\alpha f \mid \alpha \in G\}$ is a relatively compact subset of $\mathcal{C}(G/HK)$ where $f \in \mathcal{C}(G/HK)$ and $\langle\alpha f, HK\beta\rangle = \langle f, HK\beta\alpha\rangle$ $(\alpha,\beta \in G)$. Hence $\{\psi^*(\alpha f) \mid \alpha \in G\}$ is a relatively compact subset of $\mathcal{K} = \mathcal{C}(|\mathcal{K}|)$.

Set $g = \psi^*(f)$ and let me compute tg for $t \in T$. Let $s \in T$, then $\langle tg, us\rangle = \langle g, ust\rangle = \langle f, \psi(ust)\rangle = \langle f, HKustu\rangle$. Now $hustu = husuutu$ $(h \in \mathcal{K})$ whence $Kustu = Kusuutu$ and

$\langle tg,us\rangle = \langle f,HKusuutu\rangle = \langle utuf,\psi(us)\rangle = \langle\psi^*(utuf),us\rangle$. Since $\{us \mid s \in T\}$ is dense in $|\mathcal{K}|$, $tg = \psi^*(utuf)$. Hence $\{tg \mid t \in T\}$ is a relatively compact subset of $\mathcal{K}$ and so $g \in \mathcal{S}$.

Now suppose $\alpha \notin HK$. Then there exists $f \in \mathcal{C}(G/HK)$ such that $\langle f,HK\alpha\rangle \neq \langle f,HK\rangle$. If $g = \psi^*(f)$, then $\langle g,\alpha\rangle = \langle f,HK\alpha\rangle \neq \langle f,HK\rangle = \langle g,u\rangle$. Hence $g\alpha \neq g$ and so $\alpha \notin E$ because $g \in \mathcal{S}$.

Thus $E \subset HK = KH$. Since $\mathcal{K} \subset \mathfrak{U}(u)$, $H \subset H(G,\mathcal{K})$ and $KH \subset KH(G,\mathcal{K}) = H(G,\mathcal{K})$ by 2 of 14.10. The proof is completed.

15.14 <u>REMARKS</u>. 1. If $\mathcal{A}$ is a T-subalgebra of $\mathcal{K}$ then $E \subset H(G,\mathcal{A})$ and so $R(\mathcal{A}:\mathcal{A} \cap \mathcal{S}) = \{x,y) \mid (xv,yv) \in Q(\mathcal{A})$ for all minimal idempotents $v\}$.

2. Let $\mathcal{L} = \{f \mid fw = f \quad (w \in J)\}$ where J is the set of idempotents in M. Then $\mathcal{L} \subset \mathcal{K}$. To see this, first observe that if η is an idempotent with $\eta w = \eta$ and $w\eta = w$ for some $w \in J$, then $f\eta = f \quad (f \in \mathcal{L})$. Now let $t \in T$. Then tut^{-1} is just such an idempotent. Hence $ftut^{-1} = f$ and so $futu = ftu = ft = fut \quad (f \in \mathcal{L})$. Then $\mathcal{L} \subset \mathcal{K}$.

15.15 <u>PROPOSITION</u>. Let $\mathcal{A}$ be a T-subalgebra of $\mathcal{K}$. Then:

1. $\Gamma(\mathcal{A}) = e$ iff $Q(\mathcal{A}) = |\mathcal{A}| \times |\mathcal{A}|$.

2. If T is abelian (note in this case $\mathcal{K} = \mathfrak{U}(u)$) then $\Gamma(\mathcal{A}) = e$ iff $\overline{VT} = |\mathcal{A}| \times |\mathcal{A}|$ for all open subsets V of $|\mathcal{A}| \times |\mathcal{A}|$. (A transformation group satisfying this latter condition is called <u>weakly mixing</u>.)

<u>PROOF</u>. 1. Clearly if $Q(\mathcal{A}) = |\mathcal{A}| \times |\mathcal{A}|$ then $\Gamma(\mathcal{A}) = e$.

Now suppose $\Gamma(\mathcal{A}) = e$. Since $\mathcal{A} \subset \mathcal{K}$, $utu|\mathcal{A} = ut|\mathcal{A}$ $(t \in T)$. Hence $(ut|\mathcal{A},us|\mathcal{A})$ is an almost periodic point of $|\mathcal{A}| \times |\mathcal{A}|$ $(t,s \in T)$. Thus the almost periodic points of

$R(\mathcal{Q}:\mathcal{Q} \cap \mathcal{S}) = R(\mathcal{Q}:\mathbb{C}) = |\mathcal{Q}| \times |\mathcal{Q}|$ are dense in $R(\mathcal{Q}:\mathcal{Q} \cap \mathcal{S})$ and so $Q(\mathcal{Q}) = R(\mathcal{Q}:\mathcal{Q} \cap \mathcal{S}) = |\mathcal{Q}| \times |\mathcal{Q}|$ by 14.23.

2. In general if $\overline{VT} = |\mathcal{Q}| \times |\mathcal{Q}|$ for all open subsets of $|\mathcal{Q}| \times |\mathcal{Q}|$ then $Q(\mathcal{Q}) = |\mathcal{Q}| \times |\mathcal{Q}|$ and $\Gamma(\mathcal{Q}) = e$ by 1.

Now suppose T is abelian and $\Gamma(\mathcal{Q}) = e$. Let V be open in $|\mathcal{Q}| \times |\mathcal{Q}|$. Then there exist $t,s \in T$ such that $\Delta \cap V(t,s) \neq \emptyset$ because $\overline{(e,e)T \times T} = |\mathcal{Q}| \times |\mathcal{Q}|$, where $V(t,s) = \{(xt,ys) \mid (x,y) \in V\}$. Then $V(t,s)T = VT(t,s)$ is an open neighborhood of the diagonal, Δ and is therefore dense since $Q(\mathcal{Q}) = |\mathcal{Q}| \times |\mathcal{Q}|$. Consequently $VT = VT(t,s)(t^{-1},s^{-1})$ is also dense.

NOTES

1. Harry Furstenberg, <u>The Structure of Distal Flows</u>, Amer. J. of Math, vol 85 (1963), 477 515

In the above paper the author proves 15.4 for the case $\mathcal{F} = \mathbb{C}$ and $|\mathfrak{A}|$ metrizable. Also the flows $|\mathcal{F}_\nu|$ produced are such that $|\mathcal{F}_{\nu+1}|$ is an isometric extension of $|\mathcal{F}_\nu|$. Let me now say a few words about the relation between almost periodic and isometric extensions.

1.1 <u>DEFINITION</u>. Let $\mathfrak{A},\mathfrak{B}$ be T-subalgebras of $\mathfrak{U}(u)$ with $\mathfrak{A} \subset \mathfrak{B}$, and let $\varphi: |\mathfrak{B}| \to |\mathfrak{A}|$ be the restriction mapping. Then $\mathfrak{B}$ is an <u>isometric extension</u> of $\mathfrak{A}$ if there exists $\sigma: R(\mathfrak{B}:\mathfrak{A}) \to \mathbb{R}$ such that σ is continuous, $\sigma(xt,yt) = \sigma(x,y)$ $((x,y) \in R(\mathfrak{B}:\mathfrak{A}),\ t \in T)$, and σ restricted to $\varphi^{-1}\varphi(x)$ is a metric $(x \in |\mathfrak{B}|)$.

1.2 <u>PROPOSITION</u>. Let $\mathfrak{A},\mathfrak{B}$ be T-subalgebras of $\mathfrak{U}(u)$ such that $\mathfrak{A} \subset \mathfrak{B}$ and $|\mathfrak{B}|$ is metrizable. Then $\mathfrak{B}$ is an isometric extension of $\mathfrak{A}$ iff $\mathfrak{B}$ is an almost periodic extension of $\mathfrak{A}$.

<u>PROOF</u>. Let $\mathfrak{B}$ be an isometric extension of $\mathfrak{A}$ and let σ be as in 1.1. Let $(x,y) \in Q(\mathfrak{B}:\mathfrak{A})$. There exist sequences $(x_n)(y_n)$ in $|\mathfrak{B}|$ and (t_n) in T such that $x_n \to x$, $y_n \to y$. $\lim x_n t_n = \lim y_n t_n$, and $(x_n,y_n) \in R(\mathfrak{B}:\mathfrak{A})$ for all n. Then $\sigma(x,y) = \lim \sigma(x_n,y_n) = \lim \sigma(x_n t_n, y_n t_n) = 0$, whence $x = y$. Thus $Q(\mathfrak{B}:\mathfrak{A})$ is the diagonal, from which it follows that $\mathfrak{B}$ is an almost periodic extension of $\mathfrak{A}$ (14.21).

Now assume $\mathfrak{B}$ is an almost periodic extension of $\mathfrak{A}$. Let $A = \mathfrak{g}(\mathfrak{A})$, $B = \mathfrak{g}(\mathfrak{B})$ and $\psi: R(\mathfrak{B}:\mathfrak{A}) \to (A/B, \tau(\mathfrak{B}))$ such that $\psi(x,y) = B\alpha((x,y) \in R(\mathfrak{B}:\mathfrak{A}))$ where $\alpha \in A$ and $y = \alpha x$. Then ψ

is a well defined, continuous, and bijective when restricted to $x \times \varphi^{-1}\varphi(x)$ $(x \in |\mathcal{B}|)$ where $\varphi: |\mathcal{B}| \to |\mathcal{A}|$ is the restriction map. Thus $(A/B, \tau(\mathcal{B}))$ is metrizable. Let d be a metric on A/B.

Let $\mathcal{S} = [\mathcal{B}\alpha \mid \alpha \in A]$ and $S = \mathfrak{g}(\mathcal{S})$. Then A/B is a homeogeneous space of the topological group $(A/S, \tau(\mathcal{S}))$. Hence $\rho(B\alpha, B\beta) = \sup_{\gamma \in A} d(B\alpha\gamma, B\beta\gamma)$ is a metric on A/B with $\rho(B\alpha\gamma, B\beta\gamma) = \rho(B\alpha, B\beta)$ $(\gamma \in A)$. Now set $\sigma(x,y) = \rho(B, \psi(x,y))$ $((x,y) \in R(\mathcal{B}:\mathcal{A}))$. Then σ is the required map.

2. PROPOSITION. Let $\mathcal{A}$ be a T-subalgebra of $\mathbb{C}$. Then $\mathcal{A}$ is quasi-separable iff $|\mathcal{A}|$ is the inverse limit of metrizable transformation groups. (See Harvey Keynes, The structure of weakly mixing minimal transformation groups, to appear.)

PROOF. Let $|\mathcal{A}| = \varprojlim (|\mathcal{A}_i| \mid i \in I)$ with $|\mathcal{A}_i|$ metrizable. Then $\mathcal{A}_i$ is separable $(i \in I)$ and since $\mathcal{A}$ is generated by $\{\cup \mathcal{A}_i \mid i \in I\}$, $\mathcal{A}$ is quasi-separable.

On the other hand let $\mathcal{A}$ be quasi-separable. Let $\mathcal{N} = \{f \mid f \in \mathcal{A}, [f] \text{ is metrizable}\}$. Then $|\mathcal{A}| = \varprojlim ([F] \mid F$ finite subset of $\mathcal{N})$.

3. Let $\mathcal{A}$ be a T-subalgebra of $\mathcal{K}$. Then in order to prove that $\Gamma(\mathcal{A}) \neq e$ it suffices to show that $H(G,\mathcal{A}) \neq G$ (1 of 15.14). One method for doing this is to produce a nonconstant function on G to $\mathbb{C}$ with sufficient continuity properties with respect to $\tau(\mathcal{A})$ to guarantee that $H(G,\mathcal{A}) \neq G$. Let $|\mathcal{A}|$ be metrizable with metric d. Then often $\sigma(x,y) = \inf \{d(xt,yt) \mid t \in T\}$ gives rise to such a function.

3.1 LEMMA.

1. $\sigma(x,y) = \inf \{d(xp,yp) \mid p \in \beta T\}$.

2. $\sigma(x,y) = d(xp,yp)$ for some $p \in \beta T$.

3. $d(xq,yq) \geq \sigma(x,y) \quad (q \in \beta T)$.

4. $\sigma(xp,yp) \geq \sigma(x,y) \quad (p \in \beta T)$.

PROOF. 1, 2, and 3 follow immediately from the definition of σ and the fact that left multiplication is continuous on βT.

4. By 2 $\sigma(xp,yp) = d(xpr,ypr)$ for some $r \in \beta T$. Hence $\sigma(xp,yp) \geq \sigma(x,y)$ by 3.

3.2 PROPOSITION. Let $a \in \mathbb{R}$ and $K = \{\alpha \mid \alpha \in G, \sigma(u|\mathfrak{A}, \alpha|\mathfrak{A}) \geq a\}$. Then K is a $\tau(\mathfrak{A})$-closed subset of G.

PROOF. Let $\alpha \notin K$, $x = u|\mathfrak{A}$ and $y = \alpha|\mathfrak{A}$. Then $\sigma(x,y) < a$ and so there exists $t \in T$ with $d(xt,yt) < a$. Hence there exists $\mathfrak{A}$-neighborhoods $h(N)$ of u and $h(U)$ of α such that $d(pt|\mathfrak{A}, qt|\mathfrak{A}) < a \quad (p \in h(N),\ q \in h(U))$. Let $\beta \in (U,N)$. Then there exists $s \in N$ with $U \in \beta s$. Since $s|\mathfrak{A} = us|\mathfrak{A}$, $d(ust|\mathfrak{A}, \beta st|\mathfrak{A}) < a$ and so $\sigma(u|\mathfrak{A}, \beta|\mathfrak{A}) < a$. Thus (U,N) is a $\tau(\mathfrak{A})$-neighborhood of α contained in K'. The proof is completed.

Proposition 3.2 shows that the map $\alpha \to \sigma(u|\mathfrak{A}, \alpha|\mathfrak{A}) : (G, \tau(\mathfrak{A})) \to \mathbb{C}$ is upper-semicontinuous.

In a recent paper on "Point-Distal Flows", Veech shows that under certain conditions a point-distal transformation group has a non-trival equicontinuous factor. Let me indicate how this follows from 3.2.

The transformation group $|\mathfrak{A}|$ is point distal if $\mathfrak{A} \subset \mathfrak{U}(u)$ and $(x, u|\mathfrak{A}) \in P(\mathfrak{A})$ implies $x = u|\mathfrak{A}$ $(x \in |\mathfrak{A}|)$.

3.3 PROPOSITION. Let $\mathfrak{A}$ be a metrizable point distal T-subalgebra of $\mathfrak{U}(u)$. Then $\Gamma(\mathfrak{A}) \neq e$.

PROOF. Let $v^2 = v \in M$. Then $(v|\mathfrak{A}, u|\mathfrak{A}) \in P(\mathfrak{A})$

implies that $v|\mathcal{A} = u|\mathcal{A}$. Thus $\mathcal{A} \subset \mathcal{L} \subset \mathcal{K}$ and it suffices to show that $H(G,\mathcal{A}) \neq G$.

Set $\sigma(x,y) = \inf \{d(xt,yt) \mid t \in T\}$ $(x,y \in |\mathcal{A}|)$ where d is a metric on $|\mathcal{A}|$. Let $b = u|\mathcal{A}$. Since the map $x \to \sigma(b,x): |\mathcal{A}| \to \mathbb{C}$ is upper-semicontinuous there exists $x \in |\mathcal{A}|$ with $x \neq b$ at which it is continuous. Since $d(b,x) \neq 0$ and b is a distal point $\sigma(b,x) \neq 0$ and therefore there exists $a > 0$ such that $\operatorname{int} L \neq \emptyset$, where $L = \{y \mid \sigma(b,y) > 2a\}$. Hence there exists a finite subset F of T with $|\mathcal{A}| = LF$. Let $\alpha \in G$. Then $\alpha|\mathcal{A} = yt$ for some $y \in L$, $t \in F$. Let $p \in M$ with $p|\mathcal{A} = y$. Then $\sigma(u|\mathcal{A}, pu|\mathcal{A}) = \sigma(b,yu) = \sigma(bu,yu) \geq \sigma(b,y) > 2a$ by 4 of 3.1. Hence $pu \in K = \{\beta \mid \beta \in G, \sigma(u|\mathcal{A}, \beta|\mathcal{A}) \geq a\}$.

Now $\alpha|\mathcal{A} = yt$ implies that $\alpha t^{-1}|\mathcal{A} = y$ whence $\alpha u t^{-1} u|\mathcal{A} = \alpha t^{-1} u|\mathcal{A} = yu|\mathcal{A} = pu|\mathcal{A}$. Thus $\alpha \in AKS$ where S is the finite set $\{(ut^{-1}u)^{-1} \mid t \in F\}$. Since $\sigma(u|\mathcal{A}, \beta\alpha|\mathcal{A}) = \sigma(u|\mathcal{A}, \gamma|\mathcal{A})$ $(\beta \in A)$, $A \operatorname{int}_\tau K = \operatorname{int}_\tau K$ and $G \subset KS$.

By 3.2 K is $\tau(\mathcal{A})$-closed, hence τ-closed. Thus $\operatorname{int}_\tau K \neq \emptyset$ (since $G = KS$) and since u is an element of the open set K', $\operatorname{int}_\tau K \cap H(G,\tau) = \emptyset$. Then $H(G,\mathcal{A}) \cap \operatorname{int}_\tau K = AH(G,\tau) \cap \operatorname{int}_\tau K = H(G,\tau) \cap A(\operatorname{int}_\tau K) = H(G,\tau) \cap \operatorname{int}_\tau K = \emptyset$ shows that $H(G,\mathcal{A}) \neq G$.

4. I would now like to apply the Furstenberg structure theorem to prove the existence of an invariant measure μ on $|\mathcal{A}|$ for all minimal distal T-subalgebras $\mathcal{A}$.

4.1 <u>LEMMA</u>. Let $\mathcal{F}$ be a T-subalgebra of $\mathfrak{A}(u)$ and let $P: \mathcal{F}^\# \to \mathcal{F}^\#$ such that $\langle Pf,x\rangle = \int_{F/F^\#} \langle f,\hat{\alpha}x\rangle \, d\hat{\alpha}$, $\hat{\alpha} = F^\#\alpha$ $(f \in \mathcal{F}^\#, x \in |\mathcal{F}^\#|)$ where the integration is with respect to the Haar measure on $F/F^\#$. Then:

1. $P(\mathcal{F}^{\#}) = \mathcal{F}$, and $Pf = f \quad (f \in \mathcal{F})$.
2. P is linear.
3. $P(tf) = tP(f) \quad (t \in T,\ f \in \mathcal{F}^{\#})$.
4. $Pf \in \mathcal{F}_{\mathbb{R}}$ if $f \in \mathcal{F}^{\#}_{\mathbb{R}}$.
5. $Pf \geq 0$ if $f \geq 0$.

PROOF. Since the map $(\hat{\alpha},x) \to \alpha x\colon F/F^{\#} \times |\mathcal{F}^{\#}| \to |\mathcal{F}^{\#}|$ (14.11, 14.14) is continuous, Pf is continuous $(f \in \mathcal{F}^{\#})$ so that P is well defined.

1. Since the Haar measure is invariant $(Pf)\alpha = Pf$ $(f \in \mathcal{F}^{\#},\ \alpha \in F)$ whence $Pf \in \mathcal{F}$. On the other hand if $g \in \mathcal{F}$, $g\alpha = g$ $(\alpha \in F)$ whence $Pg = g$.

2, 3, 4, and 5 are immediate.

4.2 LEMMA. Let T be countable and let $\mathcal{A}$ be a distal T-subalgebra of $\mathfrak{U}(u)$. Then there exists an invariant Borel probability measure μ on $|\mathcal{A}|$.

PROOF. I shall show that there exists a positive linear functional $\mu\colon \mathcal{A}_{\mathbb{R}} \to \mathbb{R}$ such that $\mu(1) = 1$ and $\mu(tf) = \mu(f) \quad (f \in \mathcal{A}_{\mathbb{R}},\ t \in T)$.

Let $(\mathcal{A}_{\alpha} \mid \alpha \leq \gamma)$ be the family of T-subalgebras of $\mathfrak{U}(u)$ with $\mathcal{A}_{o} = \mathbb{C}$ and $\mathcal{A}_{\gamma} = \mathcal{A}$ guaranteed by 15.4.

Set $\mu_{o}(r) = r \quad (r \in \mathbb{R} = C_{\mathbb{R}})$ and assume μ_{α} defined and having the required properties for all $\alpha < \beta$ and in addition the property that $\mu_{\delta} = \mu_{\alpha} \mid (\mathcal{A}_{\delta})_{\mathbb{R}}$ if $\delta \leq \alpha < \beta$.

If $\beta = \alpha + 1$ for some α then $\mathcal{A}_{\beta}$ is an almost periodic extension of $\mathcal{A}_{\alpha}$. Hence $\mathcal{A}_{\beta} \subset \mathcal{A}^{\#}_{\alpha}$ and there exists a map $P\colon \mathcal{A}_{\beta} \to \mathcal{A}_{\alpha}$ as in 4.1. Now set $\mu_{\beta} = \mu_{\alpha} \circ P$. Then $\mu_{\delta} = \mu_{\beta} | (\mathcal{A}_{\delta})_{\mathbb{R}}$ $(\delta \leq \beta)$ and μ_{β} is an invariant measure on $|\mathcal{A}_{\beta}|$.

If β is a limit ordinal, then $\mathfrak{a}_\beta = \overline{\bigcup_{\alpha<\beta} \mathfrak{a}_\alpha}$. Then the "consistency" condition on the family $(\mu_\alpha \mid \alpha < \beta)$ allows one to define μ_β on $\bigcup \mathfrak{a}_\alpha$ and to extend it by continuity to $\mathfrak{a}_\beta$.

Thus the required measure is produced on $|\mathfrak{a}|$ by transfinite induction.

Now I remove the assumption that T be countable.

4.3 PROPOSITION. Let $\mathfrak{a}$ be a distal T-subalgebra of $\mathfrak{U}(u)$. Then there exists an invariant Borel probability measure on $|\mathfrak{a}|$.

PROOF. Let $x \in |\mathfrak{a}|$ and H a countable subgroup of T. Then $(\overline{xH}, H)$ is a distal minimal transformation group. Hence by 4.2 above there exists an H-invariant measure ν on $\overline{xH}$. For every closed subset B of $|\mathfrak{a}|$ set $w(B) = \nu(\overline{xH} \cap B)$. This defines an H-invariant measure on $|\mathfrak{a}|$ and consequently a positive linear functional w on $\mathfrak{a}_{\mathbb{R}}$ such that $w(1) = 1$ and $w(tf) = w(f) \quad (t \in H,\ f \in \mathfrak{a}_{\mathbb{R}})$.

Let $L = \{\rho \mid \rho$ is a positive linear functional on $\mathfrak{a}_{\mathbb{R}}$ with $\rho(1) = 1\}$ and topologize L with the weak-star topology i.e. the smallest topology making the maps $\rho \to \rho(f): L \to \mathbb{R}$ continuous $(f \in \mathfrak{a}_{\mathbb{R}})$.

Then L is compact and $L(H) = \{\rho \mid \rho \in L,\ \rho(tf) = \rho(f)$ $(t \in H,\ f \in \mathfrak{a}_{\mathbb{R}})\}$ is a closed non-vacuous subset of L for every countable subgroup H of T.

Now the set $\{L(H) \mid H$ countable subgroup of $T\}$ has the finite intersection property whence there exists $\mu \in \bigcap L(H)$. Then μ is the required measure.

One might now try to prove 15.4 without the assumption of quasi-separability by using the measure μ produced above.

CHAPTER 16

THE FOURIER ANALYSIS OF ALMOST PERIODIC EXTENSIONS

In this chapter, $\mathfrak{F}, \mathfrak{G}$ will denote fixed T-subalgebras of $\mathfrak{A}(u)$ such that $\mathfrak{G}$ is an almost periodic extension of $\mathfrak{F}$ with $A \lhd F$ where $A = \mathfrak{g}(\mathfrak{G})$ and $F = \mathfrak{g}(\mathfrak{F})$. The compact topological group $(F/A, \tau(\mathfrak{F}^*))$ will be denoted by H.

The assumption that $A \lhd F$ is made in order to simplify the exposition and is not essential. Since $F^{\#} \lhd F$ all the operators defined in this chapter could be defined on all of $\mathfrak{F}^{\#}$ and then restricted to the T-subalgebra under consideration. Moreover, the most important operators considered (those obtained from the irreducible representations of H) have the property that they map every T-subalgebra $\mathfrak{S}$ with $\mathfrak{F} \subset \mathfrak{S} \subset \mathfrak{F}^{\#}$ into itself (see 16.5).

In the case $\mathfrak{F} = \mathbf{C}$, $\mathfrak{G}$ consists of almost periodic functions (15.7) and classical Fourier analysis is applicable. This suggests the problem of extending the theory to arbitrary $\mathfrak{F}$. The present chapter is devoted to an exposition of Knapp's work on this problem [1].

Since $A \lhd F$, $\mathfrak{G}F \subset \mathfrak{G}$ whence $\mu x \in |\mathfrak{G}|$ $(\mu \in F,\ x \in |\mathfrak{G}|)$. This induces an action of H on $|\mathfrak{G}|$ which makes $(H, |\mathfrak{G}|, T)$ a bitransformation group with $(|\mathcal{G}|/H,T) \cong (|\mathcal{F}|,T)$ (12.12).

16.1 NOTATION AND DEFINITION. In chapter 16 and 17 $B(H)$ will denote the set of bounded Borel functions on H and $K(H)$ those elements of $B(H)$ which are constant on conjugacy classes of H (i.e. $\varphi(hjh^{-1}) = \varphi(j)$ $(h,j \in H, \varphi \in K(H))$).

Let $\varphi \in B(H)$ and $f \in \mathcal{G}$. Then $L_\varphi f$ is the map of $|\mathcal{G}|$ into C such that $\langle L_\varphi f,x\rangle = \int_H \varphi(h^{-1}) \langle f,hx\rangle dh$ $(x \in |\mathcal{G}|)$ where the integration is with respect to the Haar measure on H.

16.2 REMARKS. Let $\varphi \in B(H)$. Then:

1. It is immediate that $L_\varphi f$ is continuous $(f \in \mathcal{G})$. Hence L_φ maps $\mathcal{G}$ into $\mathcal{G}$.

2. L_φ is linear and $L_\varphi(tg) = tL_\varphi(g)$ $(t \in T, g \in \mathcal{G})$. Indeed $L_\varphi(fg) = fL_\varphi(g)$ $(f \in \mathcal{F}, g \in \mathcal{G})$, whence $L_\varphi(f) = L_\varphi(f\cdot 1) = fL_\varphi(1) = (\int_H \varphi dh)f$ $(f \in \mathcal{F})$.

16.3 DEFINITION. Let $\varphi,\psi \in B(H)$ and $h \in H$. Then:

(i) $(\varphi h)(j) = \varphi(hjh^{-1})$ $(j \in H)$.

(ii) $\varphi^*(j) = \overline{\varphi(j^{-1})}$ $(j \in H)$.

(iii) $\varphi*\psi(j) = \int\psi(k)\varphi(jk^{-1})dk$.

It is clear that φh, φ^*, and $\varphi*\psi$ are all in $B(H)$.

Thus $\varphi \in K(H)$ iff $\varphi h = \varphi$ $(h \in H)$.

16.4 PROPOSITION. Let $\varphi,\psi \in B(H)$ and $h \in H$. Then:

1. $L_{\varphi h}(fh) = (L_\varphi f)h$ $(f \in \mathcal{G})$.

2. $L_\varphi L_\psi = L_{\varphi*\psi}$.

PROOF. 1. Let $x \in |\mathcal{G}|$. Then $\langle (L_\varphi f)h,x\rangle = \langle L_\varphi f,hx\rangle = \int\varphi(k^{-1})\langle f,khx\rangle dk$. Now set $j = h^{-1}kh$. Then $\langle (L_\varphi f)h,x\rangle =$

$\int\varphi(hj^{-1}h^{-1})\langle f,hjx\rangle dj = \langle L_{\varphi h}(fh),x\rangle$ by the invariance of Haar measure.

2. Let $f \in \mathfrak{a}$ and $x \in |\mathfrak{a}|$. Then $\langle L_\varphi L_\psi f,x\rangle =$ $\int\varphi(h^{-1})\langle L_\psi f,hx\rangle dh = \int\varphi(h^{-1})(\int\psi(j^{-1})\langle f,jhx\rangle dj)dh = \int\varphi(h^{-1})$ $(\int\psi(hn^{-1})\langle f,nx\rangle dn)dh = \int\langle f,nx\rangle(\int\varphi(h^{-1})\psi(hn^{-1})dh)dn =$ $\int\langle f,nx\rangle(\int\varphi(n^{-1}r^{-1})\psi(r)dr)dn = \int(\varphi*\psi)(n^{-1})\langle f,nx\rangle dn =$ $\langle L_{\varphi*\psi}f,x\rangle$ (use $n = jh$ and $r = hn^{-1}$).

16.5 <u>COROLLARY</u>. Let $\mathfrak{S}$ be a T-subalgebra with $\mathfrak{F} \subset \mathfrak{S} \subset \mathfrak{a}$ and $\varphi \in B(H)$ such that $\varphi h = \varphi$ for all h of the form $A\nu(\nu \in \mathcal{G}(\mathfrak{S}))$. Then $L_\varphi(\mathfrak{S}) \subset \mathfrak{S}$. Thus $L_\varphi(\mathfrak{S}) \subset \mathfrak{S}$ $(\varphi \in K(H))$.

<u>PROOF</u>. Let $f \in \mathfrak{S}$, $\nu \in S = \mathfrak{g}(\mathfrak{S})$, and $h = A\nu$. Then $(L_\varphi f)\nu = (L_\varphi f)h = L_{\varphi h}(fh) = L_\varphi(f\nu) = L_\varphi f$. Thus $L_\varphi f \in \mathfrak{a} \cap \mathfrak{A}(S) =$ $\mathfrak{S}$ (13.21).

16.6 <u>COROLLARY</u>. Let $\varphi \in B(H)$ and $\psi \in K(H)$. Then:

1. $L_\varphi L_\psi = L_\psi L_\varphi$.
2. $L_\varphi(\text{im }\psi) \subset \text{im }\psi$.

<u>PROOF</u>. 1. Let $h \in H$. Then $\varphi*\psi(h) = \int\psi(j)\varphi(hj^{-1})dj =$ $\int\psi(k^{-1}h)\varphi(k)dk = \int\varphi(k)\psi(hk^{-1})dk = \psi*\varphi(h)$ (set $k = hj^{-1}$ and use the invariance of Haar measure and the fact that $\psi \in K(H)$).

Thus $\varphi*\psi = \psi*\varphi$ whence 1 follows from 2 of 16.4.

2 follows from 1.

16.7 <u>REMARKS</u>. 1. Let $r\colon |\mathfrak{a}| \to |\mathfrak{F}|$ be the restriction map, $b \in |\mathfrak{F}|$, and $f,g \in \mathfrak{a}$ with $\langle f,x\rangle = \langle g,x\rangle$ $(x \in r^{-1}(b))$. Then it is immediate from the definition that $\langle L_\varphi f,x\rangle =$ $\langle L_\varphi g,x\rangle$ $(x \in r^{-1}(b),\ \varphi \in B(H)$.

Thus if we set $\mathfrak{a}_b = \{f|r^{-1}(b) \mid f \in \mathfrak{a}\}$, then $\mathfrak{a}_b$ is a vector subspace of $\mathfrak{A}$ and L_φ induces a linear map of $\mathfrak{A}_b$ into $\mathfrak{A}_b$ $(\varphi \in B(H))$.

2. The most important operator from our point of view is L_1, the linear map corresponding to the function which is identically one. We have already encountered this map in 4.1 of the notes to chapter 15. Let me list some of its properties.

2.1. $L_1 g \in \mathcal{F}$ $(g \in \mathfrak{A})$ and $L_1 f = f$ $(f \in \mathcal{F})$ by 2 of 16.2.

2.2. Since $1*1 = 1$, L_1 is a projection of $\mathfrak{A}$ onto $\mathcal{F}$ and $\mathfrak{A} = \mathcal{F} \oplus \ker L_1$.

3. Henceforth we shall write $(f|g)$ instead of $L_1(f\bar{g})$ $(f,g \in \mathfrak{A})$. This mapping has the following easily verified properties.

3.1. $(f,g) \to (f|g)\colon \mathfrak{A} \times \mathfrak{A} \to \mathfrak{A}$ is conjugate bilinear.

3.2. $(f|g) \in \mathcal{F}$ $(f,g \in \mathfrak{A})$. Thus we may view $(f|g)$ either as a function on $|\mathfrak{A}|$ or as one on $|\mathcal{F}|$.

3.3. $(fg_1|g_2) = f(g_1|g_2)$ $(f \in \mathcal{F},\ g_1,g_2 \in \mathfrak{A})$.

3.4. $(tf|tg) = t(f|g)$ $(t \in T,\ fg \in \mathfrak{A})$.

4. Using the notation of 1 of 16.7 and setting $f_b = f|r^{-1}(b)$ we see that $(f_b,g_b) \to (f|g)_b\colon \mathfrak{A}_b \times \mathfrak{A}_b \to \mathbb{C}$ is a well-defined inner product on the vector space $\mathfrak{A}_b$. (Notice that $(f|f)_b = 0$ implies that $\int |f|^2(hx)dh = 0$ $(x \in r^{-1}(b))$ and so $f_b = 0$.)

5. Let $f,g \in \mathfrak{A}$; $\varphi \in B(H)$ and $x \in |\mathfrak{A}|$. Then $(L_\varphi f|g)(x) = \int\langle L_\varphi f,hx\rangle\overline{\langle g,hx\rangle}\,dh = \int\overline{\langle g,hx\rangle}\left(\int\varphi(h^{-1})\langle f,jhx\rangle dj\right)dh =$ $\int\overline{\langle g,hx\rangle}\left(\int\varphi(hn^{-1})\langle f,nx\rangle dn\right)dh = \int\langle f,nx\rangle\left(\int\varphi(hn^{-1})\overline{\langle g,hx\rangle}dh\right)dn =$ $\int\langle f,nx\rangle\left(\int\varphi(k)\overline{\langle g,knx\rangle}dh\right)dn = \int\langle f,nx\rangle\overline{\langle L_{\varphi^*}g,nx\rangle}\,dn = (f|L_{\varphi^*}g)(x)$ (set $n = jh$ and $k = hn^{-1}$).

Thus $(L_\varphi f|g) = (f|L_{\varphi^*}g)$.

I would now like to introduce an important class of operators on $\mathcal{G}$. These arise via 16.1 using functions associated with unitary representations of H.

16.8 DEFINITION. A *unitary representation*, λ *of* H is a continuous homomorphism of H into U(n), the group of unitary n x n matrices, for some positive integer n. The space $\mathbb{C}^n$ on which U(n) acts is called the *representation space of* λ and is denoted V_λ. The integer n is called the *dimension of* λ and denoted d_λ.

The collection of unitary representations of H will be denoted by U(H).

Let $\lambda, \sigma \in U(H)$. Then λ and σ are said to be *equivalent* ($\lambda \equiv \sigma$) if there exists an isomorphism $\varphi: V_\lambda \to V_\sigma$ such that $\varphi(\lambda(h)v) = \sigma(h)\varphi(v)$ $(h \in H, v \in V_\lambda)$.

Let $\lambda \in U(H)$. Then $\varphi_\lambda : H \to \mathbb{C}$ will denote the map such that $\varphi_\lambda(h) = d_\lambda \mathrm{tr}(\lambda(h))$ and L_λ the corresponding linear map L_{φ_λ}, where tr(A) is the trace of the matrix A $(A \in U(d_\lambda))$.

16.9 REMARKS. 1. Let $\lambda \in U(H)$. Then the map $(h,v) \to \lambda(h)v: H \times V_\lambda \to V_\lambda$ makes the pair (H,V_λ) into a left transformation group. If $\sigma \in U(H)$, then $\lambda \equiv \sigma$ iff $(H,V_\lambda) \cong (H,V_\sigma)$.

2. Let $\lambda, \sigma \in U(H)$ with $\lambda \equiv \sigma$. Then by an elementary property of the trace function, $\mathrm{tr}(\lambda(h)) = \mathrm{tr}(\sigma(h))$ $(h \in H)$. Hence $L_\lambda = L_\sigma$ and so the linear operators defined above depend only on the equivalence class of the representation.

16.10 DEFINITION. Let $\lambda \in U(H)$. Then λ is *irreducible* if the only non-zero H-invariant subspace of V_λ is V_λ itself. The set of equivalence classes of irreducible unitary representations of H will be denoted by Λ.

For $\lambda \in \Lambda$, P_λ will denote the linear operator determined by the class λ (see 2 of 16.9 and 16.8).

16.11 PROPOSITION. Let $\lambda, \sigma \in \Lambda$ with $\lambda \neq \sigma$. Then:

1. $P_\lambda^2 = P_\lambda$.
2. $P_\lambda P_\sigma = P_\sigma P_\lambda = 0$.
3. $(P_\lambda f \mid P_\sigma g) = 0 \quad (f, g \in \mathcal{G})$.

PROOF. The following results about the trace function are classical (see e.g. Theorems 2.4 and 2.5 of [2]).

(i) $\varphi_\lambda * \varphi_\lambda = \varphi_\lambda$.

(ii) $\varphi_\lambda * \varphi_\sigma = 0$.

(iii) $\varphi_\lambda^* = \varphi_\lambda$.

Now 1 and 2 follow from (i), (ii) and 16.4; and 3 follows from (iii) and 5 of 16.7.

16.12 PROPOSITION. Let $f \in \mathcal{G}$. Then $(f|f) = \sum_{\lambda \in \Lambda} (P_\lambda f | P_\lambda f)$, the convergence being uniform. This means given $\varepsilon > 0$ there exists a finite subset K_o of Λ such that $\left| (f|f)(x) - \sum_{\lambda \in K} (P_\lambda f | P_\lambda f)(x) \right| < \varepsilon \quad (x \in |\mathcal{G}|$ and K finite with $K_o \subset K \subset \Lambda)$.

PROOF. Let $F(\Lambda)$ denote the collection of finite subsets of Λ. For $x \in |\mathcal{G}|$ and $K \in F(\Lambda)$ set $s_K(x) = \sum_{\lambda \in K} (P_\lambda f | P_\lambda f)(x)$. Then 16.11 implies that $s_K(x) \leq s_N(x) \leq (f|f)(x) \quad (x \in |\mathcal{G}|_\lambda\ K, N \in F(\Lambda)$ with $K \subset N)$. Thus $\lim_{F(\Lambda)} s_K(x)$ exists and the Peter-Weyl theorem (Theorem 1.4 of [2]) implies that $\lim s_K(x) = (f|f)(x) \quad (x \in |\mathcal{G}|)$. Proposition 16.12 now follows from Dini's theorem.

16.13 <u>COROLLARY</u>. Let $f \in \mathfrak{a}$. Then $\lim_{F(\Lambda)} \| f - P_K f \| = 0$, where $\| g \|^2 = (g|g)$ and $P_K = \sum_K P_\lambda$ $(g \in \mathfrak{a},\ K \in F(\Lambda))$.

<u>PROOF</u>. Let $\varepsilon > 0$. Choose $K_o \in F(\Lambda)$ such that $|(f|f) - \sum_{\lambda \in K} (P_\lambda f | P_\lambda f)| < \varepsilon$ $(K_o \subset K \in F(\Lambda))$ (16.12).

Then by 16.11 $\| f - P_K f \|^2 = (f - \Sigma P_\lambda f \mid f - \Sigma P_\lambda f) = |(f|f) - 2\Sigma(P_\lambda f | P_\lambda f) + \Sigma(P_\lambda f | P_\lambda f)| < \varepsilon$.

16.14 <u>LEMMA</u>. Let U be a neighborhood of e in H. Then there exists $\varphi \in K(H)$ such that φ is continuous, real valued and positive with $\varphi(h) = 0$ $(h \notin U)$ and $\int_H \varphi = 1$.

<u>PROOF</u>. Let ρ: H x H → H be such that $\rho(h,j) = hjh^{-1}$ $(h,j \in H)$. Then ρ defines a left action of H on H such that the orbit space X is just the conjugacy classes of H.

Let Π: H → X be the canonical map. Since Π is open and X is compact Hausdorff (by (4.10) and the almost periodicity of (ρ,H,H)), there exists a continuous, positive, real valued function ψ on X such that $\psi(y) = 0$ $(y \notin \Pi(U))$ and $\psi \neq 0$. Then $\varphi = c \cdot \psi\Pi$ is the desired function where $1/c = \int_H \psi \Pi dh$.

16.15 <u>PROPOSITION</u>. Let $f \in \mathfrak{a}$ and $\varepsilon > 0$. Then there exists $K_o \in F(\Lambda)$ such that if $K_o \subset K \in F(\Lambda)$, then $|f(x) - f_K(x)| < \varepsilon$ $(x \in |\mathfrak{a}|)$ and some $f_K \in \operatorname{im} P_K$.

Thus the direct sum of im P_λ $(\lambda \in \Lambda)$ is dense in $\mathfrak{a}$.

<u>PROOF</u>. Since the map $(h,x) \to hx$: H x $|\mathfrak{a}| \to |\mathfrak{a}|$ is continuous (see 14.11) there exists a neighborhood U of the identity of H such that $U = U^{-1}$ and $|f(x) - f(hx)| < \varepsilon/2$ $(x \in |\mathfrak{a}|,\ h \in U)$.

Let φ be as in 16.14 and L the linear operator associated with φ. Then (i) $| f(x) - L_U f(x) | =$

$| f(x) - \int\varphi(h^{-1})f(hx)dh | \leq \int\varphi(h^{-1})|f(x) - f(hx)|dh \leq$

$\epsilon/2\int\varphi(h^{-1})dh = \epsilon/2 \quad (x \in |\mathcal{G}|)$.

By 16.13 there exists $K_o \in F(\Lambda)$ such that $\| f - P_K f \| \cdot \|\varphi\| \leq \epsilon/2$ where $\| \cdot \|$ is the L_2-norm $(K_o \subset K \in F(\Lambda))$. Let $x \in |\mathcal{G}|$ and $K_o \subset K \in F(\Lambda)$. Then (ii) $| Lf(x) - LP_K f(x) | \leq \int\varphi(h^{-1})|(f(hx) - P_K f(hx))|dh \leq$ $\|\varphi\| \cdot \| f - P_K f \| (x) \leq \epsilon/2$ (by Schwarz's inequality).

Since $\varphi \in K(H)$, $LP_K = P_K L$. Hence if $f_K = P_K Lf$, then (i) and (ii) show that $|f(x) - f_K(x)| \leq \epsilon \quad (x \in |\mathcal{G}|)$.

NOTES

1. A. W. Knapp, *Distal functions on groups*, Trans. A.M.S., vol.128 (1967), 1-40.

2. G. Hochschild, *The Structure of Lie Groups*, Holden-Day, Inc. 1965.

CHAPTER 17

REPRESENTATIONS, T-$\mathcal{F}$-SUBMODULES, AND T-VECTOR BUNDLES

Although I have tried to make it self-contained, the material in chapter 17 may prove to be a bit sketchy for one with no background in the theory of fiber bundles. Such a reader is advised that he may skip this chapter since chapter 18 is independent of it.

17.1 NOTATION AND DEFINITION. The notation of chapter 16 will be maintained with $\mathfrak{a} = \mathcal{F}^*$.

Let $h \in H$, $\lambda \in U(H)$ and $f \in C(H)$. Then $hf: H \to \mathbb{C}$ is the map such that $hf(j) = f(jh^{-1})$ $(j \in H)$ and $Q_\lambda f$ the one such that $Q_\lambda f(j) = d_\lambda \cdot \int \operatorname{tr} \lambda(k^{-1})f(kj)dk$ $(j \in H)$.

17.2 REMARKS. 1. The above definition defines a left action of H on C(H).

2. The operators Q_λ are similar to the P_λ defined in chapter 16. The first two of the following results are immediate and the others are standard (see 2 and 3).

2.1. $h(Q_\lambda f) = Q_\lambda(hf)$ $(h \in H,\ f \in C(H),\ \lambda \in U(H))$.

2.2. im Q_λ is invariant under H $(\lambda \in U(H))$.

2.3. $\dim(\operatorname{im} Q_\lambda) < \infty$ $(\lambda \in U(H))$.

2.4. If $\lambda, \sigma \in \Lambda$ with $\lambda \neq \sigma$ and M and N are H-invariant subspaces of im Q_λ and im Q_σ respectively, then the only linear map $L: M \to N$ with $L(hf) = hL(f)$ ($h \in H$, $f \in M$) is the 0-map.

17.3 <u>NOTATION</u>. Let $r: |\mathcal{F}^\#| \to |\mathcal{F}|$ be the restriction mapping, $\mathcal{M}$ a subset of $\mathcal{F}^\#$, $f \in \mathcal{F}^\#$, and $b \in |\mathcal{F}|$. Then f_b will denote the restriction of f to $r^{-1}(b)$ and $\mathcal{M}_b$ the set $\{g_b \mid g \in \mathcal{M}\}$.

Recall that if $\varphi \in B(H)$ then the associated operator L_φ induces a linear map of $\mathcal{F}_b^\#$ into $\mathcal{F}_b^\#$. This induced map will be denoted $(L_\varphi)_b$.

17.4 <u>PROPOSITION</u>. Let $\lambda \in \Lambda$. Then im P_λ is a subspace of $\mathcal{F}^\#$ such that:

1. im P_λ is an $\mathcal{F}$-submodule of $\mathcal{F}^\#$, i.e. $fg \in$ im P_λ ($f \in \mathcal{F}$, $g \in$ im P_λ).
2. $tf \in$ im P_λ ($t \in T$, $f \in$ im P_λ).
3. $\dim (\text{im } P_\lambda)_b < \infty$ ($b \in |\mathcal{F}|$).

<u>PROOF</u>. 1 and 2 follow from 2 of 16.2.

3. Let $x \in r^{-1}(b)$. Then the map $h \to hx: H \to r^{-1}(b) \subset |\mathcal{F}^\#|$ is a homeomorphism onto and induces an isomorphism $\psi: \mathcal{F}_b^\# \to C(H)$ where $\psi(f_b)(h) = f(hx)$ ($f \in \mathcal{F}^\#$, $h \in H$).

Moreover $\psi(P_\lambda)_b = Q_\lambda \psi$ whence $(\text{im } P_\lambda)_b = \text{im } (P_\lambda)_b \cong$ im Q_λ and so 3 follows from 2.3 of 17.2.

Proposition 17.4 motivates the following.

17.5 <u>DEFINITION</u>. Let $\mathcal{M}$ be a vector subspace of $\mathcal{F}^\#$. Then $\mathcal{M}$ is a T-$\mathcal{F}$-<u>submodule</u> if:

1. $fg \in \mathcal{M}$ ($f \in \mathcal{F}$, $g \in \mathcal{M}$), i.e. $\mathcal{M}$ is an $\mathcal{F}$-module.
2. $tf \in \mathcal{M}$ ($t \in T$, $f \in \mathcal{M}$), i.e. $\mathcal{M}$ is T-invariant.
3. $\dim \mathcal{M}_b < \infty$ ($b \in |\mathcal{F}|$) (Note that $\mathcal{M}_b$ is a vector

space over $\mathbb{C}$.)

$\mathcal{M}$ is <u>irreducible</u> if the only T-$\mathcal{F}$-submodules contained in $\mathcal{M}$ are $\{0\}$ and $\mathcal{M}$.

Let $\mathcal{M}$ and $\mathcal{N}$ be T-$\mathcal{F}$-modules and φ a linear map of $\mathcal{M}$ into $\mathcal{N}$. Then φ is a T-$\mathcal{F}$-<u>homomorphism</u> if in addition φ is continuous, $\varphi(fg) = f\varphi(g)$ and $\varphi(tg) = t\varphi(g)$ $(f \in \mathcal{F},\ g \in \mathcal{M},\ t \in T)$.

17.6 <u>LEMMA</u>. Let $\mathcal{M},\mathcal{N}$ be T-$\mathcal{F}$-submodules, $\varphi\colon \mathcal{M} \to \mathcal{N}$ a T-$\mathcal{F}$-homomorphism and $b \in |\mathcal{F}|$. Then φ induces a linear map $\varphi_b\colon \mathcal{M}_b \to \mathcal{N}_b$.

<u>PROOF</u>. Let $f \in \mathcal{M}$ with $f_b = 0$. Then it suffices to show that $(\varphi f)_b = 0$.

To this end let $\varepsilon > 0$. Pick $\delta > 0$ such that $\|g\| \leqslant \delta$ implies $\|\varphi g\| \leqslant \varepsilon$ where $\|g\| = \sup_{x\in|\mathcal{F}^{\#}|} |g(x)|$.

There exist U an open subset of $|\mathcal{F}^{\#}|$ and $g \in \mathcal{F}$ such that $r^{-1}r(U) = U$, $\|g\| \leqslant 1$, $g(x) = 1$ $(x \in r^{-1}(b))$, $g(x) = 0$ $(x \notin U)$ and $|f(x)| \leqslant \delta$ $(x \in U)$.

Then $\|gf\| \leqslant \delta$ whence $\|g\varphi(f)\| = \|\varphi(gf)\| \leqslant \varepsilon$ and so $\varphi(f)(x) \leqslant \varepsilon$ $(x \in r^{-1}(b))$.

17.7 <u>LEMMA</u>. Let $\mathcal{M}$ be a T-$\mathcal{F}$-submodule, $b \in |\mathcal{F}|$, $x \in r^{-1}(b)$ and $\varphi\colon \mathcal{M}_b \to C(H)$ such that $(\varphi f_b)(h) = f(hx)$ $(f \in \mathcal{M},\ h \in H)$. Then im φ is an H-invariant subspace of C(H) (see 1 of 17.2).

<u>PROOF</u>. It is clear that φ is a monomorphism whence im φ is a finite dimensional subspace of C(H).

Let $f \in \mathcal{M}$, $j \in H$, and (t_n) a net on T with $t_n \to p \in T$ with $xp = j^{-1}x$ (such exists since $j^{-1}x \in |\mathcal{F}^{\#}|$).

Since the map $(h,y) \to hy\colon H \times |\mathcal{F}^{\#}| \to |\mathcal{F}^{\#}|$ is continuous, the net $\varphi(t_n f_b)$ converges uniformly to $g \in C(H)$

which must be in im φ since this latter being finite dimensional is closed.

Now $g(h) = \lim \varphi(t_n f_b)(h) = \lim (t_n f)(hx) = \lim f(hxt_n) = f(hj^{-1}x) = (j\varphi(f_b))(h)$. Thus $g = j\varphi(f_b)$.

17.8 PROPOSITION. Let $\mathcal{M},\mathcal{N}$ be non-zero irreducible T-$\mathcal{F}$-submodules. Then:

1. There exists a unique $\lambda = \lambda(\mathcal{M}) \in \Lambda$ such that $\mathcal{M} \subset \operatorname{im} P_\lambda$.

2. If $\mathcal{M} \cong \mathcal{N}$ then $\lambda(\mathcal{M}) = \lambda(\mathcal{N})$. (It is also true that if $\lambda(\mathcal{M}) = \lambda(\mathcal{N})$ then $\mathcal{M} \cong \mathcal{N}$ but this will not be proved at this point (see 17.32).)

PROOF. 1. Let $\lambda \in \Lambda$. Then $\ker P_\lambda \cap \mathcal{M}$ is a T-$\mathcal{F}$-submodule of $\mathcal{M}$. Hence $\mathcal{M} \subset \ker P_\lambda$ or $\mathcal{M} \cap \ker P_\lambda = \{0\}$.

By 16.12 there is at least one $\lambda \in \Lambda$ with $\mathcal{M} \cap \ker P_\lambda = \{0\}$. This means that $\mathcal{M} \cong P_\lambda(\mathcal{M})$.

Now suppose $\lambda,\sigma \in \Lambda$ with $\lambda \neq \sigma$ and $P_\lambda(\mathcal{M}) \cong \mathcal{M} \cong P_\sigma(\mathcal{M})$. Let $\psi: P_\lambda(\mathcal{M}) \cong P_\sigma(\mathcal{M})$, $b \in |\mathcal{F}|$, and $x \in r^{-1}(b)$. Let $\varphi: P_\lambda(\mathcal{M})_b \to C(H)$ and $\rho: P_\sigma(\mathcal{M})_b \to C(H)$ be as in 17.7. Then $\operatorname{im} \varphi \subset \operatorname{im} Q_\lambda$, $\operatorname{im} \rho \subset \operatorname{im} Q_\sigma$, and ψ induces an isomorphism η of im φ onto im ρ (proof of 3 of 17.4, and 17.6).

Let $f \in P_\lambda(\mathcal{M})$, $j \in H$ and (t_n) a net on T which converges in βT and such that $xt_n \to j^{-1}x$.

Then $\eta(j\varphi f_b) = \eta \lim (t_n \varphi f_b) = \lim \eta\varphi(t_n f_b) = \lim \rho\psi_b(t_n f) = \lim \rho(t_n \psi_b f) = j(\rho\psi_b f) = j\eta(\varphi f_b)$.

Thus $\eta(jg) = j\eta(g)$ $(g \in \operatorname{im} \varphi,\ j \in H)$ whence $\eta = 0$ by 2.4 of 17.2. Then $0 = \eta(\varphi f_b) = \rho(\psi_b f)$ whence $(\psi f)_b = 0$ $(f \in P_\lambda(\mathcal{M}),\ b \in |\mathcal{F}|)$ and so ψ cannot be an isomorphism.

Hence there is exactly one $\lambda \in \Lambda$ with $\ker P_\lambda \cap \mathcal{M} =$

$\{0\}$. Thus $P_\lambda f = f$ ($f \in \mathfrak{m}$ by 16.12).

2. Let $\mathfrak{m} \cong \mathfrak{n}$, $\mathfrak{m} \subset \operatorname{im} P_\lambda$ and $\mathfrak{n} \subset \operatorname{im} P_\sigma$. Then the above argument shows that $\lambda = \sigma$.

Let $\lambda \in U(H)$. I wish to describe a construction which starting with λ will yield a transformation group (E_λ, T) and a homomorphism $\nu_\lambda : (E_\lambda, T) \xrightarrow{\sim} (|\mathcal{F}|, T)$.

Define an action of T on $|\mathcal{F}^{\#}| \times V_\lambda$ by setting $(x,v)t = (xt,v)$ ($x \in |\mathcal{F}^{\#}|$, $v \in V_\lambda$). Then this together with the diagonal action of H on $|\mathcal{F}^{\#}| \times V_\lambda$ (see 16.9) gives a bitransformation group $(H, |\mathcal{F}^{\#}| \times V_\lambda, T)$. Let $(E_\lambda, T) = (|\mathcal{F}^{\#}| \times V_\lambda/H, T)$ and $\nu_\lambda \Pi(x,v) = r(x)$ where $\Pi: |\mathcal{F}^{\#}| \times V_\lambda \to E_\lambda$ is the canonical map.

17.9 <u>REMARKS</u>. 1. Let $x \in |\mathcal{F}^{\#}|$, $v \in V_\lambda$ and $t \in T$. Then $\nu_\lambda(\Pi(x,v)t) = \nu_\lambda(\Pi(xt,v)) = r(xt) = r(x)t = \nu_\lambda(\Pi(x,v))t$. Thus $\nu_\lambda : (E_\lambda, T) \xrightarrow{\sim} (|\mathcal{F}|, T)$.

2. Let $b \in |\mathcal{F}|$, $x \in r^{-1}(b)$ and $\varphi_x : V_\lambda \to E_\lambda$ such that $\varphi_x(v) = \Pi(x,v)$ ($v \in V_\lambda$). Then $\varphi_x(V_\lambda) \subset \nu_\lambda^{-1}(b)$ and since $\Pi(hx,v) = \Pi(x,h^{-1}v)$ ($h \in H$, $v \in V_\lambda$), φ_x is onto. Moreover $\varphi_x(v) = \varphi_x(w)$ implies that $\Pi(x,v) = \Pi(x,w)$ whence $h(x,w) = (x,v)$ for some $h \in H$. Since H acts freely on $|\mathcal{F}^{\#}|$, $w = v$. Thus φ_x is a bijective map of V_λ onto $\nu_\lambda^{-1}(b)$.

Now let $y \in r^{-1}(b)$. Then there exists $h \in H$ with $y = hx$. Hence $\varphi_y(v) = \Pi(hx,v) = \Pi(x,h^{-1}v) = \varphi_x(h^{-1}v)$ and so $\varphi_y = \varphi_x \circ h^{-1}$. Since h is a unitary transformation of V_λ into V_λ this implies that φ_x and φ_y induce the same inner product space structure on $\nu_\lambda^{-1}(b)$.

Let $c,d \in E_\lambda$ with $\nu_\lambda(c) = \nu_\lambda(d)$. Then $(c|d)$ will denote $(v|w)$ where $\varphi_x(v) = c$ and $\varphi_x(w) = d$ for some $x \in r^{-1}(b)$.

Summing up: $\Pi(x,v) + \Pi(x,w) = \Pi(x,v + w)$, $\Pi(x,\mu v) = \mu\Pi(x,v)$, and $(\Pi(x,v) \mid \Pi(x,w)) = (v,w)$ $(x \in |\mathcal{F}^{\#}|,\ v,w \in V_\lambda,\ \mu \in \mathbb{C})$.

17.10 <u>DEFINITION AND NOTATION</u>. Let $\lambda \in U(H)$. Then the pair (E_λ,ν_λ) constructed above will be denoted $\nu(\lambda)$ and called the T-<u>vector bundle</u> (over $|\mathcal{F}|$) associated with λ.

For each $b \in |\mathcal{F}|$, $\nu_\lambda^{-1}(b)$ is called the <u>fiber over</u> b.

A continuous map $\sigma\colon |\mathcal{F}| \to E_\lambda$ with $\nu_\lambda\sigma$ = identity is called a <u>section</u> of $\nu(\lambda)$. The set of sections provided with the topology of uniform convergence will be denoted $\Gamma(\lambda)$.

Notice that $\Gamma(\lambda)$ may be given the structure of an $\mathcal{F}$-module. Let $\sigma,\eta \in \Gamma(\lambda)$. and $f \in \mathcal{F}$. Then define $(\sigma+\eta)(x) = \sigma(x) + \eta(x)$ and $(f\sigma)(x) = f(x)\sigma(x)$ $(x \in |\mathcal{F}|)$. Also, if $\sigma \in \Gamma(\lambda)$ and $t \in T$, $t\sigma$ will denote that element of $\Gamma(\lambda)$ such that $(t\sigma)(x) = \sigma(xt)t^{-1}$ $(x \in |\mathcal{F}|)$.

17.11 <u>PROPOSITION</u>. Let $\lambda \in U(H)$. Then:

1. The map $c \to ct\colon E_\lambda \to E_\lambda$ induces a linear isometry of $\nu_\lambda^{-1}(b)$ onto $\nu_\lambda^{-1}(bt)$ $(b \in |\mathcal{F}|,\ t \in T)$.

2. The map $(c,d) \to (c|d)\colon R(\lambda) \to \mathbb{C}$ is continuous, where $R(\lambda) = \{(c,d) \mid c,d \in E_\lambda \text{ and } \nu_\lambda(c) = \nu_\lambda(d)\}$.

17.12 <u>NOTATION</u>. Let $\lambda \in U(H)$. Then $\mathrm{Hom}(\lambda)$ will denote the set of homomorphisms of $(H,|\mathcal{F}^{\#}|)$ into (H,V_λ) provided with the topology of uniform convergence.

Notice that $\mathrm{Hom}(\lambda)$ may be given the structure of an $\mathcal{F}$-module by setting $(\sigma + \eta)(x) = \sigma(x) + \eta(x)$ and $(f\sigma)(x) = f(x)\sigma(x)$ $(\sigma,\eta \in \mathrm{Hom}(\lambda),\ f \in \mathcal{F}$, and $x \in |\mathcal{F}^{\#}|)$.

Let $\sigma \in \mathrm{Hom}(\lambda)$ and $t \in T$. Then $t\sigma$ will denote that element of $\mathrm{Hom}(\lambda)$ such that $(t\sigma)(x) = \sigma(xt)$ $(x \in |\mathcal{F}^{\#}|)$.

17.13 PROPOSITION. Let $\lambda \in U(H)$. Then φ: $\mathrm{Hom}(\lambda) \to \Gamma(\lambda)$ is an isomorphism onto where $\varphi\sigma(b) = \Pi(x,\sigma(x))$ $(b \in |\mathcal{F}|)$. (Here $b = r(x)$ and Π: $|\mathcal{F}^{\#}| \times V_\lambda \to E_\lambda$ is the canonical map.)

PROOF. Since $\Pi(x,\sigma(x)) = \Pi(hx,h\sigma(x)) = \Pi(hx,\sigma(hx))$ $(x \in |\mathcal{F}^{\#}|,\ \sigma \in \mathrm{Hom}(\lambda))$, $\varphi\sigma$ is well defined.

Clearly $\varphi\sigma$ is continuous.

Now suppose $\varphi\sigma = \varphi\eta$ for $\sigma,\eta \in \mathrm{Hom}(\lambda)$. Then $\Pi(x,\sigma(x)) = \Pi(x,\eta(x))$ whence $\sigma(x) = \eta(x)$ $(x \in |\mathcal{F}^{\#}|)$ since H acts freely. Thus φ is one-one.

Let $\rho \in \Gamma(\lambda)$ and $x \in |\mathcal{F}^{\#}|$. Since H acts freely on $|\mathcal{F}^{\#}|$ there exists a unique $\sigma(x) \in V_\lambda$ with $\Pi(x,\sigma(x)) = \rho(r(x))$. Then it is obvious from the definition that $\varphi\sigma = \rho$.

Let (x_n) be a net on $|\mathcal{F}^{\#}|$ with $x_n \to x \in |\mathcal{F}^{\#}|$. Then $\Pi(x_n\sigma(x_n)) \in \rho(|\mathcal{F}|)$ for all n. Since $\rho(|\mathcal{F}|)$ is compact, we may assume $\Pi(x_n,\sigma(x_n)) \to \Pi(y,v)$ with $r(y) = r(x)$ and $v \in V_\lambda$. Since Π is open, there exists a net (h_n) on H with $h_n(x_n,\sigma(x_n)) \to (y,v)$. We may assume $h_n \to h$. Then $hx = y$ and $h\sigma(x_n) \to v$. Thus $\sigma(x_n) \to h^{-1}v$ and $\Pi(x,h^{-1}v) = \Pi(hx,v) = \Pi(y,v) = \lim \Pi(x_n,\sigma(x_n)) = \lim \rho(r(x_n)) = \rho(r(x))$, whence $h^{-1}v = \sigma(x)$ and so σ is continuous.

It is immediate that φ is an $\mathcal{F}$-module homomorphism.

Let $t \in T$, $b \in |\mathcal{F}|$, and $x \in r^{-1}(b)$. Then $\varphi(t\sigma)(b) = \Pi(x,(t\sigma)(x)) = \Pi(x,\sigma(xt)) = \Pi(xt,\sigma(xt))t^{-1} = (\varphi\sigma)(bt)t^{-1} = (t\varphi\sigma)(b)$. Thus $\varphi(t\sigma) = t(\varphi\sigma)$.

I leave the proof that φ is a homeomorphism to the reader.

This completes the proof.

Let $\lambda \in U(H)$. Then one can produce elements of $\mathrm{Hom}(\lambda)$ in the following way. Let $\psi\colon |\mathcal{F}^{\#}| \to V_\lambda$ be continuous. Since H is compact and the map $h \to h^{-1}\psi(hx)\colon |\mathcal{F}^{\#}| \to V_\lambda$ is continuous, there exists $\varphi(x) \in V_\lambda$ such that $L(\varphi(x)) = \int L(h^{-1}\psi(hx))dh$ for all $L \in V_\lambda^*$, the dual space of V_λ (see [4]).

Let us write $\varphi(x) = \int h^{-1}\psi(hx)dh$. Then it is immediate that φ is a continuous mapping of $|\mathcal{F}^{\#}|$ into V_λ.

Moreover $\varphi(jx) = \int h^{-1}\psi(hjx)dh = \int jn^{-1}\psi(n)dn = j\varphi(x)$, i.e. $\varphi \in \mathrm{Hom}(\lambda)$.

17.14 <u>LEMMA</u>. Let $\lambda \in U(H)$, $v \in V_\lambda$, and $x \in |\mathcal{F}^{\#}|$. Then there exists $\varphi \in \mathrm{Hom}(\lambda)$ with $\varphi(x) = v$.

<u>PROOF</u>. Since the map $h \to hx\colon H \to |\mathcal{F}^{\#}|$ is a homeomorphism, there exists by Tietze's extension theorem a continuous map $\psi\colon |\mathcal{F}^{\#}| \to V_\lambda$ such that $\psi(hx) = hv$ $(h \in H)$.

Set $\varphi(y) = \int h^{-1}\psi(hy)dh$. Then $\varphi \in \mathrm{Hom}(\lambda)$ and $\varphi(x) = \int h^{-1}hvdh = v$.

17.15 <u>LEMMA</u>. Let $\lambda, \sigma \in U(H)$, φ a homomorphism of $\mathrm{Hom}(\lambda)$ into $\mathrm{Hom}(\sigma)$, $\mu, \nu \in \mathrm{Hom}(\lambda)$ and $x \in |\mathcal{F}^{\#}|$ with $\mu(x) = \nu(x)$. Then $(\varphi\mu)(x) = (\varphi\nu)(x)$.

<u>PROOF</u>. Set $\delta = \mu - \nu$. Then $\delta(hx) = h\delta(x) = h\cdot 0 = 0$ $(h \in H)$.

The proof that this implies that $(\varphi\delta)(x) = 0$ is analogous to the proof of 17.6 and will therefore be omitted.

17.16 <u>PROPOSITION</u>. Let $\lambda, \sigma \in U(H)$. For each homomorphism $\varphi\colon (H, V_\lambda) \to (H, V_\sigma)$ let $\varphi_*\colon \mathrm{Hom}(\lambda) \to \mathrm{Hom}(\sigma)$ be such that $\varphi_*(\mu) = \varphi \circ \mu$ $(\mu \in \mathrm{Hom}(\lambda))$ and for each homomorphism

ψ: Hom(λ) $\to$ (σ) let $\bar{\psi}$: $V_\lambda \to V_\sigma$ be such that $\bar{\psi}(\mu(x)) =$ $(\psi\mu)(x)$ ($x \in |\mathcal{F}^{\#}|$, $\mu \in$ Hom(λ)). Then:

1. φ_* is a homomorphism.

2. $\bar{\psi}$: $(H,V_\lambda) \to (H,V_\sigma)$ is a homomorphism.

3. $\overline{\varphi_*} = \varphi$.

4. $\bar{\psi}_* = \psi$.

(Note that $\bar{\psi}$ is well defined by 17.15 and everywhere defined by 17.14.)

<u>PROOF</u>. 1, 3, and 4 are immediate.

2. $\bar{\psi}(h\mu(x)) = \bar{\psi}(\mu(hx)) = (\psi\mu)(hx) = h(\psi\mu)(x) =$ $h\bar{\psi}(\mu(x))$ ($h \in H$, $\mu \in$ Hom(λ), $x \in |\mathcal{F}^{\#}|$).

17.17 <u>COROLLARY.</u> Let $\lambda,\sigma \in U(H)$. Then $\lambda \equiv \sigma$ iff $\nu(\lambda) \cong \nu(\sigma)$. Thus the vector bundle $\nu(\lambda)$ depends only on the equivalence class of the representation λ.

<u>PROOF</u>. Let $\lambda \equiv \sigma$ then $(H,V_\lambda) \cong (H,V_\sigma)$ and it follows from the definition of the bundles $\nu(\lambda)$ and $\nu(\sigma)$ that $\nu(\lambda) \cong \nu(\sigma)$.

On the other hand $\nu(\lambda) \cong \nu(\sigma)$ implies that $\Gamma(\lambda) \cong \Gamma(\sigma)$ whence Hom(λ) $\cong$ Hom(σ) by 17.13 and $(H,V_\lambda) \cong (H,V_\sigma)$ by 17.16.

17.18 <u>LEMMA</u>. Let $\lambda \in U(H)$, $n = d_\lambda$, and $x \in |\mathcal{F}^{\#}|$. Then there exist $\varphi_1,\ldots,\varphi_n \in$ Hom(λ) and a saturated neighborhood U of x (i.e. one with $r^{-1}r(U) = U$) such that given $\rho \in$ Hom(λ) there exist $f_1,\ldots,f_n \in \mathcal{F}$ with $\rho(y) = \Sigma f_i(y)\varphi_i(y)$ ($y \in U$).

<u>PROOF</u>. By 17.14 there exist $\varphi_1,\ldots,\varphi_n \in$ Hom(λ) such that $\varphi_1(x),\ldots,\varphi_n(x)$ span V_λ. Let $d(y)$ denote the determinant of the matrix $(\varphi_i(y) \mid \varphi_j(y))$ ($y \in |\mathcal{F}^{\#}|$). Then d is

continuous, $d(hy) = d(y)$, and $\varphi_1(y),\ldots,\varphi_n(y)$ span V_λ iff $d(y) \neq 0$ $(h \in H,\ y \in |\mathcal{F}^{\#}|)$. Hence there exists an open saturated neighborhood W of x such that $\varphi_1(y),\ldots,\varphi_n(y)$ spans V_λ $(y \in W)$.

There exist open saturated neighborhoods U and N of x, and $g \in \mathcal{F}$ such that $U \subset N \subset \overline{N} \subset W$, and $g(y) = 1$ $(y \in U)$ $g(y) = 0$ $(y \notin \overline{N})$.

Now let $\rho \in \mathrm{Hom}(\lambda)$. Then $\rho(y) = \Sigma j_i(y)\varphi_i(y)$ $(y \in W)$ for some functions $j_1,\ldots,j_n$ on W. Since these functions satisfy the system of equations $(\rho(y) \mid \varphi_j(y)) = \sum_{i=1}^{n} j_i(y)(\varphi_i(y) \mid \varphi_j(y))$, $1 \leq m \leq n$, they are continuous on W and $j_i(hy) = j_i(y)$ $(h \in H,\ 1 \leq i \leq n,\ y \in W)$. Set $f_i(y) = g(y)j_i(y)$ $(y \in W)$ and $f_i(y) = 0$ $(y \notin W)$ $(1 \leq i \leq n)$. Then $f_1,\ldots,f_n \in \mathcal{F}$ and $\rho(y) = \Sigma f_i(y)\varphi_i(y)$ $(y \in U)$.

17.19 <u>LEMMA</u>. Let $\lambda \in U(H)$ and V,W invariant subspaces of V_λ with $V_\lambda = V \oplus W$. Then $\mathrm{Hom}(\lambda) = \mathrm{Hom}(|\mathcal{F}^{\#}|,V) \oplus \mathrm{Hom}(|\mathcal{F}^{\#}|,W)$.

<u>PROOF</u>. Let $\rho \in \mathrm{Hom}(\lambda)$, and $x \in |\mathcal{F}^{\#}|$. The representation λ induces representations σ and δ with $V_\sigma = V$ and $V_\delta = W$. Hence we may apply 17.18 to obtain an open saturated neighborhood U_x of x and $\varphi_1,\ldots,\varphi_k \in \mathrm{Hom}(\sigma)$ and $\psi_i,\ldots,\psi_r \in \mathrm{Hom}(\delta)$ such that $\rho(y) = \Sigma f_i(y)\varphi_i(y) + \Sigma g_i(y)\psi_i(y)$ $(y \in U_x)$ where $f_1,\ldots,f_k,g_1,\ldots,g_r \in \mathcal{F}$. Thus $\rho(y) = \varphi_x(y) + \psi_x(y)$ $(y \in U_x)$ with $\varphi_x \in \mathrm{Hom}(\sigma)$ and $\psi_x \in \mathrm{Hom}(\delta)$.

Let $|\mathcal{F}^{\#}| = \cup\{U_x \mid x \in L\}$ where L is a finite subset of $|\mathcal{F}^{\#}|$ and let $(g_x \mid x \in L)$ be a partition of unity subordinate to the cover $(U_x \mid x \in L)$ with $g_x \in \mathcal{F}$ $(x \in L)$.

Then $g_x\rho = g_x\varphi_x + g_x\psi_x$ $(x \in L)$ whence $\rho = \sum_L g_x\rho = \sum_L g_x\varphi_x + \sum_L g_x\psi_x \in \mathrm{Hom}(\sigma) + \mathrm{Hom}(\delta)$. Since $\mathrm{Hom}(\sigma) \cap \mathrm{Hom}(\delta) = \{0\}$, the proof is completed.

17.20 LEMMA. Let $\lambda \in U(H)$, $x \in |\mathcal{F}^{\#}|$, and $\mathcal{W}$ a T-invariant $\mathcal{F}$-submodule of $\mathrm{Hom}(\lambda)$. Then:

1. $W_x = \{\sigma(x) \mid \sigma \in \mathcal{W}\}$ is an invariant subspace of V_λ.

2. $W_x = W =$ subspace generated by the set $\{\sigma(y) \mid \sigma \in \mathcal{W},\ y \in |\mathcal{F}^{\#}|\}$.

3. $\mathcal{W} = \mathrm{Hom}(|\mathcal{F}^{\#}|, W)$.

PROOF. Since $\sigma(xt) = (t\sigma)(x) \in W_x$ $(t \in T,\ \sigma \in \mathcal{W})$, $\sigma(y) \in W_x$ $(y \in |\mathcal{F}^{\#}|,\ \sigma \in \mathcal{W})$ by continuity. Thus $W_x = W$.

Moreover $h\sigma(x) = \sigma(hx) \in W$ $(h \in H,\ \sigma \in \mathcal{W})$ shows that W is invariant. Hence 1 and 2 are proved.

3. Clearly $\mathcal{W} \subset \mathrm{Hom}(|\mathcal{F}^{\#}|, W)$. Now let $\rho \in \mathrm{Hom}(|\mathcal{F}^{\#}|, W)$ and $y \in |\mathcal{F}^{\#}|$. Then as in the proof of 17.19 there is a saturated open neighborhood U_y of y and $\sigma_y \in \mathcal{W}$ with $\rho(z) = \sigma_y(z)$ $(z \in U_y)$.

Let L be a finite subset of $|\mathcal{F}^{\#}|$ such that $|\mathcal{F}^{\#}| = \cup\{U_y \mid y \in L\}$ and $\{f_y \mid y \in L\}$ a partition of unity subordinate to the cover $\{U_y \mid y \in L\}$ with $f_y \in \mathcal{F}$ $(y \in L)$. Then $\rho = \sum_L f_y\rho = \sum_L f_y\sigma_y \in \mathcal{W}$.

17.21 PROPOSITION. Let $\lambda \in U(H)$. Then λ is irreducible iff $\mathrm{Hom}(\lambda)$ is an irreducible T-$\mathcal{F}$-module.

PROOF. Use 17.19 and 17.20.

17.22 PROPOSITION. Let $\lambda \in \Lambda$ and $0 \neq v \in V_\lambda$. Then $\varphi\colon \mathrm{Hom}(\lambda) \to \mathcal{F}^{\#}$ such that $\varphi\sigma(x) = (\sigma(x)|v)$ is an isomorphism onto an irreducible T-$\mathcal{F}$-submodule of im P_λ.

PROOF. It is evident that φ is a non-trivial homomorphism. Hence φ is injective for Hom(λ) is irreducible by 17.21.

I leave the proof that φ is a homeomorphism onto its image to the reader.

Now $(P_\lambda \varphi\sigma)(x) = d_\lambda \cdot \int tr(h^{-1})(\sigma(hx)|v)dh =$ $d_\lambda \cdot \int tr(h^{-1})(\sigma(x)|h^{-1}v)dh = (\sigma(x)|v)$ (use theorem 2.5 of [2]). Thus $P_\lambda(\varphi\sigma) = \varphi\sigma$, whence $\varphi\sigma \in \text{im } P_\lambda$ $(\sigma \in \text{Hom}(\lambda))$.

In the past few propositions we have been analyzing vector bundles over $|\mathcal{F}|$ which arise from unitary representations of H. Now I would like to define a T-vector bundle over $|\mathcal{F}|$ without reference to a representation of H and to show that there is a representation from which it may be obtained.

17.23 DEFINITION. A T-vector bundle ζ over $|\mathcal{F}|$ is a pair consisting of a transformation group $(E(\zeta),T)$ and a homomorphism (also denoted ζ) of $(E(\zeta),T)$ onto $(|\mathcal{F}|,T)$ such that:

1. $\zeta^{-1}(a)$ is a finite dimensional vector space over $\mathbb{C}$ $(a \in |\mathcal{F}|)$.

2. There exists a continuous map $\rho: R(\zeta) \to \mathbb{C}$ such that $\rho|\zeta^{-1}(a) \times \zeta^{-1}(a)$ is an inner product $(a \in |\mathcal{F}|)$, where $R(\zeta) = \{(x,y) \mid \zeta(x) = \zeta(y)\} \subset E(\zeta) \times E(\zeta)$.

3. The map $x \to xt: \zeta^{-1}(a) \to \zeta^{-1}(at)$ induced by t is an isometry $(a \in |\mathcal{F}|, t \in T)$.

4. ζ is locally trivial, i.e. there exists a vector space W_ζ such that given $b \in |\mathcal{F}|$ there exist a neighborhood N of b and a homeomorphism $\varphi: \zeta^{-1}(N) \to W \times N$ such that $\zeta(x) = p\varphi(x)$ $(x \in \zeta^{-1}(N))$ and $\varphi: \zeta^{-1}(c) \cong W_\zeta$ $(c \in N)$ where p is the projection of $W_\zeta \times N$ onto N.

17.24 PROPOSITION. Let $\lambda \in U(H)$. Then $\nu(\lambda)$ is a T-vector bundle over $|\mathcal{F}|$.

PROOF. Property 1 of 17.23 is immediate and properties 2 and 3 are the content of 17.11.

I prove 4. Let $b \in |\mathcal{F}|$. Then by 17.13 and 17.18 there exist a neighborhood N of b and elements $\sigma_1,\ldots,\sigma_n$ of $\Gamma(\lambda)$ such that $\sigma_1(a),\ldots,\sigma_n(a)$ span $\nu_\lambda^{-1}(a)$ $(a \in N)$. Using the Gram-Schmidt orthonormalization process we may assume that $\sigma_1(a),\ldots,\sigma_n(a)$ is an orthonormal basis for $\nu_\lambda^{-1}(a)$ $(a \in N)$.

Now let $e_1,\ldots,e_n$ be an orthonormal basis for V_λ, and let $L_a: \nu_\lambda^{-1}(a) \to V_\lambda$ be the linear map such that $L_a\sigma_i(a) = e_i$ $(1 \leqslant i \leqslant n,\ a \in N)$.

Then $x \to (L_a(x),\nu_\lambda(x)): \zeta^{-1}(N) \to V_\lambda \times N$ is the required isomorphism (where $a = \nu_\lambda(x)$).

Now let γ be a T-vector bundle over $|\mathcal{F}|$. I would like to show that $\gamma \cong \nu(\lambda)$ for some $\lambda \in U(H)$.

To this end provide $V_\gamma = V$ with an inner product and set $E(\eta) = \{x \mid x: V \to \gamma^{-1}(a),\ x$ is an isometry for some $a \in |\mathcal{F}|\}$. Topologize $E(\eta)$ with the compact open topology, i.e. $x_n \to x$ iff x_n converges uniformly to x on compact subsets of V.

For $x \in E(\eta)$ and $t \in T$ set $\eta(x) = a$ where $x: V \to \gamma^{-1}(a)$ and $xt: V \to \gamma^{-1}(at)$, the composition x followed by t. (Recall t maps $\gamma^{-1}(a)$ isometrically onto $\gamma^{-1}(at)$ $(a \in B(\gamma))$.) Then $xt \in E(\eta)$ and $\eta: E(\eta) \to |\mathcal{F}|$ is a homomorphism onto.

Let K be the group of unitary transformations of V, $k \in K$, and $x \in E(\eta)$. Then the map $kx: V \to \gamma^{-1}(a)$ such that $(kx)(v) = x(k^{-1}v)$ $(v \in V)$ is in $E(\eta)$, where $\eta(x) = a$. The map $(k,x) \to kx$ of $K \times E(\eta) \to E(\eta)$ makes $(K,E(\eta),T)$ into a bitransformation group when K is provided with the norm topology. Then K is compact, it acts freely on $E(\eta)$ and η induces an isomorphism of $(E(\eta)/K,T)$ onto $(|\mathcal{F}|,T)$.

17.25 PROPOSITION. With the above notation:

1. Given $b \in |\mathcal{F}|$ there exist a neighborhood U of b and a homeomorphism $\varphi: \eta^{-1}(U) \to U \times K$ with $\pi(\varphi(x)) = \eta(x)$ $(x \in \eta^{-1}(U))$ and $\varphi|\eta^{-1}(a) : \eta^{-1}(a) \cong K$ $(a \in U)$ where π is the projection of U x K onto U.

2. $E(\eta)$ is compact T_2.

3. The map $\psi: E(\eta) \times V \to E(\gamma)$ such that $\psi(x,v) = x(v)$ $(x \in E(\eta), v \in V)$ induces an isomorphism of $((E(\eta) \times V)/K,T)$ onto $(E(\gamma),T)$.

PROOF. 1. Let $b \in |\mathcal{F}|$ and $n = \dim V$. Since γ is locally trivial we can find a neighborhood U of b and sections $\sigma_1,\ldots,\sigma_n$ of γ such that $\sigma_1(a),\ldots,\sigma_n(a)$ is a basis for $\gamma^{-1}(a)$ $(a \in U)$. Using the Gram-Schmidt orthonormalization process and cutting down U if need be, we may assume that $\sigma_1(a),\ldots,\sigma_n(a)$ are orthonormal $(a \in U)$.

Let $e_1,\ldots,e_n$ be a fixed orthonormal basis for V and $L_a: \gamma^{-1}(a) \to V$ the isometry such that $L_a\sigma_i(a) = e_i$ $(1 \leq i \leq n, a \in U)$. Then the map $\varphi: \eta^{-1}(U) \to U \times K$ such that $\varphi(x) = (\eta(x), L_a(x))$ $(x \in \eta^{-1}(U), \eta(x) = a)$ has the desired properties.

2. Since $E(\eta)$ is clearly T_2, 2 follows from 1 and the fact that both K and $|\mathcal{F}|$ are compact T_2.

3. Let $x \in E(\eta)$, $v \in V$ and $k \in K$. Then $\psi(kx,kv) = (kx)(kv) = x(k^{-1}kv) = x(v) = \psi(x,v)$.

On the other hand suppose $\psi(x,v) = \psi(y,w)$, where $x,y \in E(\eta)$ and $v,w \in V$. Then $x(v) = y(w)$ whence $\eta(x) =$

$\eta(y)$. Thus $k = x^{-1} o y \in K$ and $y = x o x^{-1} o y = x o k = k^{-1}x$. Then $x(v) = y(w) = x(kw)$ whence $v = kw$ and $(y,w) = k^{-1}(x,v)$.

Since ψ is onto, it induces a bijective map $\bar{\psi}: (E(\eta) \times V)/K \to E(\gamma)$. That $\bar{\psi}$ is a homeomorphism follows from 1, and that it is a transformation group homomorphism is immediate.

17.26 LEMMA. With the notation of 17.25 let $x_o \in E(\eta)$, $M = \overline{x_o T}$, and $S = \{k \mid k \in K, kx_o \in M\}$. Then the inclusion map $M \times V \to E(\eta) \times V$ induces an isomorphism of $((M \times V)/S, T)$ onto $((E(\eta) \times V)/K, T)$.

PROOF. We know that S is a closed subgroup of K so that S acts on V and we do indeed have a bitransformation group $(S, M \times V, T)$.

Let $f: M \times V \to (M \times V)/S$ and $g: E(\eta) \times V \to (E(\eta) \times V)/K$ be the canonical maps. Then it is immediate that $f(x_1,v_1) = f(x_2,v_2)$ implies that $g(x_1,v_1) = g(x_2,v_2)$. Hence there is induced a continuous map $\psi: M \times V/S \to (E(\eta) \times V)/K$ such that $\psi f(x,v) = g(x,v)$ $(x \in M, v \in V)$.

Now let $\psi(f(x_1,v_1)) = \psi(f(x_2,v_2))$. Then there exists $k \in K$ with $(x_2,v_2) = k(x_1,v_1)$. Hence $kx_1 = x_2$ and so $k \in S$ because $x_1, x_2 \in M$ (see chapter 6). Consequently $f(x_1,v_1) = f(x_2,v_2)$ and ψ is one-one.

Now let $x \in E(\eta)$ and $v \in V$. Since $\eta(M) = |\mathcal{F}|$, there exists $k \in K$ with $kx \in M$. Then $\psi(v(kx,kv)) = g(kx,kv) = g(x,v)$ whence ψ is onto.

I leave the proof that ψ is a homeomorphism and that ψ preserves all the structures involved to the reader.

17.27 PROPOSITION. Let γ be a T-vector bundle over $|\mathcal{F}|$. Then there exists $\lambda \in U(H)$ with $\nu(\lambda) \cong \gamma$.

PROOF. In the notation of 17.26, 17.26 and 17.25 together show that $((M \times V)/S,T) \cong \gamma$.

Since (M,T) is minimal, S compact T_2, and (S,M,T) a bitransformation group with $(M/S,T) \cong (|\mathcal{F}|,T)$, (M,T) is an almost periodic extension of $(|\mathcal{F}|,T)$ (14.26).

There exists a T-subalgebra $\mathcal{G}$ of $\mathcal{F}^{\#}$ with $\mathcal{F} \subset \mathcal{G}$, $(|\mathcal{G}|,T) \cong (M,T)$ and $F/A \cong S$ (12.12) where $A = \mathfrak{g}(\mathcal{G})$. Since $F^{\#} \subset A$ there is induced a homomorphism $\lambda: H \to S$. Thus $\lambda \in U(H)$ with $V_\lambda = V$ and $E_\lambda = |\mathcal{F}^{\#}| \times V/H$.

To see that $\nu(\lambda) \cong \gamma$ let $L = \ker \lambda$. Then $jv = v$ $(j \in L,\ v \in V)$ and $(L,|\mathcal{F}^{\#}|,T)$ is a bitransformation group with $(|\mathcal{F}^{\#}|/L,T) \cong (|\mathcal{G}|,T)$, the isomorphism being induced by the restriction map $\rho: |\mathcal{F}^{\#}| \to |\mathcal{G}|$.

Let $\rho: |\mathcal{F}^{\#}| \times V \to E_\lambda$ and $g: |\mathcal{G}| \times V \to (|\mathcal{G}| \times V)/S$ be the canonical maps.

Let $f(x_1,v_1) = f(x_2,v_2)$. Then there exists $h \in H$ with $x_2 = hx_1$ and $v_2 = hv_1$. If $s = \lambda(h)$ then $r(x_2) = sr(x_1)$ and $v_2 = sv_1$ whence $g(x_1,v_1) = g(x_2,v_2)$.

Hence there exists a continuous map $\psi: E_\lambda \to (|\mathcal{G}| \times V)/S$ such that $\psi f(x,v) = g(x,v)$ $(x \in |\mathcal{F}^{\#}|,\ v \in V)$. The verification that ψ is an isomorphism is tedious but straightforward and will be omitted.

Now I would like to show how starting with a T-$\mathcal{F}$-submodule $\mathcal{M}$ of $\mathcal{F}^{\#}$ one can construct a T-vector bundle ζ over $|\mathcal{F}|$ with $\Gamma(\zeta) \cong \mathcal{M}$.

17.28 LEMMA. Let $\mathcal{M}$ be a T-$\mathcal{F}$-submodule of $\mathcal{F}^{\#}$. Then there exists a positive integer n with $\dim \mathcal{M}_a = n$ $(a \in |\mathcal{F}|)$.

PROOF. Since the map $(f_a,g_a) \to (f|g)(a): \mathcal{M}_a \times \mathcal{M}_a \to \mathbb{C}$ is an inner product, the elements $f_a^1,\ldots,f_a^k$ of $\mathcal{M}_a$ are independent iff $\det(f^i|f^j)(a) \neq 0$ $(a \in |\mathcal{F}|)$. Thus the map $a \to \dim \mathcal{M}_a$: $|\mathcal{F}| \to \mathbb{C}$ is lower semicontinuous, whence $\dim \mathcal{M}_a$ is constant by the T-invariance of $\mathcal{M}$.

17.29 <u>LEMMA</u>. Let $\mathcal{M}$ be a T-$\mathcal{F}$-submodule of $\mathcal{F}^{\#}$, and $b \in |\mathcal{F}|$. Then there exist $g^1,\dots,g^n$ in $\mathcal{M}$ and a neighborhood N of b such that given $g \in \mathcal{M}$ there exist $f^1,\dots,f^n$ in $\mathcal{F}$ with $g_c = \sum_{i=1} f^i(c)g_c^i$ $(c \in N)$. (Here $n = \dim \mathcal{M}_b$.)

The proof is similar to that of 17.18 and will be omitted.

Now let $\mathcal{M}$ be a T-$\mathcal{F}$-submodule of $\mathcal{F}^{\#}$ with $\dim \mathcal{M}_a = n$ $(a \in |\mathcal{F}|)$. I shall construct a locally trivial T-vector bundle ζ with $\Gamma(\zeta) \cong \mathcal{M}$.

Let us set $E(\zeta) = \underset{a \in |\mathcal{F}|}{+} \mathcal{M}_a$, the disjoint union of the $\mathcal{M}_a$. For $f \in \mathcal{M}$ and $a \in |\mathcal{F}|$ set $\zeta(f_a) = a$.

The action of T on $E(\zeta)$ is defined by the formula $f_a t = (t^{-1}f)_{at}$ $(f \in \mathcal{M}, a \in |\mathcal{F}|, t \in T)$. It is straightforward to check that this defines an action of T on $E(\zeta)$ and that $\zeta(f_a t) = \zeta(f_a)t$.

For $\mathcal{F} \in \mathcal{M}$ let σ_f: $|\mathcal{F}| \to E(\zeta)$ be such that $\sigma_f(a) = f_a$ $(a \in |\mathcal{F}|)$. Let $\mathcal{N} = \{L|L$, an n-element ordered subset of $\mathcal{M}\}$. Then each $L \in \mathcal{N}$ defines a map L: $|\mathcal{F}| \times \mathbb{C}^n \to E(\zeta)$, namely $L(a,v)$ = image of v under the linear map which sends e_i into $\sigma_{f_i}(a)$ $1 \leqslant i \leqslant n$ where $e_1,\dots,e_n$ is the canonical basis for C^n and $L = \{f_1,\dots,f_n\}$. Now provide $E(\zeta)$ with the largest topology making L continuous $(L \in \mathcal{N})$.

17.30 <u>PROPOSITION</u>. With the above notation ζ is a locally trivial T-vector bundle with $\mathcal{M} \cong \Gamma(\zeta)$.

PROOF. Recall that in order to prove that a map $f: N \to X$ is continuous, where N is an open subset of $E(\zeta)$, it suffices to prove that the composition $f \circ L: L^{-1}(N) \to X$ is continuous ($L \in \mathcal{N}$).

Let $t \in T$ and $L = \{f_1,\ldots,f_n\} \in \mathcal{N}$. Then the map $(a,v) \to (L(a,v))t: |\mathcal{F}| \times \mathbb{C}^n \to E(\zeta)$ is just the composition $(a,v) \to (at,v): |\mathcal{F}| \times \mathbb{C}^n \to |\mathcal{F}| \times \mathbb{C}^n$ followed by K, where $K = \{tf_1,\ldots,tf_n\}$, because $\sigma_f(a)t = \sigma_{t^{-1}f}(at)$ ($a \in |\mathcal{F}|$, $f \in \mathcal{M}$, $t \in T$). Thus the map $x \to xt: E(\zeta) \to E(\zeta)$ is continuous ($t \in T$).

Again let $L \in \mathcal{N}$. Then $\zeta \circ L: |\mathcal{F}| \times \mathbb{C}^n \to |\mathcal{F}|$ is just a projection whence ζ is continuous. Since $\zeta(f_a t) = \zeta(f_a)t$ ($a \in |\mathcal{F}|$, $f \in \mathcal{M}$, $t \in T$), it is a homomorphism onto.

Now let $b \in |\mathcal{F}|$. Then there exist an open neighborhood N of b and n elements $f^1,\ldots,f^n$ of $\mathcal{M}$ such that given $f \in \mathcal{M}$ there exist $h_1,\ldots,h_n \in \mathcal{F}$ with $f_a = \sum_{i=1}^{n} h_i(a)f_a^i$ ($a \in N$) by 17.29.

Let $L = \{f^1,\ldots,f^n\}$ and f be as above. Then $\sigma_v(a) = L(a,v(a))$ ($a \in N$) where $v: N \to \mathbb{C}^n$ is such that $v(a) = \Sigma h_i(a)e_i$. Hence σ_f is continuous and since $\zeta\sigma_f$ = identity, $\sigma_f \in \Gamma(\zeta)$.

The map $L: N \times \mathbb{C}^n \to \zeta^{-1}(N)$ is continuous and bijective. Let $K \in \mathcal{N}$. Then the above remarks show that there exists a continuous map $H: N \times \mathbb{C}^n \to \mathbb{C}^n$ such that $K(a,v) = L(a,H(a,v))$ ($a \in N$, $v \in \mathbb{C}^n$). Hence $L^{-1} \circ K$ is just the continuous map $(a,v) \to (a,H(a,v)): N \times \mathbb{C}^n \to N \times \mathbb{C}^n$. Thus L^{-1} is continuous and ζ is locally trivial with fiber $\mathbb{C}^n$.

We have already seen that $\sigma_f \in \Gamma(\zeta)$ ($f \in \mathcal{M}$). Hence there is a map $\varphi: \mathcal{M} \to \Gamma(\zeta)$ with $\varphi(f) = \sigma_f$ $(f \in \mathcal{M})$. It is clear that φ is an isomorphism into so that all that remains to be shown is that φ is onto.

To this end let $\sigma \in \Gamma(\zeta)$. For each $b \in |\mathcal{F}|$ there exist a neighborhood N_σ of b, $f^{1b},\ldots,f^{nb} \in \mathcal{M}$ and $h_1^b,\ldots,h_n^b$ with $\sigma(a) = \Sigma h_i^b \sigma_{f^{ib}}(a)$ $(a \in N_b)$. If we set $f^b = \Sigma h_i^b f^{ib}$ then $\sigma(a) = \sigma_{f^b}(a)$ $(a \in N_b)$.

Let K be a finite subset of $|\mathcal{F}|$ with $|\mathcal{F}| = \cup \{N_b \mid b \in K\}$ and $\{j_b \mid b \in K\}$ a partition of unity subordinate to the cover $\{N_b \mid b \in K\}$. Then $j_b\sigma = j_b\sigma_{f^b} = \sigma_{j_b f^b}$ $(b \in K)$ whence $\sigma = \Sigma j_b \sigma = \Sigma \sigma_{j_b f^b} = \sigma_f$ where $f = \Sigma j_b f^b$. Thus $\sigma \in \operatorname{im} \varphi$.

With regards to the "inner product" on $E(\zeta)$, I leave it to the reader to verify that the following is well defined and satisfies the requirements: Let $x,y \in E(\zeta)$ with $\zeta(x) = \zeta(y) = a \in |\mathcal{F}|$. Pick $f,g \in \mathcal{M}$ with $f_a = x$, $g_a = y$ and define $(x|y)$ to be $(f|g)(a)$. (Hint: chose $L = \{f^1,\ldots,f^n\}$ such that $\{\sigma_{f^i}(a)\}$ form an orthonormal basis for $\zeta^{-1}(a)$ $(a \in N)$.)

17.31 <u>LEMMA</u>. Let ζ,η be T-vector bundles over $|\mathcal{F}|$. Then $\zeta \cong \eta$ iff $\Gamma(\zeta) \cong \Gamma(\eta)$.

<u>PROOF</u>. Let $\varphi: E(\zeta) \to E(\eta)$ be an isomorphism. Then the map $\sigma \to \varphi \circ \sigma: \Gamma(\zeta) \to \Gamma(\eta)$ is the desired isomorphism.

On the other hand let $\psi: \Gamma(\zeta) \to \Gamma(\eta)$ be an isomorphism. As in 17.15 if $\sigma(a) = \tau(a)$ then $(\psi\sigma)(a) = (\psi\tau)(a)$ $(\sigma,\tau \in \Gamma(\zeta),\ a \in |\mathcal{F}|)$. Then the map $\varphi: E(\zeta) \to E(\eta)$ such that $\varphi(x) = (\psi\sigma)(a)$ $(x \in E(\zeta),\ \sigma \in \Gamma(\zeta)$ with $\sigma(a) = x)$ is the required isomorphism.

In order to sum up the main results of this chapter,

let me introduce some notation.

Let ζ be a T-vector bundle over $|\mathcal{F}|$. Then ζ is <u>irreducible</u> if $\Gamma(\zeta)$ is an irreducible T-$\mathcal{F}$-module.

Thus U will denote the collection of isomorphism classes of irreducible T-vector bundles over $|\mathcal{F}|$ and $\mathfrak{G}$ will denote the collection of isomorphism classes of T-$\mathcal{F}$-submodules of $\mathcal{F}^{\#}$. If $\mathfrak{m}$ is an irreducible T-$\mathcal{F}$-submodule of $\mathcal{F}^{\#}$, $[\mathfrak{m}]$ will denote the element of $\mathfrak{G}$ determined by $\mathfrak{m}$.

17.32 <u>PROPOSITION</u>. With the above notation let $\rho: \Lambda \to U$, $\psi: \Lambda \to \mathfrak{G}$ and $\varphi: \mathfrak{G} \to U$ be the maps such that $\rho(\lambda)$ is the class to which $\nu(\lambda)$ belongs, $\psi(\lambda)$ is the class to which some irreducible T-$\mathcal{F}$-submodule of im P_λ belongs, and $\varphi\,\mathfrak{m}$ is the class to which $\nu(\mathfrak{m})$ belongs ($\lambda \in \Lambda$, $\mathfrak{m} \in \mathfrak{g}$). Then:

1. ρ, ψ, and φ are well defined and bijective.
2. $\varphi\psi = \rho$.

<u>PROOF</u>. 1. The map ρ is well defined by 17.21 and 17.16. It is injective by 17.16, 17.13, and 17.31. It is surjective by 17.27.

To see that ψ is well defined let $\mathfrak{m},\mathfrak{n}$ be irreducible T-$\mathcal{F}$-submodules of im P_λ. We must show that $\mathfrak{m} \cong \mathfrak{n}$. By 17.30 there exist vector bundles ζ and η with $\Gamma(\zeta) \cong \mathfrak{m}$ and $\Gamma(\eta) \cong \mathfrak{n}$. By 17.27 there exists $\gamma,\delta \in \Lambda$ with $\nu(\gamma) \cong \zeta$ and $\nu(\delta) \cong \eta$. By 17.31 and 17.13

$$(*) \mathrm{Hom}(\gamma) \cong \mathfrak{m} \text{ and } \mathrm{Hom}(\delta) \cong \mathfrak{n}$$

By 17.22 Hom(γ) is isomorphic to a T-$\mathcal{F}$-submodule of im P_γ and Hom(δ) is isomorphic to a T-$\mathcal{F}$-submodule of im P_δ. Since $\mathfrak{m}$ and $\mathfrak{n}$ are both submodules of im P_λ, then by 17.8 $\gamma = \delta = \lambda$. Thus $\mathfrak{m} \cong \mathfrak{n}$ by (*).

The map ψ is clearly surjective. It is injective by 17.8.

That φ is well defined follows from 17.31. It is injective by 17.31 and that it is surjective will follow from 2 and the fact that ρ is surjective.

2. Let $\lambda \in \Lambda$ and $\mathfrak{M}$ an irreducible T-$\mathfrak{F}$-submodule of im P_λ with $\mathfrak{M} \cong \mathrm{Hom}(\lambda)$ (such exists by 17.22). Then $\varphi\psi(\lambda)$ is the class to which $\nu(\mathfrak{M})$ belongs. Since $\Gamma(\nu(\mathfrak{M})) \cong \mathfrak{M} \cong \mathrm{Hom}(\lambda) \cong \Gamma(\lambda)$ (17.30 and 17.13), $\nu(\mathfrak{M}) \cong \nu(\lambda)$ (17.31), whence $\varphi\psi(\lambda) = \rho(\lambda)$.

NOTES

1. The results in this chapter are due to A. Knapp [see [1] of chapter 16.]

2. G. Hochschild, The Structure of Lie Groups, Holden-Day, Inc., 1963.

3. L. Loomis, Abstract Harmonic Analysis, Van-Nostrand, 1953.

4. N. Bourbaki, Elements de mathematique, Livre VI, Chapitre III, Hermann, Paris, 1952 (see Para.4, Proposition 2).

5.0. The material in chapter 17 may also be discussed from the point of view of "locally trivial" bitransformation groups. Thus let (H,X,T) be a bitransformation such that H is compact T_2 and such that H acts freely on X. Let $(Y,T) = (X/H,T)$ and let $\pi: X \to Y$ be the canonical map. Then (H,X,T) is locally trivial if there exist an open cover $(U_i \mid i \in I)$ of Y and homeomorphisms $\varphi_i: \pi^{-1}(U_i) \to H \times U_i$ such that $\varphi_i(hx) = h\varphi_i(x)$ and $pr_i\varphi(x) = \pi(x)$; where $pr_i: H \times U_i \to U_i$ is the projection and $h(j,y) = (hj,y)$ $(h,j \in H,\ x \in \pi^{-1}(U_i),\ y \in Y,\ i \in I)$.

5.1. Notice that the group T is not involved in the above definition. Indeed 5.0 is just the definition of a locally trivial principal bundle with base space Y, total space X, and structure group H.

5.2. Let γ be a T-vector bundle. Then 17.25 shows that $(U(n), E(\eta),T)$ is a locally trivial bitransformation group, where n is the dimension of γ and η is as in 17.25.

5.3. By taking into account the action of T one

obtains Knapp's "crossed representations" [see [1] of chapter 16]. To see this let me introduce some notation in addition to that used in 5.0 above.

Let $\sigma_i : U_i \to \pi^{-1}(U_i)$ be the map such that $\varphi_i\sigma_i(y) = (e,y)$ $(i \in I,\ y \in U_i)$. Now suppose $y \in U_j$ and $yt \in U_i$. Then $\pi(\sigma_j(y)t) = \pi(\sigma_j(y))t = yt = \pi(\sigma_i(yt))$. Hence there exists $D_{ij}(y,t) \in H$ with $D_{ij}(y,t)\sigma_j(y)t = \sigma_i(yt)$.

For $i,j \in I$ set $A_{ij} = \{(y,t) \mid y \in U_j,\ yt \in U_i\}$. Then A_{ij} is an open subset of $Y \times T$ and D_{ij} is a continuous function from A_{ij} into H.

The set $\{D_{ij} \mid i,j \in I\}$ constitutes a crossed representation in the sense of Knapp and satisfies the following relations:

(i) $D_{ki}(y,t)\psi_{ij}(y) = D_{kj}(y,t)$

$((y,t) \in A_{ki} \cap A_{kj})$

(ii) $\psi_{ij}(yt)D_{jk}(y,t) = D_{ik}(y,t)$

$((y,t) \in A_{jk} \cap A_{ik})$

(iii) $D_{ki}(y,ts) = D_{kj}(yt,s)D_{ji}(y,t)$

$((y,t) \in A_{ji},\ (yt,s) \in A_{kj},\ (y,ts) \in A_{ki})$

(vi) $D_{ii}(y,e) = e \quad (y \in U_i)$

where $\psi_{ij} : U_i \cap U_j \to H$ are the so-called coordinate functions of the bundle defined by the relation $\varphi_j\varphi_i^{-1}(h,y) = (h\psi_{ij}(y),y)$ $(h \in H,\ y \in U_i \cap U_j)$.

The proofs of the above follow directly from the definitions. To illustrate I prove (i).

Let $(y,t) \in A_{ki} \cap A_{kj}$. Then $\sigma_k(yt) = D_{ki}(y,t)\sigma_i(y)t$

and $\sigma_k(yt) = D_{kj}(y,t)\sigma_j(y)t$. Hence $D_{ki}(y,t)\sigma_i(y) = D_{kj}(y,t)\sigma_j(y)$. Then $(D_{ki}(y,t)\psi_{ij}(y),y) = \varphi_j\varphi_i^{-1}(D_{ki}(y,t),y) = \varphi_j(D_{ki}(y,t)\varphi_i^{-1}(e,y)) = \varphi_j(D_{ki}(y,t)\sigma_i(y)) = \varphi_j(D_{kj}(y,e)\sigma_j(y)) = D_{kj}(y,t)\varphi_j\sigma_j(y) = D_{kj}(y,t)(e,y) = (D_{kj}(y,t),y)$; whence $D_{ki}(y,t)\psi_{ij}(y) = D_{kj}(y,t)$.

5.4. Now suppose one is given a locally trivial principal bundle with total space X, base space Y and structure group H together with an action of T on Y and a crossed representation $(D_{ij} \mid i,j \in I)$. Then one can define an action on X by means of the relation

$$(*)\quad xt = hD_{ji}^{-1}(y,t)\sigma_j(yt) \quad (x \in \pi^{-1}(U_i),\ t \in T)$$

where $y = \pi(x)$ and $x = h\sigma_i(y)$. That (*) does indeed define an action of T on X follows from (i),(ii),(iii), and (iv) of 5.3 above.

The situation is considerably simplified when the bundle involved is the product; i.e. $X = H \times Y$ and H acts in the obvious way. In this case a crossed representation is just a continuous map $D: Y \times T \to H$ such that:

(i) $D(y,ts) = D(yt,s)D(y,t)$ $(y \in Y,\ t,s \in T)$ and

(ii) $D(y,e) = e$ $(y \in Y)$. (This is what the conditions in 5.3 reduce to when there is only one coordinate neighborhood.)

Let $x = (h,y)$ and $t \in T$. Then (*) gives $xt = (hD^{-1}(y,t),yt)$.

If the group T is the integers then D is obtained from a continuous function $f: Y \to H$ as follows: set $D(y,0) = y$, $D(y,1) = f(y)$, $D(y,n+1) = D(yn,1)D(y,n)$, and $D(y,-n) = D(y,n)^{-1}$ $(n \leqslant 0,\ y \in Y)$.

CHAPTER 18

DISJOINTNESS

In this chapter I would like to discuss the concept of disjointness introduced by Furstenberg [1] from the algebraic point of view.

18.1 STANDING ASSUMPTIONS AND DEFINITIONS.

Throughout this chapter all T-subalgebras are assumed to be contained in $\mathfrak{A}(u)$.

The T-subalgebras $\mathcal{A},\mathcal{B}$ are said to be disjoint (written $\mathcal{A} \perp \mathcal{B}$) if the transformation group $(|\mathcal{A}| \times |\mathcal{B}|,T)$ is minimal.

The pull-back of $\mathcal{A}$ and $\mathcal{B}$ (denoted $|\mathcal{A}| \circ |\mathcal{B}|$) is the subset $\{(x,y) \mid x \in |\mathcal{A}|, y \in |\mathcal{B}|, x|\mathcal{A} \cap \mathcal{B} = y|\mathcal{A} \cap \mathcal{B}\}$ of $|\mathcal{A}| \times |\mathcal{B}|$.

18.2 REMARKS. 1. The pull-back of $\mathcal{A}$ and $\mathcal{B}$ is a closed invariant subset of $|\mathcal{A}| \times |\mathcal{B}|$ and so will be regarded as a transformation group with phase group T. In general $(|\mathcal{A}| \circ |\mathcal{B}|,T)$ is not a minimal set.

2. Let $\mathcal{A},\mathcal{B}$ be T-subalgebras with $\mathcal{A} \perp \mathcal{B}$. Then $|\mathcal{A}| \times |\mathcal{B}| = |\mathcal{A}| \circ |\mathcal{B}|$ whence $p|\mathcal{A} \cap \mathcal{B} = u|\mathcal{A} \cap \mathcal{B}$ $(p \in \beta T)$.

Thus $\mathcal{A} \perp \mathcal{B}$ implies that $\mathcal{A} \cap \mathcal{B} = \mathbb{C}$; i.e. if $\mathcal{A}$ and $\mathcal{B}$ are disjoint then they have no non-trivial common factor. The converse, however, is false as will be presently shown.

I shall be concerned with the problem: (i) under what conditions on $\mathcal{A}$ and $\mathcal{B}$ does $\mathcal{A} \cap \mathcal{B} = C$ imply that $\mathcal{A} \perp \mathcal{B}$?

Now if $\mathcal{A} \cap \mathcal{B} = \mathbb{C}$, then $|\mathcal{A}| \circ |\mathcal{B}| = |\mathcal{A}| \times |\mathcal{B}|$. Thus (i) may be subsumed under the more general question (ii) under what conditions is $|\mathcal{A}| \circ |\mathcal{B}|$ minimal?

18.3 <u>PROPOSITION</u>. Let $\mathcal{A},\mathcal{B}$ be T-subalgebras, and let $\varphi\colon |[\mathcal{A} \cup \mathcal{B}]| \to |\mathcal{A}| \circ |\mathcal{B}|$ be the map such that $\varphi(x) = (x|\mathcal{A}, x|\mathcal{B})$ $(x \in |[\mathcal{A} \cup \mathcal{B}]|)$. Then φ is an injective homomorphism and $(|\mathcal{A}| \circ |\mathcal{B}|,T)$ is minimal iff φ is surjective. Thus when $|\mathcal{A}| \circ |\mathcal{B}|$ is minimal, the algebra corresponding to it is $[\mathcal{A} \cup \mathcal{B}]$.

<u>PROOF</u>. Let $x,y \in |[\mathcal{A} \cup \mathcal{B}]|$ with $\varphi(x) = \varphi(y)$. Then $x|\mathcal{A} \cup \mathcal{B} = y|\mathcal{A} \cup \mathcal{B}$ whence $x = y$ on $\mathcal{A} \cup \mathcal{B}$, i.e. $x = y$. Thus φ is injective.

It is clear that φ is continuous and that $\varphi(xt) = \varphi(x)t$ $(x \in |[\mathcal{A} \cup \mathcal{B}]|,\ t \in T)$.

Since $|[\mathcal{A} \cup \mathcal{B}]|$ is minimal, im φ is a minimal subset of $|\mathcal{A}| \circ |\mathcal{B}|$. Thus $|\mathcal{A}| \circ |\mathcal{B}|$ is minimal iff φ is surjective.

18.4 <u>PROPOSITION</u>. Let $\mathcal{A},\mathcal{B}$ be T-subalgebras with $|\mathcal{A}| \circ |\mathcal{B}|$ minimal. Then $\mathfrak{g}(\mathcal{A} \cap \mathcal{B}) = AB = BA$, where $A = \mathfrak{g}(\mathcal{A})$ and $B = \mathfrak{g}(\mathcal{B})$.

<u>PROOF</u>. Since $\mathcal{A} \cap \mathcal{B}$ is contained in both $\mathcal{A}$ and $\mathcal{B}$, $A \cup B \subset \mathfrak{g}(\mathcal{A} \cap \mathcal{B})$ whence $AB \cup BA \subset \mathfrak{g}(\mathcal{A} \cap \mathcal{B})$.

Now let $\mu \in \mathfrak{g}(\mathcal{A} \cap \mathcal{B})$. Then $(\mu|\mathcal{A}, u|\mathcal{B}) \in |\mathcal{A}| \circ |\mathcal{B}|$ whence by 18.4 there exists $p \in M$ with $p|\mathcal{A} = \mu|\mathcal{A}$ and $p|\mathcal{B} = u|\mathcal{B}$. Set $\nu = pu$. Then the above relations remain valid when p is replaced by ν. Then $\nu \in B$ and $\mu\nu^{-1} \in A$ so that

$\mu = (\mu\nu^{-1})\nu \in AB$. Thus $\mathfrak{g}(\mathfrak{A} \cap \mathfrak{B}) \subset AB$, and a similar argument shows that $\mathfrak{g}(\mathfrak{A} \cap \mathfrak{B}) \subset BA$.

18.5 LEMMA. Let $\mathfrak{A},\mathfrak{B}$ be T-subalgebras such that $\mathfrak{g}(\mathfrak{A} \cap \mathfrak{B}) = AB$ and let (x,y) be an almost periodic point of $|\mathfrak{A}| \circ |\mathfrak{B}|$. Then $(x,y) \in \operatorname{im} \varphi$ where $\varphi: |[\mathfrak{A} \cup \mathfrak{B}]| \to |\mathfrak{A}| \circ |\mathfrak{B}|$ is the map such that $\varphi(z) = (z|\mathfrak{A}, z|\mathfrak{B})$ $(z \in |[\mathfrak{A} \cup \mathfrak{B}]|)$.

PROOF. There exists an idempotent $v \in M$ with $xv = x$ and $yv = y$ (3.7). Let $p,q \in M$ with $p|\mathfrak{A} = x$ and $q|\mathfrak{B} = y$. We may assume $pv = p$ and $qv = q$. Hence there exists $\gamma \in G$ with $p = \gamma q$ (3 of 3.5).

Since $(x,y) \in |\mathfrak{A}| \circ |\mathfrak{B}|$, $p|\mathfrak{A} \cap \mathfrak{B} = q|\mathfrak{A} \cap \mathfrak{B}$ whence $\gamma \in \mathfrak{g}(\mathfrak{A} \cap \mathfrak{B}) = AB$. Let $\gamma = \mu\nu$ with $\mu \in A$ and $\nu \in B$, and set $r = \mu^{-1}p = \nu q$. Then $r|\mathfrak{A} = p|\mathfrak{A} = x$ and $r|\mathfrak{B} = q|\mathfrak{B} = y$.

18.6 PROPOSITION. Let $\mathfrak{A},\mathfrak{B}$ be T-subalgebras with $\mathfrak{g}(\mathfrak{A} \cap \mathfrak{B}) = AB$ and $\mathfrak{A} \cap \mathfrak{B} \leqslant \mathfrak{A}$ or $\mathfrak{A} \cap \mathfrak{B} \leqslant \mathfrak{B}$. Then $|\mathfrak{A}| \circ |\mathfrak{B}|$ is minimal.

PROOF. Assume $\mathfrak{A} \cap \mathfrak{B} \leqslant \mathfrak{A}$. Let $(x,y) \in |\mathfrak{A}| \circ |\mathfrak{B}|$ and v an idempotent in M with $yv = y$. Then $x = xv$ on $\mathfrak{A} \cap \mathfrak{B}$ whence $x = xv$ on $\mathfrak{A}$. Hence $(xv,yv) = (x,y)$ and so (x,y) is an almost periodic point of $|\mathfrak{A}| \circ |\mathfrak{B}|$. 18.6 now follows from 18.5 and 18.3.

18.7 PROPOPOSITION. Let $\mathfrak{A},\mathfrak{B}$ be T-subalgebras of $\mathcal{K} = \{f|ft \in \mathfrak{U}(u)\ (t \in T)\}$. Then $\mathfrak{A} \perp \mathfrak{B}$ iff $AB = G$.

PROOF. Let $\mathfrak{A} \perp \mathfrak{B}$. Then $\mathfrak{A} \cap \mathfrak{B} = \mathbb{C}$ by 2 of 18.2 whence $G = \mathfrak{g}(\mathfrak{A} \cap \mathfrak{B}) = AB$ by 18.4.

Now suppose $AB = G$. Since $A \cup B$ is contained in the group $\mathfrak{g}(\mathfrak{A} \cap \mathfrak{B})$, $\mathfrak{g}(\mathfrak{A} \cap \mathfrak{B}) = G$.

Let $f \in \mathfrak{A} \cap \mathfrak{B}$ and $t \in T$. Then $utu \in G$ whence $f = futu$. Hence $f = ft$ since $f \in \mathcal{K}$. Thus $\mathfrak{A} \cap \mathfrak{B} = \mathbb{C}$, and so

$|\mathcal{A}| \circ |\mathcal{B}| = |\mathcal{A}| \times |\mathcal{B}|$.

Since $[\mathcal{A} \cup \mathcal{B}] \subset \mathcal{K}$, $utu|\mathcal{A} = ut|\mathcal{A}$ and $utu|\mathcal{B} = ut|\mathcal{B}$ $(t \in T)$. Thus $(ut|\mathcal{A}, us|\mathcal{B})$ is an almost periodic point of $|\mathcal{A}| \circ |\mathcal{B}|$ $(t,s \in T)$. Hence im φ contains the dense subset $\{(ut|\mathcal{A}, us|\mathcal{B}) \mid t,s \in T\}$ of $|\mathcal{A}| \circ |\mathcal{B}|$ by 18.5 where φ is as in 18.3 and 18.5. Since im φ is closed, φ is surjective and 18.7 follows from 18.3.

18.8 <u>COROLLARY</u>. Let $\mathcal{A},\mathcal{B},\mathcal{F},\mathcal{H}$ be T-subalgebras of $\mathcal{K}$ with $\mathcal{A} \perp \mathcal{B}$, $\mathfrak{g}(\mathcal{A}) = \mathfrak{g}(\mathcal{F})$, and $\mathfrak{g}(\mathcal{B}) = \mathfrak{g}(\mathcal{H})$. Then it follows immediately from 18.7 that $\mathcal{F} \perp \mathcal{H}$.

18.9 <u>PROPOSITION</u>. Let $\mathcal{A},\mathcal{B}$ be T-subalgebras such that $\mathcal{B} \leqslant [\mathcal{A} \cup \mathcal{B}]$ and $\mathcal{A}B \subset \mathcal{A}$. Then $|\mathcal{A}| \circ |\mathcal{B}|$ is minimal.

<u>PROOF</u>. Let $(x,y) \in |\mathcal{A}| \circ |\mathcal{B}|$, and let $p,q \in M$ be such that $p|\mathcal{A} = x$ and $q|\mathcal{B} = y$. Then $(p|\mathcal{B}, q|\mathcal{B}) \in R(\mathcal{B}:\mathcal{A} \cap \mathcal{B}) = R(\mathcal{B}:\mathcal{A})$ by 13.10. Hence there exist $r,s \in M$ with $r|\mathcal{B} = p|\mathcal{B}$, $s|\mathcal{B} = q|\mathcal{B}$, and $r|\mathcal{A} = s|\mathcal{A}$. Let v be an idempotent in M with $r = rv$ and let $\mu \in G$ with $\mu r = pv$. Then $pv|\mathcal{B} = rv|\mathcal{B} = r|\mathcal{B} = p|\mathcal{B}$ implies that $\mu \in B$ and that $pv|\mathcal{A} = p|\mathcal{A}$. Finally $\mu s|\mathcal{A} = \mu r|\mathcal{A} = pv|\mathcal{A} = p|\mathcal{A} = x$ and $\mu s|\mathcal{B} = s|\mathcal{B} = y$. Hence 18.10 follows from 18.3.

18.10 <u>COROLLARY</u>. Let $\mathcal{A},\mathcal{B}$ be T-subalgebras with $A = \mathfrak{g}(\mathcal{A})$ and $B = \mathfrak{g}(\mathcal{B})$. Then any one of the following conditions implies that $|\mathcal{A}| \circ |\mathcal{B}|$ is minimal:

1. $\mathcal{A}$ distal and $B \subset N(A)$, the normalizer of A.
2. $\mathcal{A}$ distal and regular.
3. $\mathcal{A} \cap \mathcal{B} \leqslant \mathcal{A}$ and $\mathcal{A}B \subset \mathcal{A}$.
4. There exists a T-subalgebra $\mathcal{F}$ with $\mathcal{F} \leqslant \mathcal{A}$, $\mathcal{F} \subset \mathcal{B}$ and $A \lhd F = \mathfrak{g}(\mathcal{F})$.

<u>PROOF</u>. 1. $\mathcal{A}$ distal implies that $\mathcal{B} \leqslant [\mathcal{A} \cup \mathcal{B}]$ (12.5, 12.8) and $B \subset N(A)$ implies that $\mathcal{A}B \subset \mathcal{A}$ (12.10). Thus 1

follows from 18.9.

2. follows immediately from 1 since when $\mathfrak{A}$ is regular $N(A) = G$.

3. $\mathfrak{A} \cap \mathfrak{B}$ $\mathfrak{A}$ implies that $\mathfrak{B} \leqslant [\mathfrak{A} \cup \mathfrak{B}]$ whence 3 follows from 18.9.

4. Since $\mathcal{F} \leqslant \mathfrak{A}$ and $\mathcal{F} \subset \mathfrak{B}$, $\mathfrak{B} \leqslant [\mathfrak{A} \cup \mathfrak{B}]$. Also $\mathcal{F} \leqslant \mathfrak{A}$ implies that $\mathfrak{A} = \mathfrak{U}(A) \cap \mathcal{F}^*$ (13.21).

Let $\mu \in B$. Then $\mu \in F$ and $\mathcal{F}\mu = \mathcal{F}$, whence $\mathcal{F}^*\mu = \mathcal{F}^*$ (2 of 12.6). Also $\mu \in F$ implies, since $A \lhd F$, that $\mathfrak{U}(A)\mu = \mathfrak{U}(A)$. Hence $\mathfrak{A}\mu = \mathfrak{U}(A)\mu \cap \mathcal{F}^*\mu = \mathfrak{U}(A) \cap \mathcal{F}^* = \mathfrak{A}$. Statement 4 now follows from 18.9.

18.11 <u>REMARKS</u>. 1. Even if $\mathfrak{A}$ and $\mathfrak{B}$ are equicontinuous with $\mathfrak{A} \cap \mathfrak{B} = \mathbf{C}$, they need not be disjoint as the following example of Knapp's [2] shows:

Let T be a finite group. Then all the minimal sets are of the form $(T/H,T)$ where H is a subgroup of T and the action is given by the map $(Ht,s) \to Hts: T/H \times T \to T/H$. Hence in this case every minimal set is equicontinuous.

It is easy to verify that $(T/K,T)$ is a homomorphic image of $(T/H,T)$ iff $H \subset g^{-1}Kg$ for some $g \in T$. Thus T/H and T/L have no non-trivial common factor iff $\langle gHg^{-1}, tLt^{-1}\rangle$, the subgroup generated by $gHg^{-1} \cup tLt^{-1}$ is all of T $(g,t \in T)$. On the other hand one can verify directly or use 18.6 to show that T/H and T/K are disjoint iff $HK = T$. (When T is finite the whole algebraic theory degenerates. Thus $\beta T = T = G$ and e is the only idempotent. If $\mathfrak{A}$ is the T-subalgebra corresponding to T/H then $\mathfrak{g}(\mathfrak{A}) = H$.)

Now let T be the symmetric group on four letters, H the subgroup generated by some four-cycle, and K the subgroup generated by a three-cycle. Since gHg^{-1} and tKt^{-1} are also generated by a four and three-cycle respectively

$(g,t \in T)$, $\langle gHg^{-1}, tKt^{-1}\rangle = T$ and so T/H and T/L have no factor in common. However, HL has at most twelve elements, whence $HL \neq T$ and so T/H and T/L are not disjoint.

2. The situation in 1 above can not obtain when T is abelian. Thus let T be abelian, $\mathfrak{A}, \mathfrak{B}$ T-subalgebras with no non-trivial common factors, and let $\mathfrak{A}$ be equicontinuous. Then $\mathfrak{A}$ is regular (4.6, 11.21) and so $\mathfrak{A} \perp \mathfrak{B}$ by 2 of 18.10.

It is not known whether there exist two minimal distal transformation groups with an abelian phase group. which have no non-trivial common factors but are not disjoint.

NOTES

1. H. Furstenberg, *Disjointness in ergodic theory, minimal sets, and a problem in Diophantine approximation*. Math. Systems Theory 1 (1967), 1-50.

2. A. W. Knapp, *Functions behaving like almost automorphic functions*, Topological Dynamics, an International Symposium edited by J. Auslander and W. H. Gottschalk, 299-317.

INDEX

1 3 5 7 8 7 4